THE FIRST

MW00422671

Hebrews 5:12

"the first principles of the oracles of God"

Record your name, and the name and telephone number of your discipler here...

Your Name: _____
Date Study Began: _____
Date Completed: _____

Your Discipler's Name is: _____
Their Telephone: _____
Their E-mail: _____

An Educational Ministry of

Bible Baptist Church of Ballincollig, Ireland
Pastor Craig Ledbetter, B.A., Th.G.
Unit B Enterprise Business Park, Inishmore
Ballincollig, Cork, Ireland   P31K594
Telephone within Ireland: **(021) 487-1234**
From USA: **011-353-21-4871234**
Int'l: **+353-21-487-1234**
E-Mail: **craig1611@gmail.com**
Web: **www.biblebc.com**
US Contact Address: **c/o PO Box 849, Rossville, GA 30741 USA**

© 1993-2020 Craig Ledbetter's *In-House* Publications – Specially Printed in Ireland

Eighteenth Edition Printing - April, 2020 (with Embedded Fonts)

TABLE OF CONTENTS

All Scripture references, unless otherwise noted are from
the Word of God – the King James Bible

Welcome

The First Principles Bible Study Course

When the Lord Jesus was on this earth, He spent three and a half years personally teaching His disciples all the things they needed to know to find forgiveness and full life in the kingdom of God. By setting aside time to study His word, you are showing God that you too wish to become more than just a believer, but a follower of Jesus Christ.

The *First Principles Bible Study Course* was written to equip believers to live for Jesus through the study of God's word from Genesis to Revelation.

The Bible

You need another book in your hands as well as this Study Course... the Bible. As Christians, we firmly believe the Bible is the inerrant, infallible, inspired Word of Almighty God. We further believe that God's word has been preserved by God in the English language in the King James Bible. The goal of this Study Course is for you to learn the Bible and apply its truths to your life, not correct it, or think anyone can improve upon it. The Bible was given to us to correct, and improve us!

How Long Does the Study Course take to Complete?

Depending upon your interest level from week to week, the Study Course is usually completed in less than two years.

Do You Have to Have a Teacher?

Yes, and no. Learning most things is always best with a passionate teacher, who takes the time to answer questions as they arise, and helps make things clear in your own understanding. But not everyone has a personal teacher that is available to teach them, so this Study Course is written in an expanded fashion to answer as many normal questions as possible.

What is the Fruit of the Study Course?

An unsaved person will thoroughly learn how to be saved, and usually will decide to get born again; A new believer will become more passionate for God, and get trained to study the Bible and stand for the Lord; backslidden Christians will get encouraged to get right with God, and get back in the spiritual battle for souls; and hungry believers will get fed by the "meat" subjects of God's word.

Concerning Section Tests

Every section ends with a test, that presents questions concerning the previous five lessons (or in the case of the fourth section, it covers the previous six lessons). These tests need to be taken on your own, and then either presented to your Discipler, or posted to the **First Principles Academy** for grading.

How to Use the Answer Key

The information in the Answer Key section of the Discipleship Course looks kind of cryptic, but is just an easy way to list the answers to the blanks in this kind of a study. The first thing you will notice is the Chapter Title and Heading (i.e., **Lesson One** – Biblical Salvation). Following that, on each line is the location of the question blank, as follows:

VI.A.1.b.   hand

The first part locates where the blank is – **Section VI**. Each roman numeral (I, II, III, IV, etc.) is used in the study outline as a main topic. Find the part of the lesson that starts with the roman numeral VI (six), and then look down until you find the paragraph starting with capital '**A.**'. Under that, the paragraph marked '**1.**' will have a sub-paragraph marked, small '**b.**' at its start. In THAT paragraph, is the statement with the blank you are checking your answer against. Now, thankfully, not all of the answers are in sections so deep, with so many sub-sections, but you see how it works. There can be a few blanks that are actually not part of a paragraph that is numbered, so, the previous section number will be used.

Two other points need to be made concerning answers.

1. Usually there is only one answer that is correct for the fill in the blank, so one answer will be listed. But if another answer would be acceptable, it will be listed in parenthesis brackets "(…)".
2. If there are more than one fill in the blank in a paragraph for you to locate answers for, the answers will simply be separated by semi-colons (;).

Study Introduction

PARAGRAPH	ANSWERS
V.A.1.	Truth
V.A.2.	truth
V.A.3.	word
V.B.3.	true
VI.A.	believe
VI.B.	know
VII.A.	grow
VII.B.	unfruitful

Each lesson is in the above format and is clearly identified, with the answer matching the blank lines in the paragraphs marked in the outline.

Please Note – if you are only looking *in the Answer Key* for the answers to the fill in the blanks of the Study Guide, you are looking in the wrong place. The answers are found in the Bible, in the Scripture location referred to in the Study. Always look there first! The answers in the Answer Key could be wrong, so make sure you know what the Bible says, and not just what the Answer Key says.

How much lee-way does an instructor have when the disciple offers another answer than what is expected? Let's look at another example, still using Lesson One, but this time, let's see multiple possible answers in the Answer Key, and learn how to deal with them.

Lesson 1 - Biblical Salvation

Turn to page 13, and notice how that some of the answers have semi-colons ';' in them that are answers to more blanks on that line. If there is something in parentheses (…), it is offering other possible answers to a question.

IX.A.	No
IX.A.1.b.	hand
IX.A.2.	chastising
IX.A.2.b.	loves
IX.A.2.c.	bastard (*that's a real Bible word*)
IX.B.	Confess it as a sin and forsake it right away
X.A.	saved; hell
X.B.	Bible
X.C.	Lamb; sins
X.D.	our sins
X.E.	death (or blood)
X.F.	internal
X.G.	mine (or all people of the world)
X.H.	it is instant (or straight away)
X.I.	(*the answer is up to the individual*)
X.J.	(*the answer is up to the individual*)

THE FIRST PRINCIPLES   21st Century Edition   Lesson One

IX. Dealing With Sin Once You Are Already Saved

A. Can a Christian be happy while *disobeying* God? **Yes** or **No**?

   1. Notice how it will affect us (Psalm 32:2-5) When you keep silent about your sin (**Iniquity** is another word for sin):

     a. You will age faster.

     b. God's _____ will be hard against you, not blessing you.

     c. You will basically "dry up" like a desert.

   2. See in Hebrews 12:5-11 where God always *endeavors* to make us mature, and holy in our lives by _____ us when we sin.

     a. Chastening means "correcting" NOT punishing. God brings trouble into your life to get you back "on the strait (hard path) *and narrow*"

     b. God chastens His children because He _____ them.

     c. If a person never experiences God's **chastisement**, it is evident that person never became a Christian at all and is a _____ (Heb 12:8) – God calls them *illegitimate* – not the real thing – a faker).

B. What should a believer do when they sin? (1 John 1:9; Proverbs 28:13) _____ and _____. To "confess" means to **agree** with God about the sinfulness of your life, and especially specific acts where you broke His direct commandments!

X. Concluding Questions - Fill in these questions from memory.

A. The Bible was written for us to know that we are _____, and that as sinners we needed God to reach down to us (not for us to reach up), and to save us from _____.

B. God has revealed truth through the _____ alone.

C. The theme of the Bible from start to finish is all about "*the* _____ of God which *taketh* away the _____ of the world" (John 1:29).

D. What has separated all of humanity from God?

E. Our salvation depends only upon whether we are willing by faith to let the _____ of Jesus Christ be sufficient to pay off all our sin-debt to God, instead of trying to pay it off ourselves with our own good works.

F. The term "*born again*" refers to what? An **external** birth, or an **internal** birth? (Circle one).

G. When Jesus died, whose place was He taking? _____

H. When a person repents of their sins, and calls upon Jesus Christ to save them from hell, how long does it take before they are forgiven of all sins, past, present, and future?

I. Have you **let** *Him* take *your* place, and been born again yourself? **Yes** or **No**

J. Is Jesus Christ worthy of your life being lived for His glory from now on? **Yes** or **No** (Circle one).

Date Lesson Completed _____	Discipler _____

BIBLICAL SALVATION   • 13

STUDY INTRODUCTION

I. How to Use This Study Guide

A. **Along-side your Bible.** Never put anything above the authority of the word of God. Use *tools* to help your Bible study, but never let them take its place!

B. **Look up all the Scriptures listed in this Study.** Each Scripture for you to look up appears in parenthesis and coloured like this: (John 3:16). The answers to every question of this Study will come from those marked Scriptures. Keep reading through all of the verses listed until you are satisfied that you understand the Bible's instruction on each topic.

C. **Pray for guidance as you study.** God gave you His word (Psalm 68:11), and if you ask Him, He will guide you through it, and help you understand it (John 16:13).

D. **Fill in every blank** with the words of Scripture as you look them up! You may not see the answer right away, but the answer is in every verse listed!

II. Memorize four Memory Verses.

They are **Matthew 4:4, Hebrews 10:25, 1 Corinthians 12:27,** and **Romans 12:11.** These will help establish your faith in the promises of God! They are located at the beginning of each of the four Sections of this Study.

III. Recommended Materials for Your Study

* A "Bible Dictionary" to explain Bible words better
* Get some writing pens and highlighters for marking your Bible
* Purchase a separate notebook/journal to record your own notes as you study your Bible
* You should purchase some small (3" x 5") record/index cards to write down Scriptures for memorizing and meditation

IV. Suggestions For Reading Your Bible.

Realize that the Bible is a book. It is not a magical good-luck charm. It was written to be read with human eyes, and tested by the human mind, and believed by the human heart. The method of reading the Bible is very simple. Here are just a few suggestions to get you going.

A. **Listen to it.** Start with a determination to "listen" to what is written. When you approach the Bible, seek to hear what the words are saying. Let God talk freely as if He were right beside you.

B. **Pray through it.** Praying is asking. So, ask God to grant unto you the true understanding of His word. There is no perfect interpreter of the word of God except the Author of the word, God Himself (1 Corinthians 2:9-13).

C. **Read the Bible from Beginning to End.** You will never get the meaning of ANY book unless you read it from cover to cover. For the first time, you should start in Matthew, and read through to Revelation. After that, then go to Genesis, and start all over, and read all the way through to the end!

D. **Read with the Heart, and not just the Mind.** The Bible is perfect and quite capable of being examined by the mind, but was written for the heart.

E. **Read the Bible Daily.** Set aside a regular time every day to spend in God's word.

F. **Read it Obediently.** Here is the big deal. Read the Bible with the goal of doing what you find commanded to be done. God says in James 1:22 that we are to "*be ye _____ of the word and not hearers only deceiving your own selves.*"

G. **Read the Scriptures Contextually.** That means, allow the Scriptures to explain themselves. A sentence is always understood within the meaning of the surrounding sentences. So, always find out **who is speaking, who are they speaking to,** and, **what are they talking about.** Sounds simple and yet few actually take the time to do this!

V. Let's begin with a question. What Is Truth?

A. **First, Compare what is said in John 18:36-38 and with John 17:17**

1. In John 18, the Lord Jesus is standing before Pilate, accused of being a King. Jesus tells Pilate that He IS a King, but not of this world, and that His design is not to set up a physical kingdom, but *to declare the* _____.
2. Pilate responds, *"What is* _____?" But notice what Pilate does next. He does not wait around for the answer. He does not believe there is any such thing as "truth." It is the same with most people. They have been lied to so many times about Santa, the tooth fairy, and Easter bunnies they think God and truth are only lies as well.
3. Yet, in John 17:17, Jesus Himself says God's _____ is truth! Now, either Jesus was a liar, or crazy, or telling the truth. Which is it?

B. **Let's agree on three things:**

1. First, there must be something, somewhere, that is *true*. Because, without *truth*, there is NO WAY of knowing what is really true or false, good or bad, or right or wrong; and anyone's guess becomes as good as another's.
2. Next, **God** is the Author of truth. He cannot "___" or He's not God (Titus 1:2).
3. Lastly, God has revealed truth through the **Bible** alone (John 17:17).
4. Do you agree with these three statements? Yes or No? (circle one).

> The Bible says, "Yea, let God be _____, but every man a **liar**." Romans 3:4

VI. The Purpose of the Bible. Why was the Bible even written?

A. There are many reasons why God took the time to put down His words on paper, but here are TWO big reasons…
B. It was written that we may "_____" that Jesus was who He said He was - the Messiah, the Son of God, who came to pay our sin-debt (John 20:31).
C. It was also written, so that we may "_____" that we have eternal life, not just "hope" for it (1John 5:13)!

VII. Things to know when you start reading a King James Bible

A. There are some older words that have important meanings to know:

1. **"Thou" and "Thee"** – these simply are words for 'you' but are spoken in a serious tone towards a single individual, see Genesis 3:9 *"And the LORD God called unto Adam, and said unto him, Where art* _____?" (Where are you?)
2. **"Ye"** – This is the plural word for 'YOU' as in "you all". See Matthew 3:2 *"And saying, Repent ___: for the kingdom of heaven is at hand."* (repent all of you…)
3. **"Hath"** and other words ending in **"th"** is the older way of having an 's' on the end. Just replace the 'th' with an 's' and it will be the same as today!

   a. See Proverbs 28:13 *"He that cover_eth_ his sins shall not prosper: but whoso confess_eth_ and forsak_eth_ them shall have mercy"*
   b. It is the same as saying "He that COVER_S_ his sins shall not prosper: but whoso CONFESS_ES_ and FORSAK_ES_ them shall have mercy."
   c. Other words with "th" at the end include: loveth, heareth, doeth, giveth… and they are not hard to understand are they?

B. Other words that you are unfamiliar with, like Propitiation, Salvation, Justification, etc., should be looked up in a Bible Dictionary, so that you don't miss what God is saying in any Scripture. Maybe you have one at the back of your Bible? If not, like suggested at the beginning of this Study, you should order and purchase one.

C. Psalm 119:140 says, "*Thy word is very* _____: *therefore thy servant loveth it.*"

VIII. The Purpose and Design of This Study Guide

A. This Study will teach you the wonderful truths of God's word, so you can _____ to "perfection" or full maturity in Christ (1Peter 2:2,3; 2Peter 3:18).

B. To do this, you need to develop in yourself the following life principles by reading, and learning from God's word daily (take the time to now read **2Peter 1:4-8**):

1. **Faith** (1:5) - you start off with this at salvation. It is how you come to God… simply believing Jesus Christ is all you need to live now.

2. **Virtue** – this is the inner strength that God will constantly give you to do right.

3. _____ – Add the knowledge about Jesus Christ (by studying the Bible)

4. **Temperance** – add the ability to keep a right balance about things.

5. **Patience** – learning how to wait on God, and wait through all your trials.

6. _____ – this simply means striving to become more like Christ.

7. **Brotherly kindness** – learn how to be kind towards people as if they are family.

8. Lastly, add _____ – this means having unconditional love towards people!

C. The Bible finishes in verse 8 by saying, "*For if these things be in you, and abound, they make you that ye shall neither be barren nor* _____." That is what God wants - spiritual fruitfulness and success as a real Christian!

Have fun!

SECTION ONE

This Section of your Discipleship study will establish you in

The Word of God

Memory Verse:

> *"But he answered and said, It is written, Man shall not live by bread alone, but by every word that proceedeth out of the mouth of God."* **Matthew 4:4**

This is your first Scripture to memorize. To understand, and memorize this Scripture verse, please read Matthew Chapter 4, verses 1 through 4, to see what all is going on and ask yourself three questions:

➤ Who is doing the talking in verse 4? _____
➤ Who are they talking to? _____
➤ What are they talking about? _____
_____

Knowing the answers to these three questions will help you easily understand each portion of Scripture you read - there is no better way to learn! So, every day, read this Scripture out-loud, at least once, and in a few days, you will have memorized it and be able to recall it without looking at it.

In this Section, you will study the following Subjects:

- **Biblical Salvation** - What Does It Mean?
- **The Eternal Security of the Believer** - Can We Lose Salvation?
- **Believer's Baptism** - What Is It For?
- **The Word of God** - How We Got Our Bible!
- **Bible Study Techniques** - How to Master God's Words!

BIBLICAL SALVATION
Lesson One

Memory Verse: *Matthew 4:4*   Lesson Verses: *1 John 5:11,12*

> *"And this is the record, that God hath given to us eternal life, and this life is in his Son. **He that hath the Son hath life; and he that hath not the Son of God hath not life.**" 1 John 5:11,12*

I. Introduction

The decision to trust Jesus Christ as the Saviour of your soul is the greatest decision you could ever make! This lesson will briefly explain what happens when a person gets *saved*, and how the decision to trust Christ forever affects their relationship with God.

WHAT IS SIN?

"Transgression of the Law"

Crossing the line of God's Law

II. Is Anyone "Good?"

A. The *spiritual* condition of **everyone** is described as what? Look in Romans 3:10, and 23, where we are described as _____.

B. What does the Bible say "**sin**" is? (1 John 3:4) _____ _____. To "*trans-gress*" is to "cross a line" that God laid-out showing what is right and wrong. When we cross *His* laws (break through them), we sin. We call it "breaking God's laws." Everybody could be doing something, but if God said NOT to do it, and we go ahead anyway, then we have sinned.

C. God says, "*There is _____ righteous; no not one*" (Romans 3:10).

III. God's Absolute Laws of Right and Wrong

A. Most everyone agrees that we all break a few of God's laws here and there, but hardly anyone believes these sins are serious enough to keep them out of heaven. The Bible says otherwise!

B. God laid out the requirements for entrance into His heaven in a simple list, and that requirement is perfection - having NO sin in us at all.

C. If you think you don't sin, then God says you are _____ (1 John 1:8)!

D. If you want to try and prove that you don't sin, take the following test:

	The Big Ten	Never	Occasionally	Most of the Time	All the Time
1	Have I made something in my life more important than loving and obeying God?				
2	Have I *bowed down* to a statue, or an idol?				
3	Have I used Gods' (or Jesus') name flippantly?				
4	Have I worked on the Sabbath?				
5	Have I dishonoured or disobeyed my parents?				
6	Have I killed somebody?				
7	Have I committed adultery?				
8	Have I stolen ANYTHING, EVER?				
9	Have I told a lie?				
10	Have I coveted something?				

E. The above list is not anything new. What do we call this list? Not the Ten Suggestions, but God's Ten _____. You find this list in every Bible in Exodus chapter 20, from verses 1 through 17.

F. So, to be classified as a sinner does not only mean being a *murderer*, or a *thief*, but it means when a person does ANY sin (James 2:9,10; like *stealing*, *cursing*, *rebelling*, *hating*, *dishonouring*, *coveting*, etc.). Therefore, anyone who sins at all, is a **sinner** in God's eyes, and needs to be saved.

G. Compare this truth to a tree – a small tree can be known for what it is, even when it has no fruit. The fruit (let's say, *apples*) comes later, but the tree will produce apples because it is an APPLE tree. In the same way, a person *sins* because he/she is a *sinner*.

H. Note that if you ticked NEVER in number 6 above, remember that God says *"Whosoever _____ his brother is a _____: and ye know that no murderer hath eternal life abiding in him."* (1John 3:15)

I. If you ticked NEVER in number 7 above, remember that Jesus said, *"But I say unto you, That whosoever looketh on a woman to _____ after her hath committed _____ with her already in his heart."* (Matthew 5:28).

J. Even if you only ticked a few of the above **NEVERS**, then you probably are a pretty good person in man's eyes, but in God's eyes, you still are a SINNER (a law breaker), and you have proven God to be correct, and ought to now realise the truth that you need something to save you from the coming penalty for your sin.

IV. The Need for Salvation

A. Ok, so we are sinners – we break God's laws. We break a lot of them! But, so what? Well, there is a BIG **penalty** for all our sins. What is it? _____ (Romans 6:23).

B. Notice the word *"wages"* in Romans 6:23. Wages are what we earn - they are the result of our actions, whether on a job, or as we live our life. So, every sin we commit, we are only earning "_____". And, that is NOT what we want is it?

C. And there are two deaths to worry about. The first death is the end of your physical life, but it is not the end of your existence. What lies beyond a person's death is *eternity*. And if a person dies in their sins, they are condemned to die for an *eternity* IN A PLACE CALLED HELL.

1. No one normally believes they will end up in a devil's hell. They would never accept that they deserve such punishment. But what does the Bible say?

2. The Bible says *hell* is a real place where Satan, his angels, and all sinful people will spend *eternity* suffering eternal punishment and separation from God.

3. It is no joking matter: There are 162 clear references to hell in the New Testament alone, and 70 of these were made by Jesus himself! They include: Matthew 13:41,42; 5:29,30; 10:28; 11:23,24; 16:18; James 3:6; Revelation 20:13,14.

D. **But WHY did God create Hell?**

1. God created hell because He is a righteous and holy God and cannot allow *sin* in His Heaven (Revelation 21:8).

2. Since all men and women, boys and girls are sinners, **God's Son** came into the world to save us from hell's punishment. How did Jesus do that? By living a perfect sinless life that none of us could ever live, and then die a death in place of all mankind, be buried for three full days and nights, and then triumphantly raised again from the grave! Jesus did all this so that sinful people could receive the free gift of eternal _____ (Romans 6:23), and thus have free access to heaven.

3. It is only by believing Jesus' *finished work* on the cross that sinners such as you and I can ever be allowed into Heaven. But those who do not accept what Jesus

did for them are destined to go to hell because they remain in their sins (John 3:18,36)!

V. The Way of Salvation is found in a *Person*, Not a Religion

A. When Jesus died on the cross, What did God make available to everyone?

1. "_____ *life*" (John 3:16,17) – think about it! Instead of an eternity in hell!
2. But to get eternal life, Jesus said we "*must be born* _____" (John 3:3,7).
3. Read Romans 6:23 again. Thankfully, God doesn't just show us our condition (as sinners), and then abandon us – He offers us a free gift. The "_____ *of God*" (which CANNOT be earned) is the opposite of the wages of our sin!
4. Specifically, that free GIFT that God offers is called, "_____ *life*."

B. Jesus was God's gift to us, like an innocent lamb, taking the place of a sinful world. John the Baptist cried out "*Behold the _____ of God which taketh away the _____ of the world*" (John 1:29). **Jesus** is our substitute in death so that we can receive the gift of eternal life!

C. What does salvation cost?

1. God's gift is given to us freely, requiring only a *committed choice* on our part **to accept it**. Take it as your own.
2. God's gift of eternal life is provided FREE to you through the willingness of Jesus Christ to take your and my place in death and God's judgment on the cross! There is no other way to heaven than *through Jesus alone* (John 14:6)!

D. Did you know that Ephesians 2:8,9, says it is **impossible** for a sinner to save themselves from the penalty of their sin through *good works?*

1. Notice getting saved is "*not of_____ , lest any man should boast.*"
2. What do we normally think are good works that should get us into heaven?

_____

3. Notice in Titus 3:5 that it is "*not by works of_____...*"
4. Have you tried to live righteously for any length of time? **Yes, No** (circle one). Was any of your righteous works good enough to get you saved? **Yes, No**.
5. The gift of Salvation is only obtained by <u>surrender to Christ</u> - allow Jesus to do all the saving of your soul – with you no longer trying to do all the right things to earn heaven. So stop working at being good, and just finally accept what Jesus did for you in your place. Believe it with all your heart that Jesus did it for YOU!

E. Just WHO are you going to trust?

1. An honourable man, named Jesus of Nazareth, who lived 2,000 years ago in Galilee? Who did amazing miracles like raising the dead, and healing blind and deaf people; who taught people how to pray, and how to love one another; who died at the hands of the Roman soldiers on a cross? Are you trusting in Jesus the MAN?
2. Or are you trusting the *GOD who became a man*, who willingly took your and my place in death on the cross *as a Man*, in the place of all men and women everywhere, and who raised Himself out of the tomb and lives forevermore to give LIFE to all that believe on Him? Are you trusting Jesus the Son of God?
3. One belief will leave you lost and unconverted. The other will transform your life!

VI. Let's explore the *two births* the Bible talks about

A. Our first birth is our **PHYSICAL** birth (read all of John 3:1-7):

1. The first birth is a **water** birth (John 3:5). It is not baptism. We all start our life in water. Every human is born out of *a water sack* in the womb.
2. Your first birth comes from your *physical* parents. Their "flesh" produced your _____ (John 3:6).
3. But that is not all there is to you! You are more than just bone and muscle and blood and brain.
4. Take a look at the chart below.

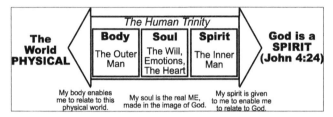

5. You are a THREE-part being, with a body, a soul and a spirit.
6. The most important part of You is the box in the middle labelled SOUL:

   a. Your soul is the real you – the part that feels, wishes, dreams, and chooses.
   b. Your body is what God gave your soul to interact with this world.
   c. Your spirit is what God gave your soul to interact with Him.

7. In simpler words, the real you (your soul) is invisible, inside you, using your body to interact with this world, and using your spirit to attempt to interact with God.
8. What is the Soul?

   a. The soul is part of the trinity of man (1Thes 5:23). Each part of you is vital, but Jesus said the _____ is the most important (Matt 16:26)
   b. It is called the *hidden* or the *inner man* (1Peter 3:3,4; 2Corinthians 4:16-18)
   c. The soul is the source of your emotions, your will, the ability to reason, and understand. It is your awareness of yourself.
   d. In other words, your soul is **the real you** – what you really are, what you think, how you feel, and why you feel that way.
   e. It is separate from the body – an immaterial, invisible part of you (2Cor 4:18).

9. Everything would be fine, except the part of you that is supposed to be able to communicate with God (your spirit) is DEAD.

   a. Sin by our first parents killed that part of us on the inside (Gen 2:17). Who were our first parents? _____ and _____.
   b. The only way to *regenerate* (give life to) the spirit is by being born again, but this time, on the inside (Ephesians 2:1; Titus 3:5)!

B. The second birth is your **SPIRITUAL** birth (John 3:5,6):

1. Your first birth only gave you human life – not eternal life. You HAVE to have a SECOND birth.
2. This birth can only come from God. John 4:24 says that "*God is a* _____." He is not *flesh* like we humans are. According to John 3:6, His Spirit will produce _____ in the life of a sinner if they would just fully believe on His Son, Jesus Christ (John 7:37-39)!

3. The second birth involves trusting God's _____ to be **true** (1Peter 1:23). You *can* fully and completely trust the death of Jesus Christ to be your payment for your sin, **because** God said in His word you could, and that He would give you a free gift, eternal salvation - eternal life!

4. If you didn't have God's perfect word to discover all this, how could you know what to believe at all? Everyone's guess would be as good as another's. No wonder there are so many religious wars!

C. Therefore, there are only two "births" that a person can experience.

1. The first birth gives only temporary life - it came from temporary parents didn't it? And it ends in death because of _____ (Rom 5:12) in all of us.

2. The second birth is only experienced by a person who turns to Christ for **salvation** from sin. It *never ends* because it came from an eternal Parent – _____ (1John 5:1)!

3. The first birth makes you physically a child of your parents. The second birth makes you spiritually and eternally a child of ____ (John 1:11,12).

D. A person desperately needs Jesus Christ to save them, because without Him, there is **no other** _____ to God (John 14:6). You cannot look to Allah, or Buddha, or Mary, etc., to get to God!

1. It is SIN that _____ all of humanity from God (Isaiah 59:2).

2. And no one can take away sin except _____ _____ (John 1:29).

3. If a person dies without having their sin paid-off by faith in what Jesus Christ did on the cross, there is only one destiny for them (John 3:36; Matthew 23:33; Matthew 25:41; Revelation 20:10-15).

   a. What is that destiny? _____

   b. That's why God calls upon everyone everywhere to _____ (Acts 17:30) and be saved when? _____ (2 Corinthians 6:2)

   c. "Succoured" means *to help you.* That means, God will even help you believe His Son when you don't know how!

E. Salvation is NOT a "process" - it is **instantly** given (Luke 18:9-14).

1. The Pharisee thought he was good enough.

2. The Publican (a public official, greedy tax collector) easily admitted he was a "_____" (Luke 18:13).

3. There is always a process to the humbling of a person, but when they know they are lost, and in need of forgiveness, once salvation is asked for, it is **IN-STANTLY** given as a free gift by God – because of Christ (Rom 6:23)!

F. What must a person do in order to be saved from hell (born again)?

1. _____ (Acts 20:20,21; 2Peter 3:9). Repentance is a determined **choice** to turn away FROM sin, and turn TO Jesus Christ for salvation. It is being *very sorry* for your sin, and hating it! It is different from "*penance*" which is you trying to PAY for your sinfulness. You cannot pay for your sins - **only Jesus can!**

2. _____ (John 1:11,12; John 5:24; 6:28,29; Acts 16:30,31).

   a. What does it mean to "*believe on Jesus?*"

     1) Not just agree with the Bible with our head (even "*the devils also _____, and tremble*"; James 2:19)

2) But it means to understand from the heart that the only payment God will accept for your sins is the death of Jesus in your place (1John 2:1,2; 5:4,5).

3) And it means to accept by faith His payment for your sins and allow Him to come into your heart and save you FROM your sins!

b. The word "**propitiation**" in 1 John 2:2, means "*full payment.*" God had to do more than just "forgive" sins, He had to completely pay-off all the broken laws that had mounted up against us, and that is what Jesus' death did - it paid *in full* all our sin debt!

G. Read carefully Romans 10:13,17. Can you be **sure** Christ will save you if you ask Him to do so? **Yes**, or **No** (circle one)

1. Would you agree that if *God said it - that should settle it?* Then believe it! That is all Jesus asks of us – just believe with all your heart!

2. Faith is "*confidence*" in God's promise, that He will never lie to you! He promises in His word over and over that He can and will save you!

Have you ever asked the Lord Jesus to **save** you from your sin and make you a child of God? _____. *When* was that? _____. **If you have not, will you ask Him, now?** (Revelation 3:20) Yes, or No. He stands at the door of your heart, knocking, and waiting. The handle is on YOUR side of the door. Open it, and let Him in! THAT's when you become BORN AGAIN.

VII. The Four 'R's of Salvation - Learn these well! You can use these four great truths and Scriptures to explain to anybody how to become a born again believer in Jesus Christ!

A. **Realize** you are a sinner, and are without the necessary righteousness to earn your entrance into heaven (Romans 3:23). God's law proves that we sin, and that we are in eternal trouble with God because of our sin! So, none of us are good enough to live with God as we are! We HAVE to be *changed* from condemned to forgiven. But how?

B. **Recognize** that you cannot fix yourself, but only by God's specific intervention can a person be saved from coming punishment (Titus 3:5). None of us have the ability to pay off our sins, no matter how much we try to go to church, say our prayers, and be nice to people! The truth is, no one can be "good enough" to make up for all the bad.

C. **Repent** of your life, and all the sin that filled it (that means: hate the sin that separates you from God, and stop trusting your attempts to be good), and then, give all that you are (sin and all) to the One who loves you and gave Himself for you on the cross (2 Corinthians 7:10). No one truly repents unless they first see themselves as a law-breaker, separated from God, and deserving of hell (John 3:36). Once you have repented, you are then empty of all self-righteousness, and are now ready to…

D. **Receive** the priceless free gift of eternal life from God by simple *faith*, asking in prayer for God to save you, all because of Jesus (John 1:12; Ephesians 2:8,9; Romans 10:13)! You will need to ask *specifically* to be saved - don't be vague or shy with God! And remember: you can ask simply because Jesus Christ paid for all your sins, past, present, and future! Nothing could be more important than knowing these four truths!

VIII. The Completion of A Person's Salvation

A. Salvation is a one-time event that changes your **destiny** forever (from hell, to heaven). It is NOT a *"continual process"*, nor a *"journey"* that a person is on! It occurs when a person decides to fully believe on the Lord Jesus Christ to save them from the punishment of their sins! Just like your first birth was a one time event, so also is your second birth! Have YOU experienced such an event? **Yes** or **No**?

B. Would you think that your salvation is now dependent upon your ability to live a *sinless*, *perfect* and *holy* life? (see Galatians 3:11) **Yes** or **No**? No one can live sinlessly, even after getting saved.

C. So, what KEEPS a person saved? JESUS! He *intercedes* with God, as _____ on behalf of a Christian who yields to temptation in a time of weakness? (1Timothy 2:5; 1 John 2:1,2). Don't ever believe that a Christian is perfect - only forgiven.

D. We therefore can **never** *lose* our gift of salvation once we have been born again! (Romans 8:37-39; John 10:27-29; Jude 24). Let's examine why not!

   1. Because we have been _____ into God's family - taken from being condemned sinners, and made into *children of God*, and heirs of everything that God has (Romans 8:15-17)! We are in God's *family* now!

   2. Because we are fully **Forgiven - all** our sins (past, present and future) were paid-for completely at the cross by Jesus Christ! There is NO further payment necessary for us to pay (Ephesians 1:7; Acts 13:38,39)!

   3. Because we have been _____ - we *exchanged* our sinfulness for the righteousness of Jesus Christ (Acts 13:38,39; 2 Corinthians 5:21)!!! Jesus did not justify *our sins*, but instead, justified *US* – made us right with God!

   4. We will learn more about this in Lesson 2.

IX. Dealing With Sin Once You Are Already Saved

A. Okay, but what happens now, when a Christian sins?

   1. The Holy Spirit first shames us, and makes us aware we are doing wrong. It is called "reproving" or convicting us – making us know we are guilty (John 16:7,8).

   2. We won't enjoy the sin like we used to (Psalm 32:1-5).

      a. Notice in how disobeying God will affect us. Iniquity is another word for sin:

      b. You will age faster.

      c. God's _____ will be hard against you, not blessing you (Psalm 32:4).

      d. You will basically "dry up" on the inside like a desert.

      e. So, Can a Christian be happy while disobeying God? **Yes** or **No**?

   3. We will be lovingly chastised by God. Hebrews 12:5-11 explains that God always endeavours to make us mature, and holy in our lives by chastening us when we sin.

      a. Chastening means "correcting" NOT punishing. God brings trouble into your life to get you back *"on the strait* (hard path) *and narrow"*

      b. God chastens His children because He _____ them.

      c. If a person never experiences God's **chastisement**, it is evident that person never became a Christian at all and is a _____ (Heb 12:8) – God calls them *illegitimate* – not the real thing – a faker.

B. What should a believer do when they sin?

1. _____ (1 John 1:9). To "confess" means to **agree** with God about the sinfulness of your life, and especially about specific acts where you broke His direct commandments!

2. _____ (Proverbs 28:13). What do you think "forsake" means?
_____

—

X. Concluding Questions - Fill in these questions from memory.

A. The Bible was written for us to know that we are _____, and that as sinners we needed God to reach down to us (not for us to reach up), and to save us from _____.

B. God has revealed absolute truth through the _____ alone.

C. What has separated all of humanity from God? _____

D. Who can actually completely take away the sins of the whole world? _____

E. Instead of trying to pay off all our sins ourselves with our own good works, our salvation depends only upon whether we are by faith willing to let the _____ of Jesus Christ be sufficient to pay off all our sin-debt to God.

F. The term "*born again*" refers to what? An **external** or an **internal** birth? (Circle one).

G. When Jesus died, whose place was He taking? _____

H. When a person repents of their sins, and calls upon Jesus Christ to save them from hell, how long does it take before they are forgiven of all sins, past, present, and future? _____

I. Have you **let** *Him* take *your* place, and been born again yourself? **Yes** or **No**

J. Is Jesus Christ worthy of you living your life by following Him and obeying His word from now on? **Yes, No.**

Well done! Lesson One is completed!

Date Lesson Completed _____	Discipler _____

ETERNAL SECURITY OF THE BELIEVER
Lesson Two

Memory Verse: *Matthew 4:4*   **Lesson Verse:** *1 John 5:13*

> *"These things have I written unto you that believe on the name of the Son of God; **that ye may know that ye have eternal life**, and that ye may believe on the name of the Son of God" 1 John 5:13*

I. Introduction – "Now that I am saved, can I ever *LOSE* my salvation?" Once a person has settled the question of how to be saved - *by grace through faith in the Saviour Jesus Christ* - it is imperative that he/she understands the security of that new relationship with God. The devil's main work on the new believer is to get them to doubt the security of that relationship.

II. What Jesus Said About Your Salvation

    A. Jesus cannot throw you away. In John 6:37, Jesus promises that *"...him that cometh to me I will in no wise _____."* To *"cast out"* would be to reject, or cast away a sinner who has come to Christ for salvation. Jesus promises *never* to do that!

    B. No one can cause you to lose your salvation – not even you! John 10:27-29 makes it clear that no one can cause you to lose your salvation. It is God that saves, and He is greater than all men. Notice that Jesus gives a person "_____ *life*", and that they shall "_____ *perish*"! How long is eternal life? _____

    C. Therefore, Your salvation is all because **God is gracious enough** to allow your simple child-like faith in Jesus, be enough to give you eternal life. It is simply a priceless *gift* from God.

        1. No one can lose their salvation because **no one can earn it!** It is *freely given* on the merit of _____ righteousness (2 Corinthians 5:21; Ephesians 2:8,9), not on the basis of our own goodness (Isaiah 64:6).

        2. Either Christ paid for ALL your sins, or He didn't (Hebrews 10:12,14,17). And if He did, then when you accepted His salvation, your eternity was settled for how long? _____ (see again 1 John 5:11-13)!

III. Is There Anything That Can Separate Us From God?

    A. Romans 8:38,39 says that **NONE** of the following can separate us from God:

        1. **Death** - you can't lose it when you die.
        2. **Life** - you can't lose it while alive.
        3. _____ - neither the good or the bad ones can take it from you.
        4. **Principalities** - no government or ruler can take it away from you.
        5. _____ - no spiritual power, including the devil himself can cause you to lose it. Spiritual powers are big, but not big enough.
        6. **Things present** - nothing happening right now can take it away.
        7. **Things to come** - nothing in the future (including sins) can make you lose it.
        8. **Height** - nothing above you can take it away.
        9. _____ - nothing from hell below you can rob you of God's forgiveness.
        10. **Nor any other creature** shall be able to _____ us from the love of God, which is in Christ Jesus our Lord.

    B. There are NO sins that you could do that could make Jesus reject you now that you have been forgiven! He took away the sins of the WHOLE _____ (John 1:29)!

And there are no Scriptures that show a believer could sin a sin and therefore lose their new life in Christ. None!

C. Your salvation is **sealed** for all eternity with the Holy Spirit (Ephesians 1:13; 4:30).

   1. To "seal" something is to "secure" it like a package is "sealed" for shipping, and like when you put a down-payment on a house (you are sealing the purchase)
   2. The Holy Spirit is our *seal* showing that _____ owns us, and will not let any-thing "spoil" or ruin us (1 Corinthians 6:19,20)!
   3. Jesus promises He will **NEVER** leave you, nor _____ you (Heb 13:5)!

D. Best of all, your _____ is written down in heaven (Luke 10:20; Rev 20:14,15) - your reservation for your trip has already been made!

E. Therefore, NOTHING can separate a believer from the love of God. *Yet the truth is, a Christian does still sin*, and is _____ if he thinks he does not sin any-more (1 John 1:8). So, what <u>effect</u> does sin have on a Christian?

   1. It will NOT send us to hell now – but it will make it so God is not close to us.

      a. Sin USED to separate us from God completely – we were in a completely different family (John 8:44).
      b. But sin now only separates us in our *fellowship* with God (our closeness)! Just as you can never break the relationship between a child and his or her parents, the same is true when we become a child of God (John 1:12,13). It is permanent.
      c. Remember, Your relationship with God is now a Father/son relationship by the new "birth" (John 3:3). Jesus teaches us to call God, *"our _____ "* (Matthew 6:9) because, by your faith in Christ, *that's just what He is!*

   2. God will have to lovingly chastise you.

      a. When a Christian sins, no matter what sin it is, if that sin is not confessed to God *as sin* (not just a "mistake"), and if not repented of, then God will have to *chastise* you (Hebrews 12:6-8).
      b. God is responsible for His children, and will not let us get away with sin like we used to before we were adopted into His family!

   3. God will ignore you – He will not answer your _____ (Psalm 66:18) until you get right with Him. He won't hear you when you pray… that's pretty serious.
   4. But, if your sinning goes on for very long, the Lord may just cause you to be-come weak, sickly, or even to die early because you have stopped living for Him (1 Corinthians 11:30-32).

F. But a believer, a born again Christian cannot ever become lost again!

   1. Remember, Jesus promises to never throw us away (John 6:37).
   2. Jesus promises that a believer will NEVER "_____" (John 10:28)
   3. Jesus promises that He will lose NO ONE that comes to Him for salvation. See John 6:39, *"And this is the Father's will which hath sent me, that of all which he hath given me I should lose _____."*
   4. Jesus put GOD the Holy Spirit inside you, and then "_____" Him in you until you reach heaven! (Rom 5:5; Eph 1:13).
   5. If someone starts seriously sinning, and leaves church, and stops believing, and does NOT experience God's chastening… then that person *"went out from us, but **they were** _____; for if they had been of us, they would no doubt have continued with us..."* 1John 2:19.

IV. What If You Don't <u>Feel</u> Saved?

ONCE \ ALWAYS
SAVED / SAVED!

A. "_____" your heart to see if you trusted Christ to **save** you, or are still *working* your own way to heaven (2 Corinthians 13:5). A "reprobate" is a faker, or a fraud. More people only "hope" they are Christians because they have prayed a prayer, or go to a certain church, or whatever. If you are saved, it will be because as a sinner, you simply repented and trusted Christ!

B. And then **Determine** in your heart, that eternal life is NOT based upon *feelings*, but only on the factual truths of the word of God and your <u>acceptance</u> of it (1 John 3:19,20; Titus 1:2).

1. He said you are forgiven by your faith alone (Acts 13:38,39).
2. He said you are now accepted (Ephesians 1:6).
3. He said you will be with Him one day (John 14:1-3).
4. At some point you are going to have to just **believe** all that God said, and settle it forever in your heart! (1John 2:25).

V. So, Once sealed, ALWAYS sealed (Ephesians 4:30). That's why a Christian can say they **know** they are saved, and actually **HAVE** right now, eternal life (1John 5:13).

VI. Things That Give Us Assurance of Salvation. Below are some things that will develop automatically in your life now that you personally know and trust Jesus Christ!

A. A love for the Bible - a love for the TRUTH (Psalm 1:1,2; 119:97)!

B. A love for God like never before - A personal walk with Him develops! He is not a Genie, or a distant Creator, but *Saviour and Friend* (Matt 22:36,37)!

C. A desire to do God's _____, instead of only your own (Psalm 40:8)!

D. No more _____ - True confidence in Christ and in the truth (2Tim 1:7)!

E. The chastening hand of the Lord in your life when you sin (Hebrews 12:6)!

F. A spiritual discernment - able to sense spiritual things going on, and focus on the eternal, instead of only on this life (Romans 8:15,16; 1Cor 2:14-16)!

VII. Some Questions to Ponder...

A. Jesus promises that "*...him that cometh to me I will in no wise* _____."

B. What kind of life did Jesus purchase for a believer? _____

C. Can anyone or anything come between and separate you from your relationship with God after you have been born again? **Yes** or **No**?

D. No one can lose their salvation, because no one can earn it! **True** or **False**?

E. How many of your sins did Jesus actually pay for when He died on the cross for you? _____

F. Name ANY sins that you could commit that would be more than Jesus died for:
_____.
Give a Scripture that proves those sins would make you lose your new life in Christ:
_____.

G. What does the Holy Spirit do to a person's soul when the get saved? _____.

H. What is written down in heaven the moment you get born again? _____.

I. What BIG thing will God have to do to you if you start sinning and not stopping?
_____

Date Lesson Completed _____ *Discipler* _____

BELIEVER'S BAPTISM
Lesson Three

Memory Verse: *Matthew 4:4*   **Lesson Verse:** *Acts 2:41*

> *"Then they that gladly received his word were **baptized**"* Acts 2:41

I. Introduction

A. The Christian life, entered through the new birth, is just that - *a life*. In the Bible, a new Christian is compared to a "baby" (1Peter 2:2), and is commanded to "_____ *in grace*" to maturity (2Peter 3:18). A Christian therefore, is not to stay as a "baby" all their life, but to GROW. And an important FIRST step of a Bible believing Christian's growth is *believer's baptism* (Acts 2:37-41; Matthew 28:18-20).

B. This simple step of obedience is NOT part of being saved - it is <u>God's test</u> of whether or not a person whole-heartily wants to follow the Lord Jesus Christ now that they ARE saved!

C. This lesson will explain what believer's baptism is, its importance, and when a Christian should get baptized.

II. What is Believer's Baptism?

A. Let's First Start with What Baptism is Not

1. **Baptism is NOT a Sacrament** - The word sacrament means doing something to **earn** God's gift of grace. The word *sacrament* is a word from Catholicism and was carried over into the Reformation, but is not a Bible word. God's grace is a free gift from God that cannot ever be earned! God gives His grace FREELY, if only we would take it by faith.

2. **Baptism is NOT a means of Salvation** - To everyone thinking their baby baptism helped them out, God's Word says in Titus 3:5 *"Not by _____ of righteousness which we have done, but according to His mercy He saved us."* God clearly declares that we are saved **by free grace** through **simple faith** in His Son. Ephesians 2:8,9 says, *"For by grace are ye saved through faith, and that not of yourselves, it is the gift of God, not of _____ lest any man should boast."* No works, no matter how good can be a part of paying for your sins. Period!

   a. Although Catechisms, Creeds, and Confessions say that baptism is necessary for your salvation, the Bible says the opposite! Anything that you are trusting in, especially your good works like baptism, is nothing compared to the perfect effort of God's son Jesus Christ in your place on the cross!

   b. Baptism cannot cleanse anyone's soul! It is only water! It never has washed anything *on the inside of us* away, and it never will! Only the perfect blood of Jesus Christ can wash away all your sin!

3. **Baptism in NOT a tradition or empty religious ceremony.** It is the FIRST thing a believer does once they have become a born again Christian. It follows salvation just about every time someone got saved in the New Testament. See again Acts 2:41 *"Then they that gladly received his word were _____: and the same day there were added unto them about three thousand souls."*

B. What Baptism Is

1. Baptism in the Bible **is the act of obedience** to the command by Jesus Christ for every new believer to be baptized in water (Matthew 28:19,20; Acts 2:41,42).

2. Baptism is **only for followers** of Jesus Christ who have made a definite decision to turn away from sin, and believe only in Jesus Christ as their Lord and Saviour! It is not for babies, or for people who just feel like getting baptized.

3. It means **to fully submerge a believer into water**, in order to identify the believer with Christ's death, burial, and resurrection (Romans 6:3,4), and to testify to the world that they are a new creature because of God's grace, not because of being baptized. Baptism is a statement that you are now a believer, not a MEANS of becoming a believer!

4. Believer's Baptism, **means to go into and then come out of WATER** (Matthew 3:16; Mark 1:9,10; Acts 8:38,39), as in *complete immersion*, and is the only thing that can picture a burial and resurrection, whereas all other definitions (like, sprinkling, dipping, pouring, etc.) cannot illustrate this.

5. Baptism **associates the new believer with the doctrine of the church administrating it.** This is important! 1 Corinthians 10:1-4 shows that the Jews coming out of Egypt were baptized unto _____ and his laws. When they went under the water, they were following Moses. Well, when a new believer gets baptized, they are deciding to agree with the doctrine of the church that is baptizing them. Be careful who is baptizing you, and make sure they are Bible-only in doctrine.

6. Baptism therefore is the method ordained by Jesus Christ to keep His church pure from false believers, and false teachers who may attempt to enter the church as ravenous wolves, not sparing the _____ (Acts 20:28,29).

C. There are Two *'Baptisms'* in the Bible

1. Water Baptism is actually the SECOND Baptism a person needs. It is NOT the most important baptism.

2. Notice these important Scriptures and truths:

   a. Every person starts off "in sins" and not "in Christ". Ephesians 2:1,5 says every one of us have lived "*IN sins*" all our lives. It was the condition we naturally lived in. We were lost, and condemned because of all our sins we constantly did against the laws of God.

   b. Then, 1 Corinthians 12:12,13 shows the sinner being **taken from** a life that had been *in sin*, and now being placed INTO the Person of _____ Himself at the time of their new birth (see also 2 Corinthians 5:17)! **This is a SPIRITUAL baptism**, and it is MUCH more important than any water baptism.

      1) Spiritual baptism is what happens when a sinner is saved from the punishment of their sins – they are PLACED INTO SALVATION HIMSELF!

      2) The placement of a sinner's life into Christ is what actually saves that sinner. As far as we are concerned, we are only trusting Christ to cleanse us from all sin in us. As far as God is concerned, we are actually being immersed into, and surrounded by our Saviour for the rest of eternity!

      3) So, at your salvation, God didn't just give you the gift of eternal life - He actually placed you INTO eternal life Himself, which is Jesus Christ!

      4) This is the most important baptism, because, if you didn't get placed *into Christ*, then you never got saved!

3. So, two baptisms need to occur in every person's life:

   a. Is it a (**spiritual** or **water**) baptism which happens <u>when</u> we are saved (placed into Jesus Christ when we ask to be saved from our sins).

   b. And THEN, is it a (**spiritual** or **water**) baptism, which happens **after** we get saved (placed into water to show the world we are burying our old life).

   c. Which baptism must happen FIRST? _____

   d. Has THAT baptism happened in your life yet? **Yes** or **No**?

D. **The importance of 'Water Baptism'.** We have learned now about *Spiritual Baptism.* The Bible also talks about '*water baptism.*' Let's find out more about it.

1. Baptism into water only occurs to those capable of 'believing' on the Lord Jesus for salvation. Therefore, only those that _____ can be baptized (Acts 8:26-39). This excludes all baby baptisms, because they can't believe! **There is not one record of the baptism of a baby in the Bible.**

2. Water baptism ALWAYS follows a sinner's salvation where they have been Spiritually baptized into Christ first.

3. Water baptism symbolizes on the outside what happened already 'inside' when a person was saved - "I died to sin (its guilt, power, and its penalty), my old life is therefore dead and buried, and I was raised to a new life IN Christ."

4. Romans 6:3-6 describes baptism as a 3-fold *memorial* of:

   a. Christ's _____

   b. His _____

   c. And His _____

   d. *According to 1Corinthians 15:1-4, the whole Gospel is contained in these three events, and that a person is SAVED if he or she simply trusts them to be sufficient to pay for their sins!*

   e. If you think water baptism is necessary for a person to be saved, 1Corinthians 15 never mentions water ANYWHERE!

   f. The apostle Paul's whole focus in life was not baptizing people, but preaching the Gospel to get people to believe (1Cor 1:13-18)! Not that water baptism is not important, but that it was *secondary* to salvation - not part of salvation!

   g. So, water baptism *identifies* or *associates* the believer no longer with their old life of sin, <u>but with Jesus Christ</u> and **His** death, burial, and resurrection. In the same way that a uniform associates a worker with the company they work for!

5. Water baptism presents a public testimony to the world that one has accepted Jesus Christ as their Saviour, and that they are willing to live a different life now for the Lord Jesus (Acts 2:41; Romans 10:11)!

III. Does Baptism Have Anything Do With Salvation?

A. So, when immersed into water in baptism, does this "wash away our sins?"

B. John the Baptist declared in Mark 1:4 "*John did baptize in the wilderness, and preach the baptism of repentance for the remission of sins.*" That sounds like a person has to be baptized to receive the removal (remission) of their sins.

C. But listen to Jesus clarify:

1. Matthew 26:28 "*For this is ___ _____ of the new testament, which is shed for many for the remission of sins.*"

   2. God says in Hebrews 9:22, "*without shedding of* _____ *is no remission.*"

D. John's Baptism was ONLY Water Baptism (Mark 1:7,8; Acts 1:5)

   1. Mark 1:7,8 *And preached, saying, There cometh one mightier than I after me, the latchet of whose shoes I am not worthy to stoop down and unloose. I indeed have baptized you with water: but he shall baptize you with the Holy Ghost.*

   2. Acts 1:5 *For John truly baptized with water; but ye shall be baptized with the Holy Ghost not many days hence.*

   3. So, Baptism of the Holy Ghost [SALVATION] is infinitely more important than baptism in water!

E. The _____ (not baptism) is the Gospel – full stop! (1Cor 1:17,18)

F. Believer's Water Baptism only pictures the Remission of sins that had happened to them when they believed!

   1. It is a joyful ceremony marking the public confession of a new believer's FAITH in Jesus, and their decision to FOLLOW the life of Christ

   2. Act 19:4,5 *Then said Paul, John verily baptized with the baptism of repentance, saying unto the people, that they should believe on him which should come after him, that is, on Christ Jesus. When they heard this, they were baptized in the name of the Lord Jesus.*

   3. Just like the Lord's Remembrance Supper is a PICTURE (it is NOT literal, even though it SOUNDS literal), so also is believer's baptism. Neither Baptism or Communion does anything for the soul of the believer!

G. Here are some more Scriptures

   1. Ephesians 2:8,9 We are saved by what? _____ Not by ANY work, effort at all other than that!

   2. 1Peter 2:24 *Who his own self bare our sins in his own body on the tree, that we, being dead to sins, should live unto righteousness: by whose stripes ye were healed.* NOT by our baptism.

   3. Ephesians 1:7 "...*we have redemption through* ____ _____ "

   4. 1John 1:7 "...*the* _____ *of Jesus Christ his Son, cleanseth us from* ___ *sin.*"

H. So... Only the _____ of Christ can wash away our sins! Not water at all!

IV. How Should A Person be Water-Baptized?

A. You must be baptized just **like Jesus was baptized**: Jesus was not sprinkled, or poured upon, but rather *immersed* into the water. Matthew 3:16 says, "*He* (Jesus) ...went **UP** straightway _____ of the water...*" He had been IN it.

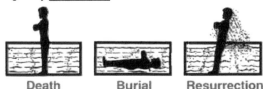

Death   Burial   Resurrection

B. You must be baptized **like ALL New Testament believers were baptized**: (Acts 8:38,39) "*... they went down both <u>into the water</u>... and when they were <u>come UP out</u> of the water...* " Note that there is NO exception to this in all the Bible examples.

C. A new Christian should be baptized **in the only way that adequately pictures Christ's death, burial, and resurrection** to save the sinner (See again 1 Corinthians 15:1-4, and Romans 6:1-6).

V. Why Get Baptized?

A. Because we are following someone who is our greatest example. Who is this example? (Matthew 3:13-16) _____

B. Because it was the *normal practice* of the Christians in the New Testament (Acts 2:41; 8:38; 9:17,18; 10:48; 16:14,15,33; 18:8; 19:4,5).

C. Because it is Christ's *command* for all nations: *"Go ye therefore and teach all nations,* _____ *them..."* (Matt 28:19,20). Jesus said, *"If ye* _____ *me, keep my* _____ *"* (John 14:15).

D. Because it *testifies* to the world that you are different now (2 Corinthians 5:17), and that you are aligning your life with what the Bible says, and not with what this world and its religions say.

E. Baptism is God's test of a person's sincerity of faith. If a person is not willing to go on record as having been saved by the grace of God through the death, burial, and resurrection of Christ, then they really are not coming to Christ for salvation, but for their own purpose. God doesn't just want "lip service" (Matthew 15:8). He wants to know if we are really serious! We already know that He is really serious - He already *died* in our place! Will you *live* for Him?

Key Truths About Baptism

❖ It means *immersion*.

❖ It is supposed to happen AFTER a person consciously repents, and accepts Jesus Christ as their Saviour from sin's penalty.

❖ Any baptism before salvation is worthless, and does not count.

❖ Baptism is a public show of your commitment to living your new life for Christ.

VI. Two Important Questions to Settle:

A. Why did Jesus die? _____
_____ .

B. Why did He rise again from the dead? Think about it! Because whatever reason He did it, proves what He wants to do IN YOUR LIFE! What one word keeps popping up in all the following Scriptures? _____ (John 10:10; 5:24; 3:16; Romans 6:23).

C. THAT answer explains the reason for getting Scripturally baptized... to **show** the world that you now have a new "_____" that you are going to live, for Him!

VII. What If I Was Baptized Already BEFORE I Got Saved?

A. Notice when true Christians got baptized (Acts 2:41; 16:30-33). Was it <u>*Before*</u> or <u>*After*</u> their repentance of sin, and acceptance of Christ? (circle one)

B. If you were baptized **before** you became born again (for example, when you were an infant, or when you joined some religion or church), then *you only got wet*, and you still need to be baptized.

C. So, if you have been saved, and have **never** been *Scripturally* baptized, and you are going to be obedient to the Saviour and His word, <u>when</u> should you be baptized?
_____ .

Have you ever been Scripturally baptized after you got saved? If so when? _____ and where? _____
If you have never been Scripturally baptized, are you ready now? **Yes, No**

Date Lesson Completed _____ *Discipler* _____

THE WORD OF GOD
Lesson Four

Memory Verse: *Matthew 4:4*   **Lesson Verse:** *Hebrews 4:12*

> *"For the word of God is quick and powerful, and sharper than any twoedged sword, piercing even to the dividing asunder of soul and spirit, and of the joints and marrow, and is a discerner of the thoughts and intents of the heart."*
> Hebrews 4:12

I. Introduction

A. What separates **Bible**-Christianity from all other types of Christianity is its claim to an absolute, written authority from God (John 17:17). So many "Christians" only *use* the Bible, but do not believe it is completely true. Having the perfect word of God is essential because the way in which a Christian is to live his or her life is only found in the pages of the Holy Bible!

B. The purpose of this lesson is to help the Christian to know what it is that they hold in their hands, and how they can trust it as *the very "word of _____"* (1 Thessalonians 2:13)! We don't just "believe" the Bible is God's word... we can PROVE it.

C. What you hold in your hands is a supernatural Book, given to us by God to show us who God is, what He expects, and how to follow Him throughout all of our lives.

II. Bible Facts

A. The Bible is **the oldest book in the world**. It has been read by more people and translated into more languages than any other book and holds the distinction of being the first book ever printed on a printing press.

B. It alone has altered the events of human history **more than any other piece of literature**. The Bible has been introduced into nations full of chaotic warlike tribes and ended up producing civilized and safe societies. This one book has defended beleaguered women and freed slaves by expressly teaching all are to be treated as equals.

C. It guides the human heart and mind on a journey that has led to the greatest discoveries and accomplishments ever attempted. And it speaks with all authority on the issues of not only life, but of death, and eternity. It does all this in words on a page, that can be held in a hand, studied by the mind, believed with the heart, and experienced in the soul. There is no other book like the Bible. And there is no better book for the soul. Read it. Test it. Believe it. And enjoy the fruits of living by it.

D. The Bible is **ONE** Book made up of **66** separate books. During the Council of Trent (1563 AD), the Roman Catholic church added 7 more books called the *Apocrypha*, but they are not inspired like the other 66, and cause great confusion by its contradictions.

E. Each book of the Bible is thankfully divided into Chapters, and each chapter into verses. There are 1,189 chapters in the entire Bible, and 31,102 verses.

F. **It is eternal.** According to Jesus Christ, "_____" and "_____" will pass away, but NOT God's word (Matthew 24:35).

G. Overall, the Bible is divided into two main sections:

  1. The **first** section is called the _____ _____ (2Cor 3:14).
  2. The **second** section is called the _____ _____ (2Cor 3:6).
  3. A "testament" is a written *testimony* about God's will for us in the form of a covenant (or agreement) with us.

H. The Bible is **God's revelation** of the origin and destiny of all things (Isaiah 46:9,10). It is a record of how God dealt with man in the past, present and future. And it reveals the plan of God for mankind here and now, and in the next life.

I. It contains **the message of eternal salvation** for all who believe in Christ, and eternal _____ for all who reject that Gospel (John 3:36).

J. It is the most remarkable Book ever! Of its divine library of 66 books, there is history, biography, poetry, proverbial sayings (true sayings), hymns (songs), laws, parables (stories that teach truth), riddles, allegories (symbolic language), prophecies, records of birth, and death, mysteries, adventure, recipes, blessings, cursings, and all other forms of human expression!

K. The Bible is superior to all philosophy because it was not given "_by man's_ _____" but by the teaching of the _____ _____ (1 Corinthians 2:13).

L. **The Bible is perfect**, having no error because it is both _inspired_, and _____ by God (Psalm 12:6,7). God wrote the Scriptures through men (that's _inspiration_, 2Timothy 3:16), and then bound Himself to keep His word from error (that's _preservation_, Matthew 24:35)! That means God's word is still here today - it has not been lost or corrupted, or else Jesus was a liar!

M. This one Book permeates all of literature. No stories are as well known as David and Goliath, Daniel in the Lion's Den, Moses at the Red Sea, and Noah's world wide flood. The words of this Book that you hold in your hand are even etched in stone upon so many public buildings all over the world as testimony to how it has been the foundation for laws and a just society.

N. And the Bible is not going away... Jesus said in Matthew 24:35, "_Heaven and earth shall pass away, but my words shall _____ _____ _____._"

O. **Psalm 119** describes the importance of the Bible in the life of the believer.

1. The Bible refers to _itself_ in Psalm 119 using <u>eight</u> different words:

   a. **The** _____ - God's definition of right and wrong (vs 1)
   b. **The** _____ - a record of what God thinks (vs 2)
   c. **God's** _____ - a record of how God works (vs 3)
   d. _____ - Truths that apply to life - principles (vs 4)
   e. _____ - fixed truths of God (5)
   f. _____ - clear commands and instructions (6)
   g. _____ - God's conclusions about various subjects (vs 7)
   h. **The** _____ - the very words of God (vs 9)

2. The Psalm also declares that God charges the believer with <u>eight</u> responsibilities concerning the Scriptures:

   a. To _love_ them (119:97,159) - How much do YOU love the Bible?
   b. _Prize_ them (119:72,127) as you would infinite **treasure**!
   c. _Memorize_ them (119:11) - learn God's words as He wrote them.
   d. _____ on them (119:15,23,48,78) - understand each word!
   e. _Study_ them (119:12,18,26,27) - See _2Tim 2:15_!
   f. _Trust_ them (119:42) Faith comes by hearing this Bible (Rom 10:17)
   g. _Obey_ them (119:8) - See _James 1:22_! Live this Bible every day!
   h. _Declare_ them (119:13) - tell others of God's word on life!

P. There are four things God wants us to learn from the Bible (2Timothy 3:16,17):

1. **Doctrine** - learn what is right and true.
2. **Reproof** - learn what is not right in our life, and in the world.

3. _____ - learn how to **get** right - most important.

4. **Instruction** in righteousness - learn how to **stay** right.

5. These four foundations prepare you so that "*...the man of God* (the mature Christian) *may be* _____, *throughly furnished unto all good works.*"

III. What The Bible Is Not - Make no mistake about it!

A. It is NOT a charm or good luck piece.

B. It is NOT a book of "heavenly utterances" in a supernatural language. It is God's revelation in the most simple human language possible.

C. It is NOT a book of mysteries. It is self interpreting, explaining all the mysteries of life, so that no mysteries remain.

D. It is NOT a book that says one thing and means another.

E. It is NOT a book that should be constantly criticized and attacked simply because you don't like what it says, or how it says it! It is God's words!

IV. How We Got Our Bible - A Brief History Lesson

A. The Bible was written not by just one or two people, but by 40 different people from 19 different occupations, including shepherds, soldiers, farmers, cattlemen, fishermen, tax collectors, a medical doctor, and even several kings and prophets, etc. These men's lives spanned a period of about 2,000 years, with the earliest book, the book of Job being written about 1,900 years before the birth of Christ. Other books, including Genesis through Deuteronomy were written around 1,400 years before Christ. And the book of the Revelation was written about 95 years AFTER the birth of Christ.

1. The first part of the Bible is called **the Old Testament**, and consists of 39 books. These books make up about 3/4ths of the entire Bible. They include Genesis, Exodus, Ruth, Esther, Psalms, Proverbs, Daniel, and ends with the book by Malachi. These 39 books were written mainly in the Jewish language of Hebrew.

2. The second part of the Bible is called **the New Testament**, and it has 27 books in it. They include Matthew, Mark, Luke, John, Ephesians, 1st and 2nd Timothy, James, and it ends with the book of Revelation. All the New Testament books were written in the Greek language starting just after Christ's resurrection, with the last ones being completed by 95 A.D.

B. The Bible is the <u>written record</u> of the very words that proceeded from the _____ of God (Matthew 4:4). They are referred to as the *Scriptures*, the *Law*, **God's *Word***, and ***the Book***. We get our word "*Bible*" from the Greek word 'Biblios', which simply means "the Book."

C. The Bible actually describes how it was written.

Old Testament   New Testament

Genesis   Revelation

39 Books   27 Books

1. The Bible came not "*by the* _____ *of* man" (2Peter 1:21). No one just sat down and decided to write something and call it Scripture.

2. The Apostle Peter continued in 2Peter 1:21, "but *holy men of God spake as they were* _____ *by the Holy Ghost*". That is called Inspiration (2Tim 3:16). This means God "breathed" (spoke) His very words into the human authors of the Bible as they wrote it - they were not invented by human imagination. They came directly from God (Matthew 4:4)!

3. God chose to use over 40 human authors to pen the books of the Bible, with the Holy Spirit always directing, and controlling their words. Let's look at some of the "sub-authors" that God used to pen this Book of books called the Bible:

   a. Who wrote Deuteronomy 31:24-26? _____
   b. Who wrote most of the Psalms? Luke 20:42_____
   c. Proverbs 1:1 _____
   d. Isaiah 1:1 _____
   e. Romans 1:1,7 _____
   f. 1Peter 1:1 _____

4. What the sub-authors spoke was written down. What was written down was copied and passed around throughout the world! These authors were serious men. They came from all walks of life. They were men of good reputation and of sound mind. Many of them were viciously persecuted and killed for the life they lived. None of the authors were ever made wealthy or powerful by the words they wrote, or the prophecies they gave. Far from it; many were impoverished. Moses, the author of the first five books of the Bible, chose to live a life of horrific hardship in the service of God as opposed to the billionaire's life he could have lived as the adopted son of Pharaoh, the king of Egypt. Many Bible writers made similar choices. Their motivation certainly was not covetousness and worldly advantage. The lives they lived, and the testimonies they held, and the deaths they died gave powerful evidence that they were telling the truth.

D. As each of the authors spoke, they then penned their words under the perfectly guided inspiration of the Holy Ghost (2Timothy 3:16 says, *"All scripture is given by* _____ *of God"*).

E. The Old Testament was written mainly in the **HEBREW** language, with the oldest book being written 2000 years before the Birth of Christ (BC) and the last being written about 350 years BC. The Hebrew (which is read from right to left) for Genesis 1:1 looks like:

בְּרֵאשִׁית בָּרָא אֱלֹהִים אֵת הַשָּׁמַיִם וְאֵת הָאָרֶץ:

F. The New Testament was written in **GREEK** from 35 AD to 95 AD (A.D. is a Latin abbreviation for, *Year of the Lord* starting from Christ's birth). The Greek for John 3:16 looks like (you read Greek from left to right):

ουτως γαρ ηγαπησεν ο θεος τον κοσμον ωστε τον υιον αυτου τον μονογενη εδωκεν ινα πας ο πιστευων εις αυτον μη αποληται αλλ εχη ζωην αιωνιον

G. Aren't you glad we can read God's words in our own language?!

H. The Bible is now **completed**. It's last book was finished in about 95 AD, when the apostle John completed the book of *Revelation*. No one can add anything to it through personal revelations, visions, or prophecies, and no one can take away from it (Rev 22:18,19) - anyone who tries to say they have any additional prophecies than already contained in the Bible is of the devil!

I. Through 3,000 years, God has preserved over **5,200** Greek and Hebrew copies and portions of His words! These copies are what our Bible is translated from.

J. From those copies, God combined His words into ONE Book at around 157 AD. This Bible was called the *Vetus Latina*, or **Old Latin Bible**. At the same time, the Bible was beginning to be translated into dozens of other languages including Coptic (Egyptian), Syriac, and Gothic (European).

K. In 382 A.D. the Roman Catholic Church had Eusebius Jerome (340-420 AD) produce a new version of the Latin Bible, called **Jerome's Latin Vulgate**. It was completed in 405. Jerom's Vulgate became the official Bible of the Roman Catholic Church for the next 1,300 years, and all other translation work was officially prohibited and was a criminal offence punishable by death. (See Council of Toulouse of 1229 A.D., the Council of Tarragona of 1234, and the Ecumenical Council of Constance in 1415). Until the Reformation of the 14th through 17th centuries the Bible was always read at great risk.

L. The *English* Bible is the result of some 1,300 years of life-threatening work, starting as far back as 700 AD (only some of the publications are listed below).

1. In 1382, a man named **John Wycliffe** (1330-1384) translated the first complete Bible into English. For this, he was *excommunicated*, and after death, his bones were *burned* by order of the pope! Here is an example of his translation of John 3:16:

for god loved so the world! that he gaf his oon bigetun sone, that eche man that bileueth in him perisch not: but have euerlastynge life.

2. The next was made by **William Tyndale** (1494-1536), who was only able to finish the New Testament and the first five books of the Old Testament by 1530. By order of the Catholic Church, Tyndale was *burned* at the stake for translating the Scriptures on October 6, 1536!

3. In 1535, **Myles Coverdale** (1485-1568) completed the first printed Bible (all others were *hand copied*, or printed without moveable type).

4. In 1539 the **Great Bible** was published. It was called *Great* because of its large size. This Bible was placed into every church, and a chain placed on it so that it could not be removed, but freely read from without worry of it being stolen.

5. In 1560, the **Geneva Bible** was produced by Bible scholars in Geneva, Switzerland because in England, Catholic *Queen Mary* had ascended the throne and forbid access to the Bible, and its publication.

6. The Roman Catholic church came out with it's *Rheims* New Testament in 1582, and *Douay* Old Testament in 1609. They were translated for the express purpose of backing up the dogma and teaching of the church instead of presenting the truths of Christ.

Genesis 17 from Geneva Bible

7. In 1604, **King James** the First, authorized 47 men to produce a complete translation of the Bible without Catholic influence in it. It was completed in 1611, and is referred to as the **King James Version** (KJV), or **Authorized Version** (AV) of 1611, and still today is God's preserved word for the English speaking people. The King James Bible has gone through **seven editions**, the last one being in **1769**, correcting spelling errors, and making very minor changes so that it is completely accurate and faithful to the texts of the original languages from which it was translated.

Page from the King James Bible of 1611

M. Since 1611 there have been over 200 attempts to falsely "modernize" the Bible. Maybe you know of some of these. They include the **New International Version** (NIV), **New American Standard Version** (NASV), **Good News Bible**, **New King James Version**, **English Standard Version**, etc. But none are as accurate, or honest in their translation, or have the effect on people's hearts like the **King James Bible**! More about this in Lesson 5.

N. Since the time of the Reformation, over 2,000 languages have received the "*words of Life*" as the Apostles called them in John 6:68, due to the sacrificial efforts of Bible believing men and women who believed with all their heart that "_____ cometh by hearing, and hearing by the word of God." (Romans 10:17). Jesus plainly declared in John 5:24, "*Verily, verily, I say unto you, He that heareth ___ _____, and believeth on him that sent me, hath everlasting life, and shall not come into condemnation; but is passed from death unto _____.*"

O. So, what you hold in your hands, has cost a great number of people a high price to make sure you can read God's words, and believe God's promises for yourself.

V. **Proofs of Inspiration** - *How We Know the Bible was Given By God!*

A. This book has been tested and proven scientifically to be absolutely accurate when it has spoken of science. Historically it has recorded ancient events that even now are being discovered to be 100% true. Prophetically the Bible has foretold hundreds of vast future events, long before they ever occurred, with 100% accuracy! There is no other book in all of history like this Book you now hold in your hands!

B. **Its Unity Proves it was Given by God.** Over 40 authors wrote the 66 books of the Bible in different lands (*Job* in Mesopotamia, *Moses* in Jordan, *Paul* in Rome and Greece, *John* in Turkey, *Peter* in Babylon), and at different times, covering a period of over 2,100 years (from 2000 B.C. to 95 A.D.), and yet never contradicting each other! Try to duplicate that! No matter what you have been told, none of the writings were "sanctioned" by some church council, or commanded to be written by some church leader. They were all written by the direct inspirational hand of _____ (2 Tim 3:16), and preserved from any human error, in spite of the fact that myriads of religious efforts were made to destroy both the prophets and their message!

C. **Its Influence on the World.** No other book has so influenced the course of human events like the Bible - it has never been *imposed* upon a people. No matter what culture a person lives in, one thing has always been true - *Religion* has always been forced upon people on a collective basis, while Biblical Christianity has always been ***chosen*** on an individual basis. This one piece of "literature" has brought about the greatest nations, and greatest freedoms no sword or any other means could! Notice the effect the word of God had upon the people of first century A.D. (Acts 8:4; 17:6) – it turned the world "_____". Compare the time of the Dark Ages (when the Bible was banned from being read or believed), and the effects of Humanism, Stalinism, Marxism, and all other forms of tyrannical dictatorship (all banned the Bible) with the Reformation, and the Renaissance! Don't let anyone take away your access to God's written word!

D. **Its Supernatural Preservation.** Whole kingdoms and religions have sought in vain to destroy the influence of the Scriptures, and yet it still reigns victorious, and indestructible (Matt 24:35). It has, and always will out-last all religions and kingdoms of this world, simply because, it is God's pure word (Ps 12:6,7)!

E. **Its Fulfilled Prophecy.** One of the most important areas of proof that God wrote the Bible involves the fact that almost 3,300 verses of prophecy have been fulfilled *to the letter*. These prophecies were predictions made hundreds and even thousands of years before their fulfilment:

   1. The prediction in Micah 5:2 of the birthplace of _____ was made 700 years before the event - see Matthew 2:1-6).

   2. Jesus would be born of a virgin, "*Behold, a _____ shall conceive, and bear a son, and shall call his name Immanuel*" (750 BC - Isaiah 7:14)

   3. Jesus would be rejected by His own people, "*He is despised and _____ of men; a man of sorrows, and acquainted with grief: and we hid as it were our faces from him*" (750 BC - Isaiah 53:3).

   4. Jesus would heal people, "*The eyes of the blind shall be _____, and the ears of the deaf shall be unstopped... The lame man leap as an hart, and the tongue of the dumb _____*" (Isaiah 35:5,6).

5. The prophet Zechariah (in Zech 11:12,13) back in 500 BC foretells that Jesus would be betrayed for 30 pieces of silver *"Give me my price; and if not, forbear. So they weighed for my price _____ _____ of silver"*. See Mt 26:15

6. Jesus' hands and His feet would be pierced by nails, *"They _____ my hands and my feet."* (Ps 22:16), *"and they shall look upon me whom they have pierced"* (500 BC Zech 12:10). Normally criminals were stoned.

7. Jesus would be in the grave for 3 days and 3 nights, *"For as Jonas was three days and three nights in the whale's belly;* **so shall the Son of man be three days and three nights in the heart of the earth.**" (Matthew 12:40). The Book of Jonah was written 800 years before Christ.

8. Jesus would rise from the grave, *"But God will redeem (resurrect) my soul from the power of the _____ "* (written 1000 years BC - Psalm 49:15)

9. Not one detail has failed, and there are over 300 more yet to be fulfilled! Deuteronomy 18:20-22 says God promises that everything His prophets speak will be fulfilled, and if not, then they were *false* prophets, and should die! No human authored book would dare to make so many predictions, so far in advance, and subject its authenticity to such chance - yet God did!

F. **Its Scientific Accuracy.** There are more than 300 clearly scientific statements in the Bible, that only God could have shown people – they could not have figured it out on their own.

1. The Bible describes the earth not as a flat world, but as a _____ (like a *sphere*, Isaiah 40:18,22). The Bible expressed this as FACT long before Columbus discovered it was right!

2. It says the earth is suspended in space (Job 26:7) hanging upon _____ . There is no way anyone could have known that to be true back in 2000 BC! And it told us these things without the aid of an orbiting satellite.

3. The Bible explains that all the major languages were instantly divided into *confusion* 4,400 years ago at the Tower of _____ (Genesis 11:1-9).

4. The Bible reveals that there are "paths," or currents in the seas (Psalm 8:8). Again, Columbus "discovered" that this was true when he sailed to the New World on one ocean *current*, and then back to Spain on another.

5. The Scriptures in Psalm 102:24-27, and Hebrews 1:10-12 declare *the Second Law of Thermodynamics* (which states that everything **wears out**) before scientists ever figured it out on their own!

6. God's command to wash everything (Leviticus 17:15) protected His people from invisible diseases and germs that were not discovered until the 1600 and 1700's!

7. The Bible revealed that the stars are innumerable (Jeremiah 33:22). That is a big thing to say when only in the past 80 years has it been accepted as true!

8. The Bible in Genesis chapters 1 and 2 also reveals the process by which all of life began on this planet (by supernatural and instantaneous creation).

9. And there is *much, much more*! You can't beat the awesomeness of the Bible, no matter how much education you obtain - it's always years ahead of science!

G. **Its Historical Accuracy.** Noah's flood (Genesis 6-9) is described by Babylonian tablets written in 650 B.C., as well as in 250 other ancient world histories. Most of the places named in the Bible have been identified through careful archaeology, thus validating the historical accuracy of the Bible again and again! The same cannot be said however about other religious books including the Book of Mormon.

H. **The Claims of the Bible Itself.** Over 3,800 times the writers of the Bible boldly claim that God Himself spoke what they wrote (i.e., *"thus saith the Lord"*), and that what we hold in our hands are the very words of God (2Timothy 3:15,16; 1 Thes 2:13)

The Bible IS God's Word to Mankind
Read it; Believe it; Study it; Obey it; Love it, and Preach it!

Date Lesson Completed_____Discipler_____

BIBLE STUDY TECHNIQUES
A Study of the Importance and Methods of Bible Study
Lesson Five

Memory Verse: *Matthew 4:4*   **Lesson Verse:** *2Timothy 2:15*

"Study to shew thyself approved unto God, a workman that needeth not to be ashamed, rightly dividing the word of truth."
2Timothy 2:15

I. Introduction

The disciple of Jesus Christ not only believes the word of God, but studies it, obeys it, and builds his or her life around it. This goal requires work, and study so that the Christian, *like a soldier*, is prepared to live life for the Lord! No soldier enters into combat however, without first knowing his weapons, and understanding how to use them effectively against his enemy. The Bible is the Christian's weapon against sin and even Satan; and this lesson is intended to instruct him in how to study it, and then use it in his life.

II. The Bible is our Source for Truth – THE best reason to learn it.

A. About God - About Ourselves - And basically, about all the unanswerable questions that cannot be found by science or reasoning

1. It tells you what you and I are really like on the inside – in our _____ (Jer 17:9,10).
2. It tells us what _____ is like (John 4:24).
3. It tells us clearly about heaven, about hell, about Satan, demonic activities.
4. It shows us what love actually is (1Corinthians 13:1-8). It's called "_____."
5. It tells us about the future (Isaiah 46:9,10).
6. None of those things can be known unless GOD revealed them to us.
7. This Bible is an amazing Book, and MUST be studied and learned if you are going to know the truth about any of the above.

B. What's the Point?

1. If you don't take the time to actually learn what God wrote down for you, then you will be **deceived** by every other wind of doctrine and persuasion (2Tim 4:2-4).
2. First by your own heart
3. Then by the greatest liar ever... _____ (John 8:44).
4. And it will cost you, your family, and every nation to not know God's truth, or turn away from it (Psalm 9:17)!

C. Things Jesus said about the Bible

1. Jesus taught that EVERY word of Scripture in the Bible proceeded from **God** and was not from man. (Matthew 4:4)
2. He believed in the Genesis record of a six-day creation (in other words, He did not believe in evolution). (See Matthew 19:4-6; Mark 10:6-8)
3. He believed that the Flood of Noah actually occurred. (Matthew 24:37-39)
4. He believed Abraham actually lived and followed God and became the father of the Jewish nation. (John 8:56)

---

5. He believed _____ and _____ were real cities that were destroyed by God by fire and brimstone. (Matthew 10:15; 11:23-24)
6. He believed Jonah was really swallowed by a _____. (Matthew 12:39-41)
7. He believed Lot's wife was a real woman who was turned into a real pillar of salt. (Luke 17:32)
8. He believed God gave _____ from heaven to Israel for almost 40 years in the desert. (John 6:31,49,58)
9. He taught the doctrine of the preservation of Scripture – that God protected the Scriptures from loss or error after they were written down. (Matthew 5:17-18; 24:35; Luke 16:17)
10. He taught that all the Old Testament Scriptures pointed to Him alone, and not to any other man or prophet. (Luke 24:27,44)
11. He never corrected or criticized any Scripture. (John 17:17).

D. Things the Bible Claims about itself

1. That it is actually what _____ spoke (Ex 5:1) – not made up by people
2. That it is pure and perfect (Psalm 19:7; 12:6)
3. That it is preserved for all generations to have access to it (Psalm 12:7).
4. That it will stand all the tests we can throw at it (Isaiah 40:8).

E. This single Book has proven itself to be absolutely true and trustworthy

1. Science and philosophy constantly change and cannot find God (1Cor 1:21)
2. Even Religion cannot find God (Luke 10:21)
3. So, to find and know and actually understand God, it took GOD Himself revealing Himself through prophets, then the Bible and ultimately through God's Son (Hebrews 1:1,2). The only thing we lack is CHILD-LIKE faith to believe it!

III. The Bible is the Christian's Greatest Weapon

A. The Bible is a powerful Weapon against being deceived by the lies of the culture we grow up in (teaching that we are only a higher form of animal, and should act only like animals; that we are accidents; that the only life we have is here and now; that there is no God and no heaven and no hell; and that God would never send anyone to hell). Knowing the truth, overwhelms all the lies and half-truths of modern society.

B. The Bible is our Weapon against the Devil
1. What did Jesus use against the temptations and pressures of Satan? _____ _____ (Matthew 4:4,7,10).
2. Quoting and believing the TRUTH of a select Scripture instead of a fear or doubt, can enable you to _____ the devil, and make him flee from you (James 4:7).

C. The Bible also is our Weapon against Sin and Temptation. The Bible is the Christian's primary *offensive* weapon against sin in his or her life, and against the temptations that our world attacks us with. How can it actually defeat sin?
1. By replacing the lies we have believed since childhood with God's truth.
2. By feeding our faith and confidence in God (Romans 10:17).
3. By reminding us to humble ourselves and draw close to the only real power against Satan, which is God Almighty (James 4:6,7)!
4. By using the words of God as a sword against everything that attacks you!

D. The Apostle Paul lists seven powerful spiritual weapons available to the Christian in Ephesians 6:11-18, and refers to them as the "*whole* _____ *of God.*"

   1. Your loins (your body) needs to be *girt about* (covered) with _____. God's absolute truth is what all the other spiritual weapons and defences are resting upon.

   2. The *breastplate* of _____. Not our 'right'-ness, but the purity of our lives, in line with Christ's, who gave us HIS righteousness.

   3. Your feet *shod* (covered) with the preparation of the _____ of peace. Be ready to go and answer the world's need for hope from the Gospel!

   4. The *shield* of _____, wherewith ye shall be able to quench all the fiery darts of the wicked.

   5. The *helmet* of _____.

   6. The *sword* of _____ _____, **which is the word of God.**

   7. And, Praying always.

   8. None of that may look like much, but the Apostle Paul says they actually help us wrestle and win against the powers of darkness!

E. Only one of the above items can be used as an offensive weapon - "*the* _____ *of the Spirit*", which is "*the* _____ *of God*" (Ephesians 6:17; Hebrews 4:12)! All others are there to protect you when under attack.

The Christian is a soldier in God's army, armed with God's supernatural weapons against our worst enemies!

IV. Some More GREAT Reasons for Bible Study

A. It is **commanded...**"_____ *to shew thyself approved unto God* " (2Tim 2:15). This verse is not a suggestion!

B. Another reason is because it is **profitable** for the Christian (2Tim 3:16; Psalm 1:1-3) - not monetarily, but spiritually. The benefits are eternal!

C. The truths of Scripture gives the Christian **victory**! As a powerful weapon, the very words of Scriptures will give you victory over sin and temptation (Ps 37:31; 119:11).

D. The Bible is a *guiding* _____ to the Christian (Psalm 119:105). It provides instructions on *how* to go through life, *where* to go, *why* go a certain path, and even *when* to go (Ecclesiastes 3:1-8).

E. Special blessings are promised for those who _____, _____, and _____ the things written in the Bible (Revelation 1:3) - *not what another man says, or even what your church says!*

F. The Bible is the *only* means to test religious teaching - "*If they speak not according to this* _____ *it is because there is no* _____ *in them*" (Isaiah 8:19,20). God gave His word to be the only basis for truth (John 17:17).

V. HOW to Study and Really Learn the Bible

  A. Have a Personal Quiet Time

    1. A quiet time is a Christian's personal time of talking to God in prayer, and listening to God by reading His words from the Bible.

    2. King David said: "*I will* _____ *in thy precepts*" (Psalm 119:15; 1:1-2). That means King David took time out of his busy schedule to read, and think, and ponder, learn and then obey whatever God had said to do.

3. To have a *Quiet Time* you need to:

   a. **Make time** to read and study the Bible *every day*.

   1) When reading your Bible, take time to ponder what is being said. In Acts 17:10,11, the people in Berea did not simply believe what the Apostle Paul taught, but rather tested what he said by the word of God said! *"They _____ the word with all _____ of mind, and searched the Scriptures _____."*

   2) Choose a convenient time - decide when is the best time, and have it. Don't *wait* for a convenient time because it probably will never come!

   3) Be consistent - form a habit of doing it *every day*. You are going to have to make it as important as _____ and sleeping is (Job 23:12).

   b. Begin with **prayer**, asking God to speak to you, and show you His will for you daily (Psalm 119:18).

   c. **Read** your Bible - like you would any other book, reading at least one chapter each time. If you are going to read through the Bible in one year, you will need to read at least four chapters a day.

   d. When you find something that has special meaning to you, **underline** those verses with your pencil, or light coloured markers, and then copy a few select ones to the small pocket-sized note cards to memorize them later.

   e. **Write** out your thoughts and conclusions in a notebook so that you can begin to apply the Scripture to your life. Think about how the verses relate to your life. Always ask yourself **5** questions as you read:

   > 1) Who is doing the talking? *Is it Jesus, or Moses, or John, etc.*
   > 2) Who is he or she talking to? *The disciples, Jews, etc.*
   > 3) What is the subject being talked about? *Look at the context!*
   > 4) Does that subject relate to me, and what I am going through?
   > 5) How can I learn from this event in Scripture?

   f. **Obey** what you read. *"Be ye _____ of the word and not _____ only"* (James 1:22). The goal of Bible study is wrapped up in finding what the Bible says about a subject, and then doing what it says to do!

   g. Be careful to **pay attention to CONTEXT** (Isaiah 28:9,10). The Bible is not a list of do's and don'ts that can just be extracted at random, but rather a revealing description of God and His will that must be read *in context* - a verse is understood only in light of the meaning of the surrounding verses. See for example what happens when you read Matthew 27:5 with Luke 10:37! So, the wrong kind of Bible study can be deadly, because you start making the Bible say what YOU want it to say - and that is how cults are established!

   h. As you study your Bible, use a sharpened pencil, or nice pen to **record your thoughts** in the margin of your Bible, or in a good notebook for further study later on (see Deeper Study, next).

   i. Finish in **prayer**, thanking God for speaking to your heart in such a wonderful, and personal way!

B. **Public Bible Study in Church, and Study Groups**

1. Pastors are to _____ the _____ (2Tim 4:2). That means, a man is supposed to get in front of people, and boldly declare the truth from the Bible about sin, righteousness, the coming judgment, and Jesus the Lamb of God who can save any and all who come to God by Him!

2. To those who are saved, preaching in church is the _____ of God (1Cor 1:18), and is a wonderful time for the Disciple to learn and grow from what is taught by a pastor. Don't be ashamed of straight-talk-preaching, when it comes from the Bible! It is more important

Evangelist Billy Sunday boldly preached to crowds of 20,000 people!

than all the worship of all religions put together because, it is God's way of saving sinners (1Cor 1:17,18,21)!

3. As Christians, we are to receive the word with _____ like a thirsty man receives water (James 1:21). Never become unteachable, or unreachable, because preaching prepares you to serve and disciple others later! It takes a humble heart to receive instruction.

4. **Bible study groups** are great places to learn the Bible. Remember to make sure, when looking for a group, that it is under the authority of a local church (i.e., that it is sponsored by a Bible believing church and pastor). Not everything that calls itself a Bible Study really is one.

C. So, in summary, every believer should have a quiet time and every Christian family should have a family Bible time, and every Christian is to be in church, learning the Bible through preaching and teaching.

VI. Bible Study Tools - Things that can help you learn more in your Study Time

A. **Bible Cross-References.** Most Bibles have some sort of Cross Referencing system either in the centre column, or embedded in each verse. Use these references to help you understand what other portions of Scripture say about the subjects in the verse you are reading. An example can be found in Genesis 1:1-3, where a little note would direct you to see that the creation of the world is also described in John 1:1-3, and Acts 17:24, and 2Cor 4:6, etc. If your Bible does not have a similar system, then consider buying one that does because it is so helpful and easily accessible when you are reading and studying the Bible.

B. **Study Bibles** - Beyond the cross-referencing system, there are many Bibles that have *Study Notes* along with the Scripture that are designed to give the student more in-depth information about each verse and subject. These Bibles are very good to have, and are more often than not, the only Bible helps you need. Be sure to only use the notes as <u>opinions</u>, and not as absolute. They are not always going to be right!

C. **Concordances** - A Bible concordance is an alpha-
betical index of the words used in the Bible, listing
where they appear. Some Bibles come with a mini-
concordance in their back pages. But when a Christian wants to know what the entire Bible says about
a subject or word, you need a Complete Concordance. A good one is the *Dr. James Strong's Exhaustive Concordance*, which lists every word, and every
place that each word occurs in the Bible!

JESUS (je'-zus) See also BAR-JESUS; CHRIST; JESUS'; JOSHUA;
JUSTUS.
Mt 1:1 book of the generation of J. Christ, ... 2424
Mt 1:16 of whom was born J., who is called 2424
Mt 1:18 birth of J. Christ was on this wise:.... 2424
Mt 1:21 son, and thou shalt call his name J. 2424
Mt 1:25 son: and he called his name J. 2424
Mt 2:1 when J. was born in Bethlehem of..... 2424
Mt 3:13 cometh J. from Galilee to Jordan 2424
Mt 3:15 J. answering said unto him, Suffer..... 2424
Mt 3:16 J., when he was baptized, went up..... 2424
Mt 4:1 was J. led up of the spirit into the..... 2424
Mt 4:7 J. said unto him, It is written......... 2424
Mt 4:10 saith J. unto him, Get thee hence,.... 2424
Mt 4:12 J. had heard that John was cast 2424
Mt 4:17 From that time J. began to preach, ... 2424
Mt 4:18 J., walking by the sea of Galilee, ... 2424
Mt 4:23 J. went about all Galilee, teaching 2424
Mt 7:28 when J. had ended these sayings, ... 2424
Mt 8:3 J. put forth his hand, and touched 2424

D. **Bible Atlas** - This is a handy set of maps of the lands
in the Middle East where all the events of Scripture took place. They help you understand distances and terrain that people would have had to deal with back then.

E. **Commentaries, Study Guides and Bible Dictionaries**

1. The last thing a Christian may want to obtain for their library of tools is a set of
Bible Commentaries and **Study Guides**. Commentaries usually are large volumes of writings by authors on each and every verse in the Bible. They bring
together archaeology, history, various languages and other helpful tools into the
understanding of Scripture.

2. Be aware that <u>commentaries can be very destructive to the faith of young Christians.</u> Some authors do not believe the Bible is the word of God. They usually
spend more time **questioning** Scriptures instead of *commenting* on them! So,
look for ones that help you grow in grace, and not in criticism of God's word.

F. *Study Guides* are outlines of notes on Scripture. These are not as extensive as commentaries, but often more practical.

G. *Bible Dictionaries* are reference books that contain definitions of words and proper
names as found in the Bible, helping the student better understand the meaning and
context of verses.

H. There is a load of computer based Bible software available that can search and sort
through every word and phrase in the Bible, as well as provide you access to hundreds of thousands of pages of research materials and commentaries. You have NO
EXCUSE for not studying the Bible today!

VII. A Deeper Study

A. As you read each page of your Bible, when you notice something confusing, or
something important, take time after you have finished reading the current chapter,
to go back and **study** the portion of Scripture that got your attention for more in-
sights.

1. There are things in your Bible that should stand out, and make you think, like:

a. **S**ins to avoid (Col 3:5,6,8,9; 2:8; 1Cor 6:9,10).

b. **P**romises to claim (Jer 33:3; Philp 4:13,19).

c. **E**xamples to follow (1Pet 2:21-23).

d. **C**ommands to obey (Matt 28:19,20; Eph 5:18; 4:31,32).

e. **SW** – Scriptures about the Spiritual Warfare we are in (Eph 6:12; 1Pet 5:8).

2. Mark verses using multi-coloured pencils, or lightly-coloured pens, and mark-
ing them like: **Blue** for <u>Promises</u>; **Red** for <u>Warnings</u>; **Green** or **Yellow** for <u>Im-
portant Information</u>; **Orange** for <u>Prophecy</u>; and any two-colour combination for
other special identification. This helps you find the verses later when you need
them.

3. Take time to notice every important word in a Scripture, and **ponder its meaning**. An example would be to write out the words in Matthew chapter 5, and try to learn what each means - NOT just what you *think* they mean!
4. Use a Concordance to **look up those words** to see what else the Bible has to say on that subject. Remember, the Holy Spirit may be trying to get your attention about something. If your Bible has cross-references in the margins, look those up too. Be sure to write down what you found in your notebook.
5. One other practical way is to **write a Scripture down in your notebook <u>in your own words</u>**. It will show you what parts of a verse you may not really understand.

VIII. Concerning *Which* Bible - The Differences in the English Versions

A. Satan's primary attack <u>has always been</u> against the foundation of our faith, the Bible (Gen 3:1). His goal has always been to question and "______________" the Bible, so that its message gets changed (2Cor 2:17). What has happened is this: God wrote the Bible, and Satan seeks to "corrupt" its message by constantly redefining words, and ultimately, removing them, and even entire verses from what God said! A study of Satan's methods will only strengthen your faith in the Bible as the very word of God!

B. **The Two Greek Manuscript Sets of the New Testament**

1. The basis for all the different versions of the Bible are because of the existence of TWO sets of differing Greek "manuscripts": the ***<u>Majority</u>*** text, and the ***<u>Westcott and Hort</u>*** text.
2. The *Majority Text* is a group of about <u>5200</u> portions of Scripture in Greek that through the past 2,000 years has been accepted by Christians as authentic, and true. What follows is an example of what a passage in the Majority Text looks like, along with the English underneath. Note ***verse 37*** is present and marked. This is important because verse 37 **disappears** in the Westcott and Hort text!

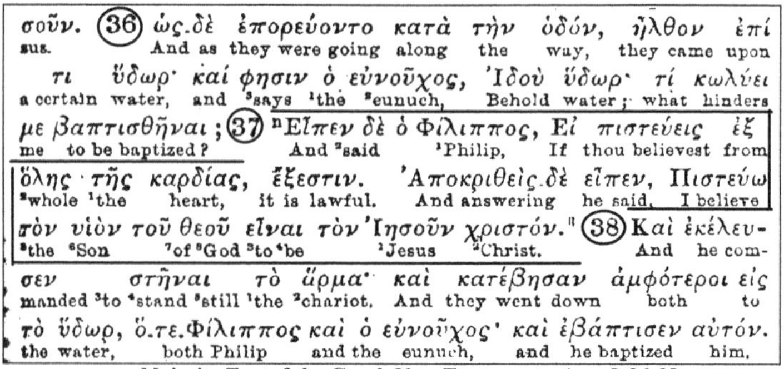
σοῦν. (36) ὡς.δὲ ἐπορεύοντο κατὰ τὴν ὁδόν, ἦλθον ἐπί
sus. And as they were going along the way, they came upon
τι ὕδωρ· καί φησιν ὁ εὐνοῦχος, Ἰδοὺ ὕδωρ· τί κωλύει
a certain water, and [3]says [1]the [2]eunuch, Behold water; what hinders
με βαπτισθῆναι; (37) [n]Εἶπεν δὲ ὁ Φίλιππος, Εἰ πιστεύεις ἐξ
me to be baptized? And [2]said [1]Philip, If thou believest from
ὅλης τῆς καρδίας, ἔξεστιν. Ἀποκριθεὶς.δὲ εἶπεν, Πιστεύω
[2]whole [1]the heart, it is lawful. And answering he said, I believe
τὸν υἱὸν τοῦ θεοῦ εἶναι τὸν Ἰησοῦν χριστόν." (38) Καὶ ἐκέλευ-
[5]the [6]Son [7]of [8]God [3]to [4]be [1]Jesus [2]Christ. And he com-
σεν στῆναι τὸ ἅρμα· καὶ κατέβησαν ἀμφότεροι εἰς
manded [3]to [4]stand [5]still [1]the [2]chariot. And they went down both to
τὸ ὕδωρ, ὅ.τε.Φίλιππος καὶ ὁ εὐνοῦχος· καὶ ἐβάπτισεν αὐτόν.
the water, both Philip and the eunuch, and he baptized him.

Majority Text **of the Greek New Testament - Acts 8:36-38**

3. The second primary Greek text is the ***Westcott and Hort*** *Text.* Brook Foss Westcott (1825-1903) and Fenton Hort (1828-1892) were two Anglican ministers who created *their own Greek text* from only **<u>two</u>** Greek manuscripts called the *Vaticanus* and *Sinaiticus*.
   a. Vaticanus showed up in a Vatican Library in 1481, and Sinaiticus was found in a the trash in a Monastery on Mt. Sinai in 1844.

b. These manuscripts were believed to be *older*, and *more accurate* (watch statements like that) than all the rest of the 5000 manuscripts of the Majority Text! Westcott and Hort rejected the authority of the Majority Text and chose rather to accept these *Roman Catholic* texts that now bears their name.

4. Notice the missing verse in the following *Westcott and Hort* text:

What happened to verse 37?

Westcott & Hort **Greek Text of the New Testament - Acts 8:35-38**

5. Did you notice what is *doctrinally* affected if you accept the Westcott and Hort over the Majority text? Satan will go to any length to confuse people by getting them to think **baptism** is the important thing, and not trusting in Christ alone (2Peter 3:15,16; 2Cor 2:17; 4:2)! The Westcott and Hort text attacks the Deity of Jesus Christ (that He is God), removes the importance of faith **before** baptism (as presented in Acts 8:36-38), waters down the clear teachings that are present only in the King James Bible.

6. The clear goal of Satan is to simply make a Bible contradict itself. If he can do that in the mind of a reader, then that reader will not trust it completely, and it makes God confusing, and ultimately a liar (1Cor 14:33)! One thing ought to be clear to the Bible believer, God is not the author of _____

7. The differences between these two sets of documents are so profound, that they cannot be ignored.

C. **The English Versions From the Two Manuscript Sets**

Comparing the English versions is very revealing. Notice how all the "new bibles" (left hand side) are from the Westcott and Hort text, and yet only the **King James Version** is from the Majority text. Therefore, the new versions are NOT <u>revisions</u> as they claim to be, but rather NEW bibles based upon completely different Greek texts than what historical Christianity accepted until 1881!

D. **Every major language has the two types of Bibles** - at least one from the Westcott and Hort texts, and the other from the Majority texts. In every language however, the Westcott and Hort versions are ALWAYS sold on the basis that they are supposedly EASIER to read, and not whether they are an honest translation from the correct texts. Is that always true????? Check out just a "few" of the supposed better words for our modern world…

BIBLE VERSE	NIV (Easier word?)	AV 1611
Isaiah 24:23	abashed	confounded
Ezekiel 40:18	abutted	over against
2 Chron 15:14	acclamation	voice
Isaiah 13:8	aghast	amazed
Ezek 40:13	alcove	little chamber
2 Chr 13:22	annotations	story
Num 31:50	armlets	chains

Acts 2:6	bewilderment	confounded
Ps 58:7	blunted	cut in pieces
Job 8:2	blustering	strong
Ex 35:22	brooches	bracelets
Dan 10:6	burnished	polished
Rev 4:3	carnelian	sardine
1 Ki 7:6	colonnade	porch
1 Ki 4:22	cors	measures
Ezek 13:22	disheartened	sad
Lk 20:23	duplicity	craftiness
Rom 2:20	embodiment	form
Mk 14:31	emphatically	vehemently
2 Chr 30:22	encouragingly	comfortably
Pro 23:10	encrouch	enter
2 Chr 17:14	enrollment	numbers
Ps 45:11	enthralled	greatly desire
Lk 9:34	enveloped	overshadowed
Jude 16	faultfinders	complainers
Ex 28:20	filigree	enclosings
Ps 89:47	fleeting	short
Acts 5:40	flogged	beaten
Is 59:13	fomenting	speaking

See all the "bibles" translated from the '2' Westcott & Hort Greek Documents	Translated from the 5,200 Majority Greek Documents
1609 Roman Catholic *Douay* version - Catholic Bible	
1881 The Revised Version	
1901 American Standard Version	
1903 Weymouth, The New Testament *in Modern Speech*	
1912 The Holy Bible An Improved Edition	
1913 James Moffatt, A New Translation *in Modern Speech*	
1937 The New Testament *in the language of the people*	
1946 Revised Standard Version New Testament	
1948 New Testament *in modern English*	
1951 Norlie, The New Testament *in Modern English*	
1952 Revised Standard Version The Holy Bible	
1952 Williams, A New Translation *in Plain English*	
1958 J B Phillips, The New Testament *in Modern English*	
1962 The King James II Bible, 1971	
1963 New American Standard New Testament	
1965 The Amplified Bible	
1966 Good News for Modern Man	
1966 The Jerusalem Bible	
1970 The New American Bible	King James Version (1611)
1970 The New English Bible	
1971 New American Standard Bible	
1971 Kenneth N Taylor The Living Bible, Paraphrased	
1972 The Bible in Living English	
1972 Today's English New Testament	
1976 Good News Bible: The Bible *in Today's English* Version	
1976 The Holy Bible *in the Language of Today*	
1978 New International Version	
1985 The New Jerusalem Bible	
1987 New Century Version	
1989 The Revised English Bible with the Apocrypha	
1990 New Revised Standard Version	
1993 The Message: The Bible *in Contemporary English*	
1994 21st Century King James Version	
1994 The Inclusive New Testament - Political correctness bible	
1995 An Understandable Version	
1995 Contemporary English Version	
1996 NIV Inclusive Language Edition	
Etc, etc, etc!	
The "New" King James Version (1982) - A *merge* of both text sets	

E. The current trend among Bible publishers is to edit their bible translations, and bring them back closer to the King James Bible. This has resulted in *"New"* Versions being published, so they now include verses that they had first removed, making them not so different than the King James anymore - can you guess why they did this? Because the KJV sets the pace! The Bible believer however must not be deceived into thinking those 'bibles' are ok to read and study now – they may be getting closer to the word of God, but why trade what is perfect, for something that is in a constant state of evolution?!

F. **Next are some Critical Scripture Changes to know about.** According to Revelation 22:18,19, God warns us to never _____, or _____ away from His words, and yet look below! Notice the verses listed in the following table, and compare what *Westcott and Hort* versions say in the verse, and then what the *King James Bible* says. It will shock you! This is only a sampling of thousands!

THE CORRUPTION LIST!

Matt 9:13	The need for sinners "to repent" is removed!
Matt 17:21	Prayer and fasting is evidently not necessary
Matt 18:11	The verse explains the very reason for Christ coming!
Matt 23:14	Somebody doesn't like attacks on money-hungry religious leaders
Matt 27:35	Last half of the verse is missing!
Mark 7:16	Someone is attempting to remove Christ's plea to the sinner's free-will
Mark 9:24	The word "*Lord*" omitted (see also Luke 23:42)
Mark 9:44,46	See if your Bible has these verses, or questions their presence!
Mark 10:24	Someone doesn't like Jesus' remarks against trusting in riches!
Mark 11:26	Someone doesn't like God's warnings against our disobedience!
Mark 15:28	Someone doesn't like all the connections back to the O.T. prophecies
Mark 16:9-10	These verses are attacked, and declared untrustworthy
Luke 2:33	The word "*father*" is substituted for "*Joseph*" making him Jesus' father!
Luke 4:4	The words "*every word of God*" omitted
Luke 17:36	Just a small verse removed - yet it is necessary for the context!
Luke 23:17	This verse is clean gone as well
John 3:13	Jesus is not allowed to be in two places at the same time!
John 5:4	This missing verse explains why the people were gathered at the pool
John 9:35	Jesus is no longer the Son of God!
Acts 1:3	The word "*infallible*" is watered down so as to not offend anyone!
Acts 4:27	Jesus is no longer God's *Son*, but rather *Servant* (no Deity)
Acts 8:37	Verse is either missing or questioned, and yet critical to salvation!
Acts 15:34	Silas is missing!
Acts 24:7	Gone!
Acts 28:29	Also missing!
2Cor 2:17	The word of God no longer is being "*corrupted*"
Col 1:14	The '*blood*' omitted - salvation no longer needs the blood of the Lamb!
1 Thes 5:22	We are to abstain from all *appearance*, not just *kinds* of evil
1Tim 3:16	'*God*' is changed to an unknown '*He*' so that you can't tell He is God!
1Tim 6:5	Godliness is the means of gain? Paul is warning about just the opposite
1Tim 6:10	The love of money is not always bad anymore.
2Tim 2:15	We do not really have to STUDY our Bible anymore
James 5:16	All the new bibles now command us to confess our *sins* to each other!
1 John 4:19	They even took GOD away so that all we can do is "love"
1 John 5:7	Verse missing, with part of verse 8 made into verse 7!
Rev 22:18,19	Talk about changing verses! Notice how '*book*' is changed to '*tree*'

G. Problems with the "New" King James Version (NKJV)

1. Changed Words = Changed Meanings (*You will need a copy of an NKJV for this*)

   a. Is Jesus God's **"Son"** or God's *"servant"*? In Acts 3:26, the NKJV calls Jesus only God's "Servant." But the KJV correctly calls Him God's "Son." These are not the same. Which one is He? To the Muslim, Jesus is only God's servant. But the Bible says He is God's CHILD/Son. Changed words like this make a great deal of difference in how we understand a passage.

   b. Do we really need to change all the "thee's" and "thou's" to 'you' and 'you'?

      1) Please decide what God is saying to Moses based on the NKJV:

         a) *"And the LORD said to Moses, "How long do you refuse to keep My commandments and My laws?"* (Exodus 16:28, NKJV)

         b) It looks like God is saying, *"Moses, you are continuing to refuse to keep My commandments and My laws."* But look carefully at the accurate King James:

         c) *"And the LORD said unto Moses, How long refuse ye to keep my commandments and my laws?"*

         d) Now we understand! It was the people, not Moses, God was upset with

         e) **"Ye"** and **"you"** mean more than one person. **"Thee,"** **"thou,"** **"thy,"** **"thine,"** **"doeth,"** **"hast,"** etc., only mean one person.

         f) How do we know? The **"y"** is plural. The **"t"** is singular. It's that easy.

      2) Now you know what Jesus meant when He said to Nicodemus, *"Marvel not that I said unto **thee** (Nicodemas, a single person), Ye (everyone, plural) must be born again"* (John 3:7).

      3) What Jesus said was, *"Nicodemus, marvel not that I said unto thee, all of you need to be born again."* This is very important. Not only Nicodemus needed to be saved. But everybody, including him, needed to be born again. That's why Jesus used the singular and the plural words!

2. Were many people *"peddling"* (selling) the word of God in Paul's day, or were they CORRUPTING it? (2Cor 2:17)

3. Do people go to **hades** or **hell**? (Matt 16:18; Luke 16:23)

   a. The NKJV claims to be "more accurate" because it leaves untranslated words like **"Gehenna,"** **"Hades"** and **"Sheol."** What do they mean? You will know from the King James the exact meaning: **"hell."** We know what that means. Meaning is very important. When's the last time you heard someone told to "go to hades", or "see you in hades"?

   b. The NKJV changes or removes the word HELL 22 times!!!

4. Are people "Saved", or only "BEING Saved"? (1Corinthins 1:18; 2Cor 2:15)

5. Are we supposed to "STUDY", or just "be diligent" so that you are not ashamed before God? (2Tim 2:15).

6. What kind of a man holds onto riches and wealth? (Prov 11:16)

7. Are we to set our *"MIND"* or our *"HEARTS"* on things above? (Col 3:2)

8. See also Acts 4:27, 1Timothy 6:5; 1Cor 6:10; James 5:16 and compare with the 'old' King James Bible.

H. Missing Words in the NKJV:

1. The Name, "*JEHOVAH*" is gone!
2. The word "REPENT" is taken out 44 times!
3. "*Nevertheless I live*" is missing in Galatians 2:20!

I. The Bible-believer settles once and for all whether we have the word of God, or not! *If we do, then we live by it!* If not, then God is a liar, and let's eat, drink, and be merry, for tomorrow we die, and who cares! But as we have seen, God does care - proven in the giving of the Son of God, and the very word of God!

IX. **The Superiority of the King James Bible of 1611 - The AV (Authorized Version).** When the Bible believer examines the facts, the King James Bible of 1611 is found to be superior to any other English Bible because of the following four main reasons:

A. **The Source of the Translation.** The simple belief is that God **both** *inspired*, and then *preserved* His word without error (Matthew 24:35; Psalm 12:6,7).

1. The AV translators chose to use the available 5,200 agreeing Greek copies of the New Testament as the source of the King James Bible.
2. All other versions primarily use only **TWO** Greek copies of the New Testament to translate from - these two documents have over **35,000** differences between them and the AV copies, including deleted verses. That's a lot of differences.

B. **The Honesty and Accuracy of the Translation (2Cor 2:17; 2Pet 3:14-16)**

1. The AV translators took no *liberties* in translating the Bible the way they wanted. They did not attempt to paraphrase, or "interpret" hard passages. Most other Bibles attempt to "*fix*" problems with the meaning of the Greek and Hebrew by trying to figure God out. Thankfully the AV translators did not! If a passage of Scripture was hard to understand in Greek or Hebrew, then it was translated that way. If they needed to add a word to help the meaning, they put it in *italics* (words that are *slanted*) to show when they had to add specific words in English so that the reader could best understand the sense of the verse being translated.
2. By the way; the italicized words are just as much the word of God as the normal words (see and compare the words of Deuteronomy 8:3 and Mt 4:4).
3. Notice the plain errors in the other versions – check these out in other versions:
   a. 2Sam 21:19 _____
   b. Heb 3:16 _____

C. **The Fruit of its Reading (Matthew 7:20)**

1. *Ease of Memorization* - The AV is much easier to memorize and retain because of the way it is written, and the way it impacts the heart.
2. *True Revivals* - No other Bible has brought about real revival (i.e., the closing of pubs and bars, the restoration of families, the fear of God instilled in entire communities) like the AV does! All other "bibles" water-down, and weaken the heart of the Christian from that of a strong soldier, to a lazy, lukewarm, and emotionally unstable compromiser.
3. *No confusion* - The AV is much clearer than the other versions, especially in areas of important doctrine. Look up the differences between the AV and another version in the following verses:
   a. 1Cor 1:18 _____
   b. Acts 8:37 _____

D. The Enemies of the Translation

1. *The Roman Catholic Church* - The AV 1611 is considered to be "anti-Catholic" - which it is - and is usually not permitted to be read by Catholics.
2. *The Liberal branch of "Christianity"* - The AV 1611 is considered to be archaic, and a hindrance to today's modern "me" philosophy - *which it is!*
3. *The Lazy Christian* - The AV requires a person to *think* and *study* instead of having all the thinking done for them with paraphrases and easy to read 'bibles'!
4. *The Carnal Christian* - The AV makes worldly Christians uncomfortable because it does not compromise on God's clear hatred of sin and try and mix holiness with modern terminology!

X. Concerning The Apocrypha

A. The books called 'Apocrypha' (which mean *extra writings*) were later added to the Bible by Catholic "church councils," and only show their ungodly desire to make the Bible into a complex, and contradicting book, instead of the perfect, and supernatural one that it always has been! Neither Jesus Christ, nor any New Testament author ever used, or even alluded to anything ever written in *any* of the Apocryphal books. This goes in the face of the fact that Christ and His apostles quote from every other Old Testament Book! The Apocrypha is made up of *1 & 2 Esdras, Tobit, Judith, Wisdom, Ecclesiasticus* (or *Sirach*), *Baruch*, and *1 & 2 Maccabees*.

B. Here are some reasons the Apocrypha is rejected by Bible believers:

1. They are not included in the original Hebrew Old Testament preserved by the Jews. Romans 3:1-2 states that God used the Jews to pen, and also to preserve His Word; therefore, we trust that He guided them in the rejection of the Apocryphal books from the canon of Scripture.
2. They contain teachings contrary to the rest of the Bible, like:

   a. **Praying for the dead**. The apocryphal book 2nd Maccabees teaches people to pray to the dead and make offerings to atone for the sins of the dead "*He also took up a collection... and sent it to Jerusalem to provide for a sin offering.... Therefore he made atonement for the dead, that they might be delivered from their sin.*" (2 Maccabees 12:43-46).

   b. **Mediators in heaven**. 2nd Maccabees contains the heresy that dead saints intercede in heaven for those on earth (2 Maccabees 15:11-14). They do not.

   c. **The Use of Magic**. A supposed good angel teaches the use of magic in Tobit! "*Then the angel said to him, 'Cut open the fish and take the heart and liver and gall and put them away safely.' ... Then the young man said to the angel, 'Brother Azarias, of what use is the liver and heart and gall of the fish?' He replied, 'As for the heart and the liver, if a demon or evil spirit gives trouble to any one, you make a smoke from these before the man or woman, and that person will never be troubled again. And as for the gall, anoint with it a man who has white films in his eyes, and he will be cured*'" (Tobit 6:4,6-8). The Bible clearly condemns magical practices such as this (consider Deut 18:10-12; Lev 19:26,31; Jer 27:9).

   d. **Salvation through works** is taught in the book of Tobit. "*For almsgiving delivers from death, and it will purge away every sin*" (Tobit 12:9). "*So now, my children, consider what almsgiving accomplishes and how righteousness delivers*" (Tobit 14:11). Leviticus 17:11 clearly says "*it is the blood that maketh an atonement for the soul.*"

3. None of these match any of the rest of the Bible, and were only added to confuse the reader and force them to look to the "church" for the truth!

XI. A Survey of What is In the Bible...

The following section lists the basic information that you need to understand as you read and study God's word. It is intended to help you understand just what is the underlying "structure" of God's ways of doing things. It won't explain "everything," but will lay-out the framework of people and truths in the Bible.

A. **The Main Events of the Bible** - what follows are the important events in history and prophecy as recorded in the Bible! Take careful note!

1. **The Creation.** The Bible teaches in Genesis 1, and throughout the Scriptures that God "created" everything there is in six literal days, about 6,000 years ago, and that everything is currently wearing out, and not improving.

2. **The Fall.** God created two people, and placed them in a perfect garden called Eden. Satan in Genesis 3 entered the garden with one purpose – lure Adam and Eve into disobeying God, and become cursed by God. Disobey they did, but God provided two lambs to take the place of Adam and Eve in death. From then on, God's promise was for a future Messiah to come who would one day "take away the sins of the world."

3. **The Flood.** About 4,600 years ago, a world-wide flood occurred that wiped-out all land-dwelling creatures, including mankind (Genesis 6-8). Everyone died except for Noah, and his family, who were saved because they obeyed God, and built an ark which contained two of every kind of land animal. It was the flood that fashioned the continents into their current shapes, and lifted the mountains to their current heights.

4. **The Calling out of Abraham.** Abraham is a cornerstone of the Old Testament. He lived in an ungodly city called Ur, but decided to obey God's word and leave Ur to follow God's will for his life. When God promised Abraham that He would give him as many children as the number of the stars, Abraham didn't doubt, but simply believed God, and became the father of the race of people called Jews, who because of Abraham, are the people of God (Genesis 12-25).

5. **The Bondage in Egypt.** The descendants of Abraham were called Jews. These Jews went to dwell in Egypt, but were enslaved by the Egyptians for over 400 years (Genesis 30 through Exodus 3).

6. **The Passover.** Just before Israel was set free from slavery in Egypt, God commanded that every believer get themselves a lamb, and to kill that lamb in their place. They were to then take the blood of that lamb, and place it visibly upon the outside doorposts of each home, and God promised to "*pass over*" them in His judgment (Exodus 12)!

7. **The Promised Land.** Abraham had been promised a piece of land known as Canaan. It was over 400 years later when Joshua led the nation of Israel into Canaan and conquered all its inhabitants (The Book of Joshua). It is where Israel now dwells, and always will be Israel's.

8. **The Kingdom Age.** Israel became a kingdom under three great kings named Saul, David, and Solomon. Many other kings followed them (1 Samuel – 2 Chronicles).

9. **The Captivity.** After about 400 years in the Promised Land, the people of Israel lost interest in following the God of the Bible, and became totally idolatrous. God gave them over to their enemies, who came into their cities, and took all the healthiest, strongest, and most beautiful away to distant lands as slaves. Israel had gone full circle, and would have to wait for 70 years before they could begin to rebuild their lives back under God (Jeremiah & Lamentations).

10. **The Exile, and the Return from Exile**. The Book of Esther is a description of how God protected the Jewish people during captivity, and the Books of Ezra and Nehemiah describe the return of the people from Babylon back to their homeland.

11. **The Old Testament**. This set of 39 Books in the Bible contains the history of the world from Creation, up to about 400 years before the birth of Jesus. It was written in Hebrew, and pointed toward Christ.

12. **The Birth, and Life of Christ** - His First Coming. God became flesh and dwelt among us on earth 2,000 years ago. He lived a sinless life for 33 years, and then died as our substitute for sins on the cross to pay off our sin-debt to God. Everyone of His day wanted Jesus to rule as King, but His first coming was not to rule, but to save (Matthew – John)!

13. **The New Testament**. This set of 27 Books in the Bible records the life of Christ, and presents the truths and freedoms that can transform any sinner into a true saint.

14. **The Rapture**. A catching away (1 Thes 4:16,17) of the Christians from the earth just before the beginning of the time called the Tribulation. It occurs so fast that people won't know what happened!

15. **The Tribulation**. Seven years of disasters and troubles that will rock the very foundations of this planet (Revelation 6-19). It will result in 1/3rd of the population of the earth dying.

16. **The Second Coming of Christ**. Christ Jesus, and all Christians are coming back again! Jesus promised that He will defeat Satan, and will establish a true kingdom of heaven on earth (Revelation 19). We don't know when it will happen, but look for it everyday expectantly!

17. **The Millennium**. This is the 1,000 year reign of Jesus Christ on this earth, who will return the earth back to what it was like in the Garden of Eden (Revelation chapters 20,21).

18. **The New Heaven and New Earth**. Once the Millennium is over, God will destroy this entire universe by fire, and start over with a perfect universe, and earth, with no more sin, or Satan around (Rev 21 & 22).

B. **The Main People of the Bible**

1. **Adam and Eve** (Gen chapters 2,3). These were the first humans on earth, and from them are all humans, and because of their disobedience to God, we have death, and sin, and separation from God.

2. **Cain and Able** (Gen 4). Here were two brothers, sons of Adam and Eve. Abel worshipped God with the sacrifice of lambs, and Cain with his own good efforts. When God only appreciated Abel's lamb, Cain ended up killing his brother out of envy, and became the first murderer!

3. **Noah** (Gen 6-9). Noah was the only man who followed and obeyed God in his day - the rest of the world was caught up in wickedness and violence. He was commanded to build a huge ark that would carry both himself, his family, and two of each kind of animal through the coming world-wide flood.

4. **Nimrod** (Gen 10). Nimrod began again false worship, and open rebellion to God's word. He built Babylon, and attracted all the world to worship his false gods, which are the basis for ALL the world's religions still (including Catholicism), except for Biblical Christianity!

5. **Abraham** (Gen 12-25). The father of the race of people called Israel, or the Jews. It was his faith in God that moved God to choose to use him to bring the

promised Messiah into the world. It was his people that God would use to pen the Scriptures, and keep them from error.

6. **Isaac** (Gen 21-35). The miraculous born son of Abraham. This boy was the promised son of Abraham, and was born when Abraham was 100 years old, and his wife Sarah was 90!

7. **Jacob** (Gen 25-49). He is one of Isaac's sons. He is a trouble-maker, but gets converted, whose name gets changed to *Israel* by God because he finally surrenders to the Lord.

8. **The Children of Israel.** These are the descendants of Jacob/Israel, and are the people of God.

9. **Joseph** (Gen 30-50). Joseph was Jacob's favourite son, and ended up being hated most by his other brothers, and sold into slavery in Egypt. While in Egypt, he was tested by temptations, and and trials, yet he remained faithful to God. Even while in prison, he honoured God and served others. And God brought him out top stand one day before Pharaoh, the king of Egypt, and foretold about the coming wealth, followed by a terrible famine that was to happen throughout the world. Pharaoh made Joseph second in command of all the empire, and became known as saviour of the world! Joseph is the greatest example of whate Jesus was going to be when he came to this world!

10. **Moses the Lawgiver.** God protects Moses from birth, when he is taken in by Pharaoh's daughter, and made into the adopted son of the king of Egypt. Moses later discovers that he is a Jew, and renounces his position so that he can be with his people which at the time were slaves. Moses ultimately leads Israel out of Egypt, and to the land promised them called Canaan, which is modern Palestine, where Israel is today. God uses Moses to pen the first five Books of the Bible, which are referred to as "the Law" of Moses (Lk 24:44).

11. **Joshua.** He leads Israel into their Promised Land, and defeats all the kingdoms of the land, allowing Israel to possess it in peace (see the Book of Joshua).

12. **The Judges.** These are leaders whom God uses to bring Israel back to God each generation after Moses and Joshua because they would spiritually drift away. They were before the time of kings in Israel (see the Book of the Judges).

13. **The Kings.** God set Israel up as a kingdom with <u>Saul</u> as its first king. After him was king <u>David</u>, followed by <u>Solomon</u>. After them, the kingdom splits in two, and each kingdom lasts for no more than 400 years before being taken captive by other countries.

14. **Job.** One of the most important books in the entire Bible, is that of Job, which deals with the reason for suffering, and tragedy, and shows God's hand in everything we go through.

15. **Daniel the prophet.** There were many prophets used by God to write much of the Bible, but Daniel stands out among them. He is used to write about the coming Messiah (Jesus), and the end times.

16. **Jesus the Saviour.** <u>Jesus is the whole theme of the Bible</u> - from the first lambs slain in the Garden of Eden, God has been pointing sinners to the only substitute acceptable - that of an innocent Lamb. God became flesh, gave His life freely on the cross, and was buried, but then after three days, rose again, and ascended to heaven victorious over both sin and death! That makes Him our only way to heaven, by faith!

17. **Satan, the devil.** Satan's name used to be *Lucifer*, an arch-angel, who turned away from God seeking to de-throne the Lord. He was kicked out of heaven, but still works destruction in God's creation. He only seeks to destroy what God has

created, and set himself up **as** God. He is doomed to burn forever with his followers in the lake of fire (Rev 20:10)!

18. **Devils**. Devils are what we call "demons" and were created by Satan to help him
work against all that God does in the world.

19. **Angels**. Angels are spiritual beings that minister for God here on earth. They
only do what God wants done, not what we want done.

C. The Main Themes of the Bible

1. **The Depravity of Mankind**. At the start of the Bible, God shows that mankind,
even in the most perfect of environments, will choose to go their own sinful way
instead of God's way (Isaiah 53:6). God however, will not give-up on the work
of redeeming us from sin's power and price. All humans, at their best, are still
sinful, and unable to enter heaven, no matter how hard they try (Psalm 39:5;
Isaiah 40:17). They MUST be "born-again" where their sins are completely forgiven, and their names are written in heaven, all by faith in Jesus Christ!

2. **The Intervention of God in Human Affairs**. In order to keep mankind from
self-destruction, and total loss, God has had to intervene sometimes with disasters (like the world-wide flood of Noah's day, etc.), and with the coming of Jesus
Christ. God is in no way ignoring our condition here on earth, but intervenes at
the right times, in the right ways (Gal 4:4,5; Heb 1:1,2). As a matter-of-fact, He
intervenes in everyone's life *daily!*

3. **The Salvation of Sinners**. The primary reason for God's intervention is to re-
store what sin has ruined, and He does that one heart at a time in the lives of
sinners who repent, and follow His Son, Jesus Christ (Lk 19:10). This theme is
played-out over and over throughout the lives of all people throughout Scripture.

4. **The Coming Physical World-wide Kingdom of Christ**. The constant struggle
with sin on this earth will NOT go on forever, but will climax with the return of
Jesus Christ the second time. He thankfully comes again to destroy the works of
the devil, and to rule as King of kings, and Lord of lords. No one knows when
He is coming again, but we know He says it is imminent (soon)!

Date Lesson Completed _____ *Discipler* _____

Section ONE Test - The Word of God

NAME: _____   DATE: _____

(Each mark = 2 points) SCORE: _____ out of 53 total

The following questions will identify how much you have learned in your Bible Study time. Answer as many as possible, and take your time so that you can think and remember the answers. Most answers are obvious, but some will be hard. All questions come from the material you just studied in Section One of the **First Principles** Course. God bless you as you become confident in knowing and growing in God's wondrous word!

1. Write out *word perfect*, Matthew 4:4 _____
_____
_____

2. What is spiritually wrong with everyone who has ever been born, besides Jesus?
_____.

3. What does the Bible say "sin" is? _____

4. List THREE of the Ten Commandments:
   a. _____
   b. _____
   c. _____

5. What is the penalty for breaking any of God's laws? _____

6. When Jesus died on the cross, What kind of life did God make available to everyone who would believe? _____

7. According to Ephesians 2:8,9 a sinner is saved by God's *what*? _____

8. If a person does NOT get "saved," their *eternal destiny* according to the Bible is **where**? _____

9. God created hell because He is a righteous and holy God and cannot allow sin in His Heaven. **True** or **False** (circle one)

10. Who is your father if you are not born again? _____

11. How many births are required for a person to get into heaven? _____

12. How many sins were forgiven at the cross when Jesus died? _____

13. List the three parts of a human being, that are referred to as the Human Trinity:
   a. _____
   b. _____
   c. _____

14. Which one is the most important part? _____

15. Which part is dead towards God until the new birth? _____

16. The first birth makes you physically a child of your parents. The second birth makes you spiritually and eternally a child of who? _____

17. What does it mean to Repent? _____
_____

18. Can a Christian be happy while living in disobedience to the word of God? ___

19. Is there anything that can separate a Christian from the love of Christ? _____

20. What is it that actually "*seals*" (preserves) the Christian's salvation for all eternity?
_____

21. List an obvious proof that a person has gotten saved _____
_____

22. Who actually lives in and through every believer? _____

23. What does God promise that He will do if a Christian starts seriously sinning, or leaves church, or stops believing? _____

24. What two things should a believer do with their sin when they give in to temptation?
   a. _____ it.
   b. _____ it.
25. Describe in simple words what water baptism is: _____
   _____
26. What kind of baptism is the most important to have? _____
27. Water baptism describes a 3-fold memorial of what:
   a. Christ's _____
   b. His _____
   c. And His _____
28. Should babies be baptized? Yes, or No.
29. What two things must have taken place before a person can be baptized?
   1) _____, and 2) _____
30. The Bible has how many books in it? _____
31. The Bible is divided into two sections:
   a. The first section is called the _____ _____
   b. The second section is called the _____ _____
32. God chose to use about how many human authors to pen the books of the Bible? ____
33. The Old Testament was written mainly in what language? _____
34. The New Testament was written in what language? _____
35. In what year was the King James Bible published? _____
36. List ONE of the seven Proofs that the Bible was Given By God: _____
   _____
37. Not only is the Bible "*inspired*," but it is also what? _____
38. If you don't take the time to actually learn what God wrote down for you in the Bible,
   then what will happen to you: _____
39. What is the Christian's Greatest Weapon against Satan? _____
40. What did Jesus *say* to defeat the temptations of the devil? "It is _____ "
41. Describe what a Personal Quiet Time should be: _____
   _____
   _____
42. List one of the Bible Study Tools that can help you learn more in your Study Time:
   _____
43. What verse is missing in Acts 8 in the "Westcott and Hort" Greek? _____.
44. What difference does that verse make to a person's salvation? _____
   _____.

How are you doing?

Have you been born again? **Yes, No.** When? _____
Have you been baptized yet? **Yes, No.** When? _____
Have you read your Bible all the way through yet? **Yes, No.**
What Book in the Bible are you reading currently? _____
Are you attending church every week? **Yes, No.**
Are you enjoying this study of the Bible? **Yes, No.**
Do you have your own King James Bible? **Yes, No.**

Well Done!

You have now completed Section ONE, and its test. Hand this test in to your Discipler, and it will be quickly graded. After going through this test, knowing what you don't know, and maybe don't understand, you may want to go back over certain portions of the Course before going on to the next Section. Otherwise, press on, and keep growing!

SECTION TWO

This Section of your Discipleship study will establish you in

Fellowship With Other Believers

Memory Verse:

> **"Not forsaking** <u>the assembling of ourselves together</u>**, as the manner of some is; but exhorting one another: and so much the more, as ye see the day approaching."** Hebrews 10:25

Every day, read this Scripture out-loud, at least once, and in a few days, you will have memorized it and be able to recall it without looking at it. And take note of the following facts about the verse in its context:

> ➢ **Who is talking?** The Apostle _____
> ➢ **Who is he talking to?** The "_____" (Jews) - Written to both those people who believed on Christ, and those who did not.
> ➢ **What is he talking about?** He is talking about how that Christians (*ourselves*) should not forsake times when we assemble (on Sundays and other days), even though some people are getting into the habit of it, because we know that "*the day*" (of the return of Christ) is approaching fast!

In this Section, we will study:

- **The Church** - What is it, and what are my responsibilities to it?
- **Scripture Memorization** - How to store God's word into your life!
- **Who is God?** - A Study of what God is really like!
- **Praise and Worship** - How to honour and bless God!
- **The Lord's Supper** - How should a Christian remember Christ's sacrifice on the cross?

MY NAME: _____

THE NEW TESTAMENT CHURCH
Lesson Six

Memory Verse: *Hebrews 10:25*   **Lesson Verse:** *Hebrews 10:25*

> *"Not forsaking **the assembling of ourselves together**, as the manner of some is; but exhorting one another: and so much the more, as ye see the day approaching."* **Hebrews 10:25**

I. Introduction. God established **three** foundational institutions on this earth: the family, civil government, and the group of Bible believing Christians that He calls "the church." Each group has a specific design, and is no less important than the other. Our focus in this lesson is on the local church which has been commissioned by God to carry out His commands of reaching the lost, and maturing the saved. Therefore, God's plan for a Christian's life will always be connected with a local body of believers called **the church.** The purpose of this lesson is to show the disciple the role which their church will play in their everyday life. Without a good understanding of what Christ's church is all about, religions have been able to abuse, confuse, and turn so many people away from living the Gospel!

II. The New Testament Kind of Church

   A. What It Is, and What It Is Not

   1. According to Hebrews 10:25 a church is referred to as the "_____ *of ourselves together*".

      a. It is the gathering of Christians together as often as possible to encourage, and minister to each other as we grow, and reach the surrounding area with the Gospel.

      b. It assembles those Christians together into one unit, one body, as a team of believers, who live as Jesus lived and taught us to. It's like a writing pen has many parts that, when assembled, works just fine.

   2. The church is something that _____ Himself started , builds, and develops as a visible testimony to the world of His grace upon repentant sinners (Matt 16:18).

   3. This "group" of believers is called the "*body of*_____" in 1Cor 12:27. That means two things:

      a. It represents His "body" (His physical presence) on earth today (like ambassadors, 2Cor 5:20), and it operates *like a human body* in the following ways (1Cor 12:12,13,17-27):

         1) Each member (part) of the body of believers has a different function - each ministering to each other's needs as a whole.

         2) No one member can function alone - we need each other! When a Christian is not committed to others, especially to other believers, then they are hindering Christ's work in the world today.

         3) Each member's contribution is vitally important to the well-being of the entire body of believers - we can't go it alone!

         4) A properly functioning body operates as a single unit – a team.

    b. All this shows that the church that Jesus started is a *living organism* constantly growing, and maturing under the never changing, and always perfect Head, Jesus Christ (Eph 5:23).

4. A church is more than just a group or a fellowship - it is a body of **committed** believers, seeking to worship and serve Christ <u>together</u>. It's called a "_____ *of saints*" (Ps 149:1, see also Eph 1:1; Col 1:1,2).

5. A New Testament church therefore is *not* a building at all. If you are looking for a temple to worship in, the Bible says "*your* _____ *is the temple of ... God*" (1Cor 6:19,20). Think about that! Your place of worship is in your heart!

6. A church is *not* a denomination, or religious organization run by a central headquarters. It is local, and run under the authority and instructions of the word of God through its pastor, and for its own people (Titus 1:5-9). *It also is not a social club - i.e., just for fun and pleasure!*

> 7. In short, a church is a group of people who **faithfully assemble together** (that means every week) because they are saved, baptized, and purposed in their hearts to "*observe* ___ *things*" Christ commanded them to do in the Bible (Mt 28:19,20).

B. The local church is also called "*the* _____ *of God*" (Eph 2:19), or in other words, the "family" of God (as His children). As part of His family, Christians MUST be able to get along (John 13:35) under the authority of the _____ (Acts 2:41-47; 20:32).

C. Remember that all members of God's family must be _____ into His family by the new birth (John 3:3; John 1:12,13) or else they are only spectators – not members.

D. Truths About the Church

1. Every local Bible-believing church is Christ's Church, where He is Head!
2. A true church is subject unto God's word in everything - we can't pick and choose.
3. Christ's church is family-oriented - not self oriented.
4. We love to give of ourselves so others get the Gospel.
5. A true church is evangelistic - on the go for souls!
6. Every Christian must be a committed part of a local church! We are not loners!

III. The Purpose of the Local Church

A. The three-fold purpose of the church is found in Mt 28:19,20 where all Christians are to be active in:

1. **<u>GOING</u>** - The world is not commanded to go to church, but the church is commanded to go into the world (see also Acts 1:8) with the Gospel of Jesus Christ, and compelling them to come to "_____" (Mt 11:28-30). Every Christian needs to be involved in going to people everywhere, telling them how to flee from the wrath to come!

2. _____ - The world needs to be **taught** about Jesus through Bible preaching, discipleship, and clear, Biblical teaching (Mt 28:19,20; Acts 20:25-27).

3. _____ - People need to turn away from their *birth-religion*, and begin following Jesus Christ according to the Bible only, and that starts when a person is **baptized** (Mt 28:19), publicly testifying that you follow Jesus now!

B. These are the **core** reasons for the existence of any church. If there is a fault in churches, it is because they have priorities that are more important than these!

IV.What a Church Does

A. **Believes the Bible** - *not criticise it* (2Tim 3:15-17; Act 24:14; Lk 24:25)

B. **Feeds the flock.** The church is to be a place for _____ and teaching the doctrine (truth) about Jesus Christ, and the Christian life (1Cor 1:17; 2:1-5)!

C. **Cherishes Doctrine** - They will pay careful attention to _____ – making sure it is right, and only from the Bible (Titus 1:9; 2 John 1:9,10).

D. **Discipleship** - They will be involved in discipling new Christians, preparing them to serve God, and not be babies or selfish anymore (2Tim 2:1-3)!

E. **Live Separated from the wicked cultures of the world around it** - They will be *different* from the world (1John 2:15; Tit 2:11-14; 2Cor 6:14-17). Not only just in beliefs, but in LIVES (clean and separated).

F. **Corporate Prayer.** The church must focus on praying with one heart about the needs of its own people, and also of the lost around them (Acts 2:42) - Christians should pray together about everything – it keeps our hearts united!

G. **Spiritual Warfare** - They use _____ weapons (not fists or guns) to fight temptation, sin and the devil (2Cor 10:3-5)!

H. **Baptize new believers by Immersion** - They *immerse* - not sprinkle - when they baptize new believers (Acts 8:36-38).

I. **Provide Christian Fellowship** - They ALL meet together every Lord's day, and as often as possible throughout the week (Acts 5:42; Heb 10:25)!

1. The church is to provide Christians with _____ with other believers (Acts 2:42) – you can't find this at the local pub or disco!

2. The church makes it possible for people to <u>minister</u> to each other's needs (Acts 2:44,45). Your greatest ministry will always be one word – OTHERS! Especially widows and _____ (James 1:27)

3. It encourages, and enables Christians to love and enjoy God (Acts 2:46,47).

4. It edifies (builds up, strengthens) the saints (which is *all of us*, Eph 4:11-16).

J. **Ordinances.** The church meeting is a time to remember the three main "_____" (1Cor 11:2), which are not "sacraments," but *commandments* that the Lord left specifically for the church to remember Him by. These ordinances are:

1. **Baptism** (Acts 2:41) Baptism is vital to mark the commitment of a new believer to Christ, and to living separated from the old life and religions of their past.

2. The **Lord's supper** ("*the breaking of* _____," Acts 2:42; 1Cor 11:23-26) is meant to remind us of the high price Jesus had to pay for our forgiveness! A church can remember this event as often as they want, but usually it happens about every one or two months.

3. **Loving** ____ _____ (Jn 15:12,17). This may sound a bit unusual, but Christ *commanded* the people of a church to love the people of that church as much as Jesus loves them. By doing this, God keeps us humble, and godly as a people!

K. **Evangelism.** A Biblical Church will be involved in _____ to the lost (Acts 1:8). A true church will boldly evangelize a lost world to Jesus Christ!

L. **Reproducing Itself.** All the above focuses a Biblical Church on reproducing itself throughout the world through soul-winning, baptizing, training, and then repeating (Acts 1:8)! A true New Testament church is not what it ought to be until it has *reproduced itself* somewhere else.

M. **How can you tell if the church to which you belong (or wish to join) is a true New Testament type of church?** It will match the pattern found in the list above!

V. Each Person's Function in a Local Church

A. During your Christian life, you should grow in three general stages:

1. **Observe and learn** - Your first priority should be to submit to the teaching of the word of God to learn how to be the man or woman that God designed you to be (Matt 11:28-30). Be teachable. Discipleship is the beginning of this stage. *The key is not to stagnate!*

2. **Participate** - In time, you will naturally grow to the point where you can begin to serve and take on basic functions through the ministries of your church (Matt 4:19; James 1:22-25).

3. **Lead** - As your growth continues, you should reach the point where you can begin to minister to others in the same way that you have been ministered to (2Tim 2:2; 1Pet 3:15).

B. These three stages can be roughly compared to the stages of your growth physically: as a <u>child</u>, then <u>youth</u>, and then mature <u>adult</u>.

C. Be patient! Growth takes time. If you work hard as a servant of the Lord Jesus Christ, you will watch yourself grow!

VI. The Organisation of the New Testament, Local Church. All believers are to be _____ (John 8:31) – that means, be students and followers of Jesus Christ, committed to living just like He would if He were in your shoes.

A. The **guide and final authority** of a church is always the _____ (Acts 20:32; John 17:17). In Christ's church, the final authority is never in people, pastors, or princes, but in the living and pure words of God! As disciples, we must follow the Bible's design for Christianity, and not try and improve on it, or adjust it – just live it!

B. There have been five positions of authority in church throughout history, all *under* the Word of God (Eph 4:11) (and none of them included Popes, priests, or canons):

1. **Apostles**: Each were "*someone specially chosen and sent out by Jesus.*" Only TWELVE apostles were chosen by Jesus personally (Mt 10:1,2) who would be the first *to establish Christianity throughout the world* - <u>they laid the foundation</u> by writing and preaching the New Testament. The twelve were made apostles by the supernatural empowerment of Jesus Christ. Their powers were specific only to themselves, and not to all of Christianity (2Cor 12:12). Once the apostles died, their powers died with them!

2. **Prophets**: A special class of people used by God to speak His word until the completion of the Bible (1Cor 13:8-10). The Apostles were also prophets, but most prophets were not apostles, like _____ (Acts 11:27,28; 21:10).

   a. The Old Testament was written by _____ (Rom 16:25,26)
   b. The New Testament was written by ***prophets and apostles***.
   c. Now that the Bible is completed, the role of prophets and apostles has **ceased** (see again 1Cor 13:8-10).

C. Well, if Apostles and Prophets are no longer around, what other leaders are there? (see again Eph 4:11).

1. **Evangelists**: These are <u>Church-starters</u> (like the Apostle Paul was), who *evangelize* the lost to a surrendered faith in Jesus Christ, and then assemble those believers into a local church fellowship (a flock), who are dedicated as a group to obeying and living by all the commands of the Lord Jesus under their own pastor (Mt 28:19,20). As each church obtains its own permanent pastor, the evangelist moves on and starts more churches somewhere else (2Cor 10:16).

2. **Pastors:** These are <u>Shepherds</u>, the Bishops, the Overseers of the "flock" of Christians that seek to serve Christ. They have the primary job of feeding the flock with the truths of the Bible, leading the flock of Christians to serve God, and protecting that flock from spiritual dangers. They are "coaches", training Christians to shine as lights in this dark world!

3. **Teachers:** These people labour together teaching the word <u>along-side</u> pastors. No pastor can do all the work to keep a church going, so God gives additional people a heart to minister *WITH* the pastor, so that the Gospel can go further!

4. Of the five leadership groups only *the last three* are in operation today (Eph 2:19-22). The first two groups (Apostles and Prophets), by their examples laid the foundation of every church (until the Bible was finished), with Christ being the cornerstone of everything. The remaining three groups (Evangelists, Pastors and teachers) simply build upon that **finished** foundation (1Corinthians 3:10,11).

D. The Work and Authority of the PASTOR.

1. The primary leadership in a church is provided by its _____ (Eph 4:11; 1Tim 3:1-5; see also Titus 1:5-9). He is the BISHOP.

   a. A bishop is a *shepherd* over a "flock" (1Pet 2:25; 5:1-4). That is what "pastor" means. **Pastor**, **bishop** and **shepherd** are all the same thing. He is to minister, preach, care for, instruct, and equip the believers.

   b. By the way: a Biblical bishop is *different from modern bishops.*

2. Every church is designed to be led by a pastor. If it has no pastor, then its main goal should be to pray, and get one, and then follow him as he follows Christ.

3. A pastor/shepherd does the following (Acts 20:28-31):

   a. He _____ his flock with the word of God (Bible teaching).

   b. He _____ his flock – knows them; cares for their needs. He keeps them in line with the Bible, and keeps them in motion, always serving the Lord.

   c. He <u>warns</u> them - that is what preaching and teaching is for! He has a responsibility not just to the "flock" but to the Great Shepherd who called him to preach (Ezek 3:17-19; Col 1:28)!

   d. Therefore, a pastor is to **oversee** and spiritually care for those to whom he ministers (by living like them, among them, and for them)! He is not to dominate their lives, but **guide**, love, protect them, and if need be, give his life for them as Christ did!

   e. The pastor is not to be a _____ (1Tim 3:1,6), but an _____ (1Tim 5:17) - He should be **mature** in the Lord, and should be respected, and followed (2Tim 2:2; Jam 1:22). All pastors *first* are elders (mature Christians), but all elders are not pastors.

      1) Every young as well as older man in a church needs to be surrendered to the Lord's will if He should call them to be a pastor.

      2) If a man is called of God to preach, then his local church is his training ground to prepare him to pastor someday!

   f. Christians are to _____ the instruction of a godly pastor, knowing he watches for your _____, and will give an account to God for how you lived your life (Heb 13:7,17). God has given him the responsibility to instruct you as you grow, and to rebuke you when you don't grow (1Tim 4:12). Every Christian needs a godly pastor to follow and learn from.

g. One of the jobs of pastors is to train more pastors (2Tim 2:2). Pastors come from within a flock. That is how God supplies men to go and reach the world with the gospel – through godly men training faithful men!

E. **The Work of Teachers.** These are people God calls to work along with a Pastor to train and mature believers in a church (Eph 4:11-12).

1. Teachers of the Bible need to know the Bible themselves! They need first to be discipled, so that they can later disciple others!
2. Everyone needs to be available should God need them to teach a Sunday School class, help with a Bible Club, or disciple a new Christian!

F. **The Office of Deacons.** This is not a leadership role, but it is an official role. Deacons are paid servants/helpers in a church (1Tim 3:8).

1. Even though there are several "official" positions of leadership, God refers to all Christians as _____ (Mt 20:25-28; 25:21), committed *as a team of servants* to obey our Lord's command to serve each other, and reach this world with the Gospel of Jesus Christ!
2. Some servants are official servants, known as **Deacons**. A deacon is a Bible word for *a God-called servant*, who gives their life to take care of the needs of folks like widows, children, and the poor, so that the pastor can continue to labour in the study and teaching of the word of God (Acts 6:1-4).
3. Ordained Deacons are paid by the church to be able to serve full time like their pastor does (Acts 6:5,6)! They serve along-side the pastor, taking some of the ministry work load off him, so that he can minister without being crushed by it.
4. A deacon must see his role as very important, and be committed to serving - not being served, even though being paid!

G. Notice what is NOT in a church: priests, gurus, canons, altar boys, monsignors, prelates, primates, clergy, popes, cardinals, nuns, etc! Every religion has to "add" to God's clearly defined standard – but these additions are only destructive.

VII. What is a Baptist Church?

A. Baptists are a group of believers that base every belief and every aspect of Christianity solely on the Bible – to the exclusion of all traditions and cultural norms.
B. Bible believers have always assembled themselves together to:

1. Preach and teach all the Bible
2. To live the Bible's commands without fear of man or king,
3. And to encourage each other.

C. The groups who believed only the Bible, were labelled "Baptists" and "**ana-baptists**" (which means *re*-baptizers) by the Catholic Church during the great persecutions of the Dark Ages because we require people who had been baptized as babies to get re-baptized once they repent and are truly born again the Bible way. Baptists are not Catholic, nor Protestant – just Bible-believing followers of the Lord Jesus! Baptists down through history were tortured and burnt at the stake by the tens of thousands during the dark ages – all because they would not submit to a pope or king who required people to either worship himself, or follow an unbiblical belief.
D. Did you know freedoms we take for granted today, were totally against the law just a few hundred years ago? Like the right to own a Bible; the right of free assembly; innocent until proven guilty; and the right of disagreement with the government.

E. Simply put, a Baptist Church is a local group of people who firmly believe and practice the following things as presented in the Bible alone:

B – Biblical Authority Only (2Tim 3:16,17). The only source for absolute truth about God, and what is right and wrong is the written word of God. All questions are settled according to *"Thus saith the Lord."*

A – Autonomy of the local church – this means a local church is fully able to make its own decisions, and govern itself (Acts 5:29). There is no hierarchy over a Bible believing church.

P – Priesthood of believers (1Peter 2:9; Gal 3:26; Mt 23:8). Every Christian can go directly to God because Jesus Christ as their High Priest has made it possible.

T – Three ordinances given by Jesus for the Church to obey: To regularly have the Lord's Supper, Baptize, and Love one another.

I – Individual Soul Liberty. A Christian answers only to God concerning his or her faith (John 12:48; Gal 5:13)! We have the freedom to believe what we want to believe. No human has power over your faith. But all people will answer to God according to whether they lived by the Bible, or by their own will.

S – Saved and Secure Membership (Acts 2:47). Only born again believers are able to be members of a church, and all believers are eternally secure in Christ.

T – Three Church Offices: Evangelist (Church Starter), Pastor, and Deacon.

S – Separation of Church and State (Mt 22:21). Baptists believe the church is under the control of the word of God, not a government. We obey the laws of the land – but when those laws go against the Bible, a Christian ignores those laws!

VIII. The Financing of a Local Church (More about this in *Lesson Fifteen*)

A. The giving of our *tithes* (1/10th of our income), and *offerings* to our local church is God's way of supporting your local church and its ministries. Faithful stewardship (the responsible handling) of our possessions involves giving the "*firstfruits of our increase*" to _____ (Pr 3:9,10)! Not because He needs our money (Ps 24:1), but rather, out of faithful obedience to His word.

B. According to Malachi 3:8-10, the Lord is very serious about the Christian making sure money does not become a "god" in his or her life (1Timothy 6:10). He helps by requiring us to keep *Him* in first place with our finances. This is called *the tithe*. If a person does not tithe, no matter how hard it may be, *he or she is* _____ *God*, and are worse off by keeping their money, than by giving it to Him!

C. Giving our money to the Lord is like the giving of our time, and our love - *it always costs us something* - and it should!

D. Giving demonstrates the proof of our love for _____ (1 John 3:18; John 14:15). If a person has a problem with giving, then it is because they do not love Jesus Christ supremely, or they are not willing to follow the word of God by faith.

E. So, why give regularly to my local church (1Cor 16:1,2)?

1. To obey God (Prov 3:9,10) - do it first out of *obedience*!

2. So that your church can be <u>self-sufficient</u> (not dependent upon the government, bazaars, or bake sales, but upon the very people who assemble together there).

3. So that God's man (the pastor) can be paid for full-time ministry serving people and the Lord, and reaching the lost, instead of having to work both a job, and do the ministry (1Tim 5:17,18)!

4. And also, so that God can bless YOU, knowing that you seek _____ to bless and honour Him (Matt 6:33).

IX.So, How Does A Person JOIN a Local Church? Every Christian is to be a dedicated member of a local Bible believing church (Heb 10:25).

A. **Fulfil God's requirements.** There are only two requirements to be added to a church: _____ (salvation) and _____ (Acts 2:41).

B. **Know whether it is God's will** to join that church (Acts 2:47). Every Christian is supposed to be a member of a local Bible believing Baptist church, and committed with that church to getting the Gospel out to everyone in their area. Ask the Lord where you should commit YOURSELF, and your family, and then join it!

C. **Request membership.** Don't expect to be a part just by attending your church. You have to **ask to be a member**.

D. **Be accepted.** *The local New Testament church is exclusionary* (that means, it does NOT have to accept everyone as members – see Acts 9:22-29). You will only be accepted if you have a clear testimony of your salvation, been Scripturally baptized, and are in agreement with the doctrines of the church you wish to join yourself to. Ask the pastor for the doctrinal statement of the church for you to review.

E. **Once you have been accepted, Make the church, YOUR church!** Be there for every meeting, pray for your pastor, and for the other people there, and ask God where He needs YOU to work so that souls get saved, and young Christians grow!

Are you an accepted member of a church that believes the Bible and *practices* it? If so, where? _____. If not, is there anything keeping you from joining with your Discipler's church? **Yes,** or **No?**

X. Finding a Place to Serve the Lord in Your Local Church (Acts 13:1,2).

A. When the Lord places you in a Bible believing Baptist church, dedicate your life, efforts, and talents in service to God so souls get saved, and Christians are matured.

B. Look around you and see where the pastor, or someone needs help. Take a look at the following list and circle SOMETHING that you might could do at church:

1. Helping Teach a children's or teen Sunday School Class.
2. Going out soul-winning regularly with other believers.
3. Helping the pastor with secretarial tasks like sending out birthday cards.
4. Correspond with missionaries to encourage them and pray for them.
5. Start up a Bible study at your workplace during lunch. You could even use this First Principles Discipleship Course as the study materials!
6. Singing special music, or even joining the choir.
7. Playing a musical instrument.
8. Having Bible Clubs in your home and back-garden.
9. Going with the pastor on visitation calls to people's homes.
10. Visiting people who are sick and in the hospital.
11. Helping in a puppet ministry.
12. Picking up people who need a ride to church.
13. Making tea and coffee for people who come early to church.
14. Ministering to older folks by mowing their grass, or repairing their homes.
15. Hosting a Ladies' Coffee Morning in your home for Christian women to fellowship and give testimony so that other lost women can hear the gospel!

C. And the list goes on… Just add your own ideas, and get started – right away!

XI.Discerning and Using Your Spiritual Gifts

A. Every believer has been given the GIFT of the Person of the Holy Spirit in their lives (Heb 2:4). HE is the source of all good and abilities in your life now!

B. The Holy Spirit has given every believer at least one gift/ability that enables them to "_____" the church (1Cor 14:12) – that means *to encourage and build up.*

C. Spiritual Gifts are a divine enablement that was lacking in a person's life prior to salvation, but are given to be used to serve God by your life through your church. These gifts enable you to do what you could NOT do before getting saved.

D. Talents are what you seem to already be good at, or enjoy doing:

1. Some people play the piano – that is a talent
2. Some people can sing – that is a talent
3. But a spiritual gift is something you could NOT do until you got saved

E. Spiritual Gifts are not earned. They are not dependent upon superior intelligence, physical power, spiritual maturity, moral character, or even the fullness of the Holy Spirit. You either have them, or you don't.

F. These are gifts of God's _____ (1Peter 4:10). Received without any merit.

G. At the time of Christ, 12 men, called Apostles had very special gifts (Mt 10:1-3):

1. They had power over demonic spirits
2. They had the ability to heal every disease and sickness! No limits!
3. They could speak in multitudes of foreign languages (tongues).
4. They could even raise the DEAD! Like it was just as easy to turn on a light bulb!

H. But, these specific gifts have all passed away (1Cor 13:8-10), and are in hibernation until the time of the Tribulation and the Millennium (*more about this in Lesson 20*).

I. The gifts that ARE available to believers today are found in Romans 12:6-8...

1. **Prophecy** – (1Cor 14:3) the ability to speak up for God / preach, when you used to be terrified of speaking in front of anybody!
2. **Ministry / Helps** – that's serving, and making sure everyone is taken cared of ahead of yourself, when before, you used to only think about yourself. It picks up the weaker brethren, the defeated, the discouraged, the empty (Gal 6:1).
3. _____ – (2Cor 3:12) the God-given ability to explain the truths of the Bible and spiritual things, when you used to not be able to explain anything spiritually!
4. **Exhorting** – being an encourager / a motivator – where you used to be so critical and discouraging to others (Heb 3:13; 10:25).
5. **Giving** – (Mt 14:15-17) Sharing what you have with others. It is the drive to give things and money away without fear or regard of your lack, out of a deep sense of appreciation towards God!
6. He that **ruleth** (Rom 12:8) – this is the gift of people management, helping manage people and events and Gospel outreaches, like a helmsman steers a ship according to the commands of the captain/governor (James 3:4).
7. He that **sheweth** _____ (Mt 9:12,13) – is the person who goes out of their way to meet the needs of the weak and infirm, and sick and poor – never condemning them, but showing mercy on them.

J. Some suggestions on how you discover your gifts:

1. Clear away any habitual sin in your life and get victory over anything that is blocking the work of the Spirit of God in your life (Heb 12:1; Eph 4:14-32).
2. Look for just ONE gift – ask God to show you what main gift He has given you.
3. Concentrate on meeting the needs of others ahead of your needs (Eph 4:8-12). Only then will you be able to sense and confirm the gifts you have been given, and you will start to supernaturally meet the needs of the church as a whole.

K. Be careful not to misuse your gifts, or fake a gift in you (Prov 25:14).

XII. Why Are There So Many Churches?

A. The Bible warns that not only does God have *His* church (Matt 16:18), but so does
_____ (2Cor 11:13-15). Satan's churches are full of:

1. False _____ (Matt 7:15)
2. False believers (Matt 7:21)
3. Traditions (Col 2:8)
4. And false doctrines – heresies (Jude 3,4)

B. When comparing "Religion" with *Christianity*, find out whether it is founded upon
what God says (in the Bible), or what **man** says (*tradition*, Mark 7:1-9)

C. There are many different churches. They all claim to be churches but are they?

1. Baptist Churches – should be strictly living by and obeying the Bible only
2. Roman Catholic – allegiance to Rome and tradition and not just Bible
3. Presbyterian Churches – protestant, and baby sprinklers
4. Methodist Churches – believe a Christian can lose their salvation
5. Lutheran Churches – protestants that follow the teachings of Martin Luther
6. Church of England, Church of Ireland – just barely different than Catholic
7. Pentecostal Churches – emphasis mainly on miracles and experiences
8. Non-denominational Churches – no strong doctrinal stand at all

D. Then there are other religious groups – which are clearly **cults:**

1. Mormons – all of them are working at becoming gods (Gen 3:4,5)
2. Jehovah's Witnesses – working their way to God without new birth (Jn 3:3)
3. Seventh day Adventists – keeping the Sabbath (Rom 10:4)
4. Churches of Christ – believe God requires baptism and good works to obtain
remission of sins (Eph 2:8,9)

E. Never mind the fact that there are lots of different **religions** all over the world

1. **Buddhism** – China – belief in the eight-fold path to nothingness
2. **Islam** – Middle East – believe in Allah and his prophet Mohammed
3. **Hinduism** – India - believe in about 2 million gods
4. **Shintoism** – Japanese – believe in dead ancestors
5. **Judaism** – Israel – believe in God of the Bible, but not Messiah
6. **Evolutionism** – fools – the belief in almighty dirt!
7. **Atheism** – fools – believe only in almighty SELF!

F. But in spite of all the above confusion, there are only two kinds of religions:

1. Either salvation is already and completely DONE by Christ…
2. Or it is that we must DO, DO, DO good works, and then DO some more.

G. There are so many churches today simply because people believe that there can be
so many different approaches to God and the Bible, which just is not true (Rev
22:18,19; John 14:6). People must take God's word literally and completely, and
come to God, only God's way - the Bible way. *Religion* has no authority other than
itself, instead of the word of God. That's why, religions are constantly changing,
while in Biblical Christianity, believers are always ***anchored*** to the unchanging
words of God!

H. A brief History of "Churches," beginning with the New Testament Church!

Early Christianity	33 AD	The Crucifixion, burial, and resurrection of Jesus Christ, and His sending out His disciples into all the world to preach and establish Christianity by getting people to repent and believe!
	65	The apostle Paul says all of the then known world had heard about Jesus Christ (Col 1:23)! New Testament style churches were spread throughout the Roman empire in every major city!
	95	The apostle John finished writing Revelation, and completes the Bible - no more prophecy! Right after this, the Bible was published as one Book of 66 books in Latin.
Church and State	...	Intense persecution against Christianity by the Roman Empire for over 200 years!
	313	The Roman Emperor **Constantine** gives in, and organises a central **state-church** in Rome with him at the head. This becomes known as the **ROMAN CATHOLIC** Church. He becomes the first POPE! Before that time, all "churches" were local, independent, and *illegal.* After this time, only the "baptistic" churches were illegal.
	375	The use of "images" was introduced along with the veneration of saints and angels – the catholic church just borrowed all the images of the pagans and made them into "Christian" symbols (idols)! God forbid in Exodus 20 the veneration of ANY image or picture!
	394	"Mass" was forced as THE method for salvation. Religious leaders made the crucifixion into a ritual that had to be constantly repeated.
	593	Purgatory was introduced as a temporary punishment of sinners. No other religious doctrine produced as much money for the catholic coffers than the teachings about "purgatory!"
The Dark Ages	850	Holy water is introduced as having special powers of healing and cleansing.
	1054	The **GREEK ORTHODOX** church split from Rome over the issue of Papal authority. Now there were two "holy apostolic catholic" churches, neither of which follow the Bible!
	1079	Celibacy of the Catholic priesthood was made mandatory. Before then, most members of the clergy were married.
	1090	The rosary was adopted as a method of praying - it was also borrowed from the pagans. The Hindus, the Buddhists AND the Muslims also have their own kind of rosary beads.
	1190	Sale of indulgences (paying a priest for your sins in money) began. It allowed people to pre-pay for sins that otherwise would have to be paid for in purgatory.
	1215	Confessions to Roman priests started, and was made mandatory to all people for salvation. The gift of Salvation was just constantly being added to!
The Reformation	1525	Martin Luther broke away from the Roman Catholic Church - started the **Lutherans.** Martin was a good monk, but wanted to get the Bible into the hands of the common people – he found he had to leave the "church" in order to live by the Bible.
	1534	Henry VIII took the English church away from Rome & started the **Church of England**
	1541	The **Presbyterian** church was formed by Christians breaking away from Church of England. They made a big step in attempting to return to Biblical Christianity – but still carried a lot of "baggage" from Catholicism and the church of England.
	1791	The **Methodist** church broke away from the Church of England - by John Wesley. They for the most part went back to Biblical Christianity.
	1827	The **Mormons** (Church of Jesus Christ of Later Day Saints) began "their church" (with their own "Bible").
Apostasy	1850	Papal infallibility was decided
	1854	The Immaculate Conception of Mary (not of Jesus) was declared as doctrine.
	1870	The pope was declared to be infalible (without error) in his teachings.
	1896	The **Jehovah's "Christian" Witnesses** were organized (with their own "Bible").
	1900's	New religions and moralities were started like the world has never seen before
	1950	The Assumption (ascension into heaven) of Mary proclaimed as doctrine.
	1980+	Even fundamental Christians no longer believe and practice the Bible (Judges 21:25)

I.   Every year there are new "cults" and flavours of "faith" for people to choose from.
J.   But Bible believers (from the time of the apostles on) have never been a part of the religious "system" listed above, but have always been separate from it, and required anyone who believed the Bible to separate themselves from it (2Cor 6:14-18).
K.   Whenever the predominant religious system (Jewish, catholic, protestant, etc) caught a Bible believer, they side-lined, vilified, hunted and tortured them, and even burned them at the stake for their beliefs all because they would not obey the church and baptize their infants, and would not confess to priests, etc. (Acts 8:3; 9:1; 24:14).
L.   So, How can a Bible believer identify *false* churches and *false* religions?

1.   The first thing to look for is whether a church or religious organisation has another authority besides just the Bible.

   a.   Either their authority will **take the place of** the Bible (i.e., Book of Mormon, Koran), or **along-side *with*** the Bible (like Catholic traditions, having equal inspiration), or they will **produce their own bibles!**
   b.   In the Catholic church, their authority is found in about 135 volumes of church traditions and writings, along-side the Bible.
   c.   In other churches, their authority is based on visions, or secret revelations by their leaders. Anytime someone claims to have a vision, a dream or special revelations from God that cannot be verified (like Mohammed's visions, Fatima, Joseph Smith, etc.) THEY are attempting to be equal with the Bible, or over-ride it. And THAT is a cult!
   d.   The Bible believer promotes an honest and clear revelation from God in the form of a Book that can be tested, and verified as authentic!

2.   Another thing to look for is whether they require blind obedience to any human leader – like a pope, or some charismatic leader, or a miracle worker.
3.   Find out if they have a history of killing or suppressing those who do not agree with them (i.e., like Islam does, and like Catholicism did in the Dark Ages).
4.   Do they emphasize obscure passages in their Bible instead of clear ones? (Like, Matt 24:13 and Acts 2:38 instead of Rom 10:13 and Eph 2:8,9).
5.   One last thing to check, is to see if they emphasize *secret* societies and groups that are not open and transparent. If secret things are going on, then they are not like Christ (Mt 26:55; Philp 2:15).

XIII. Questions

A.   According to Hebrews 10:25 a church is referred to as the "_____ *of ourselves together*".
B.   A church is like the human what? _____
C.   Who started and designed the concept of a Church? _____
D.   What are the three ordinances/commandments for the church to keep?
   1.   _____
   2.   _____
   3.   _____

E.   List one of the seven spiritual gifts that God gives to His people at salvation? _____
_____
F.   What spiritual gift do you think you might have from God? _____

Date Lesson Completed _____   *Discipler* _____

BIBLE MEMORIZATION
A Study of the Importance and Methods of Scripture Memorization
Lesson Seven
Memory Verse: *Hebrews 10:25*   **Lesson Verse:** *Psalm 119:11*

> *"Thy word have I **hid** in mine heart, that I might not sin against thee."* Psalm 119:11

I. Introduction

A. It is important for Christians to read and study the word of God daily. But study of the Bible is incomplete if what the Christian reads never takes hold and never manifests itself by a changed life (James 1:22). The only way for the word of God to direct your life is by learning to memorize and meditate on every word of God!

B. This lesson provides the *reasons* for Scripture memorization, and the *methods* that can work best for you.

II. The Importance of RIGHT THOUGHTS in the Life of the Believer

A. Four big truths about *our thinking*:

1. **You are what you _____** (Proverbs 23:7)
2. **Your thoughts come from your _____** (Luke 6:45)
3. **Your heart is messed up bad** (Jeremiah 17:9)
4. **But our heart can be fixed** (Ezekiel 36:26,27; 2Cor 5:17)

B. Even after getting born again, our biggest battle will always be in our "_____" - see 2Corinthians 10:5. Why would the battle be in there?

1. Because Satan used to own that area of our lives – our thoughts.
2. Because Satan knows every back door into it.
3. Because our heart and mind is USED to being run by wrong ideas and feelings, and so, new thoughts and truths from the Bible are often a lot harder to follow!

C. What are some wrong thoughts that you think all too often?

1. _____
2. _____
3. _____

D. How does the devil take control of our thoughts (referred to as demonic attacks)?

1. **We usually just LET him have control** without us even thinking about what we are thinking about (Luke 22:31)!
2. **He uses troubles to scare us!** The devil uses problems to scare you and get you to believe his lies, instead of resting in God's care and wisdom (1Peter 4:12).
3. **He uses re-occurring circumstances** – bad things that seem to constantly happen in our lives usually take our attention off of God, so the devil takes charge!
4. **He uses verbal suggestions** from people (including the TV, radio, music) – all of them usually speak half-truths and lies that we often believe without question!
5. **He uses spiritual influencing** – Satan especially puts ideas in your heart (Luke 9:54,55; Ephesians 6:12) – just as God speaks to your heart at times, so also does the devil if we are not careful about what we end up thinking about!

E. Everyone battles with many of the following wrong thoughts: suicide, lust, hatred, envy, worry (fretting), depression, hatred of themselves, covetousness, constant fears, and even apathy. Do you think about any of those things a lot? _____

F. So, how do we fight against and defeat such demonic attacks? *Only through...*

1. **Regular Scripture Reading** – it helps wash and cleanse our habitual thoughts that often defile us and defeat us (Eph 5:26).

2. **Scripture Memorization** – the storing away in our hearts and minds the words of God so that we can meditate on them for strength, wisdom, direction, and comfort.

3. **Scripture Meditation** – the thinking-through the meaning of every word of a Scripture so that we understand it, and so that we can obey it.

4. **Scripture Activation** – acting in obedience to what God says to think and do, instead of what we think and want to do (James 1:22).

G. The truth is, we can never change how we *feel*, but we can change *the way we think.* That's why the Bible constantly refers more to our *mind* instead of our emotions.

1. Computer programmers refer to something called G.I.G.O. which stands for *Garbage In Garbage Out.* What we have put into our thinking affects what comes out of our lives by our words, and especially our actions.

2. The opposite is true as well. G.I.G.O. could become, *Good In Good Out.* The key is to find what is truly Good and wholesome and clean, and think on that!

III. **Here is The Way to CHANGE Your Mind – change what you think about...**

A. **Through Repentance** – You have to start with this! Repentance is a regular effort of submitting your life and feelings to the Lordship of Jesus Christ over you. Allow God to show you where you are wrong, and allow Him to change. You won't be changed until you WANT Him to change you.

1. By _____ *your heart*, facing and accepting your own guilt and shame towards God (2Cor 13:5). Sorrow is good when it brings us to God for forgiveness!

2. By _____ *with all your heart* in Jesus Christ - allowing His blood, shed in your place, be the power that constantly cleanses away all your guilt and shame.

    a. Have you trusted Jesus to save your soul? (Romans 10:9,10) **Yes, No**?

    b. Well, keep trusting His blood to cleanse and protect your soul (Heb 9:14)!

3. By _____ *your heart* with a Person - yielding to *His work* in you (Eph 5:18)

4. By _____ *from your heart* every word God says in His word - living under HIS influence on your life AND thoughts (Romans 6:17)

5. Many people only "receive" the gift of salvation without ever wanting to enjoy the fullness of God's grace and forgiveness for the rest of their lives! The only way that happens is if we start memorizing and meditating on Bible truths!

B. **God Changes Our Thinking Through Scripture Memorization**

1. God calls memorizing Scripture "_____" *Scripture away in our heart* (Psalm 119:11). That means storing away the words of Scripture in your mind and heart in an organised way so that you can call it to mind whenever you need it.

2. Start off small. It takes only five minutes in the morning, and five minutes in the evening. Don't plan on hours of work, just plan on slowly collecting particular Scriptures that speak right to your heart and life so that you can be changed!

3. Copy a verse or two to small pocket-sized cards (3"x5" or 4"x6") like below:

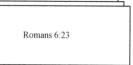

Salvation is Free
Romans 6:23
For the wages of sin is
death; but the gift of God
is eternal life through Jesus
Christ our Lord

Romans 6:23

4. Make sure that you memorize the "*address*" (*reference*) of the Scripture along with the verse(s). In the above figure, it is **Romans 6:23**. The important thing is to make the address part of what you memorize as well. This way, you will be able to find the verse again in the Bible when you need it for someone else!

5. Keep the cards together in a case or pack of some sort, so that they can be carried around easily in your pocket or purse.

6. Memorize each verse using the following pattern:

   a. Read the verse out-loud just **5** times and then put it away.
   b. Do this at least once a day for a week.
   c. At the end of the week you should be able to say the verse easily by memory
   d. Try to do a new verse each week.
   e. Make sure that you go back and review each previous verse at least once a week - maybe go back through all the older verses at one time, so to keep them fresh. You will be surprised how much you remember.

7. Soon you will see these verses help you lead someone to salvation in Jesus Christ, or help you through a struggle, or strengthen another Christian!

8. Review will be the key to retaining what you memorize! Memorization is not just a one-time event, it is repetitive so you can remember what you learn.

C. **Through Scripture Meditation** "*...and in his law doth he* _____ *day and night*" (Psalm 1:2)

1. God blesses Scripture meditation! This is not just some "duty" for a Christian to do, but it is the KEY to God's greatest blessings in every believer's life!

   a. You will prosper by it! (Psalm 1:2,3)!
   b. You will get answers to prayer! John 15:7 You will then *know* what to ask.
   c. You will become wiser than your _____, and stronger than your troubles (Psalm 119:97-100).
   d. You will be able to defeat sinful temptations! (Psalm 119:11) – best reason!

2. God commands us to, "_____ *on these things...*" (Philippians 4:8):

   a. _____ - think about more than just "facts" – true things are real and not imagined, or felt, or supposed, or guessed at, but absolute and unchanging!
   b. _____ - think on things that are in the open, not on things that are evil or hidden or dark.
   c. _____ - think on things that are right, moral, and godly – not ungodly
   d. _____ - think on things that are clean, and innocent
   e. _____ - think about beautiful, pleasant, wonderful things
   f. _____ - think about the good things in other people instead of the bad
   g. _____ - think about good inner qualities of people and God
   h. _____ - think about ways to praise other people, and especially God!
   i. All of the above describe just one Person you should think about all the time – who is that? _____ (Isaiah 26:3).

3. Meditating on the things as listed above will be the first way God helps you replace wrong and sinful thoughts with the following RIGHT kind of thoughts:

    a. Pondering God's goodness – You will need to learn to limit your mind to just dwelling on the goodness of God for a while at first – *"rejoice in the Lord"* is a command (Philp 4:4). Make a list of things that you can be thankful to God for, and then praise your way through it!

    b. Scripture meditation will help you connect God's promises, words and warnings with your everyday life.

    c. Through simple Scriptures, God will speak to you and direct your thoughts in a new and better way!

4. Meditation simply is you focusing on what God is saying **one word at a time**, asking yourself what it is saying to YOU, and how to obey it. Think about the words of a verse throughout your day, allowing it to be opened up by the teaching power of the _____ ___ _____ (John 16:13).

D. God Changes Our Thinking Through Belief!

1. You won't always see the results of meditating on Scripture right away. God will only bless your thoughts if you really start believing what you are learning to think from His word! Trust that *"...weeping may endure for a night, but _____ cometh in the morning."* (Psalm 30:5)

2. Realize how much God thinks about each of us, and loves us (Jer 29:11; Ps 40:5).

3. Believe that you are probably WRONG about how you view things (Isaiah 55:8,9; 2Corinthians 3:5)! Start to believe that God's word, works

4. You need to especially believe that God REALLY IS working everything out for your good, even when it doesn't make sense, or feels like it (Romans 8:28)! God is good; His way of doing things is good; and He only has your good in mind in everything He allows in your life!

5. Just start believing what God says and what God promises. Have you ever started collecting all God's promises to you? They are worth remembering!

E. Finally, Through Obedience! This is the final step in *Changing your mind!*

1. Just knowing God's word will not bring you joy and blessing – DOING God's word will bring you joy (John 13:17)

2. **Use what you learn!** Be involved in soul-winning and Church visitation, applying the verses you are memorizing to other people's needs for their salvation, encouragement and spiritual direction (Proverbs 11:30)!

3. We're told to *not* think "_____", hurtful, revengeful thoughts (1Cor 13:5).

4. So, will you start obeying what God says to think about, and rejecting the thoughts that He says NOT to think? **Yes, No.** If not, you are wasting your time!

5. By **Thinking** right things, you will start **Doing** right things!

IV. Final Thoughts

A. Some Goals to Set

1. Memorize verses that will help you win people to saving faith in Jesus Christ. Memorize the same verses that *helped you* see the need to be saved. Write these down and memorize them! (Heb 9:27; John 3:3; Rom 3:23; 6:23; 10:13)

2. Memorize verses that will help you in times of trouble, heartache and temptation (1Cor 10:13; John 14:1; Isa 40:31; Philp 1:6; 1Thes 5:24).

3. Memorize verses dealing with current issues facing your co-workers and neighbours (like evolution, eternal life, that the unborn child is human and true life).

B. **A Verse a Day, actually <u>KEEPS</u> the Devil away!** These goals are not obtained in just one month, or even one year. They are obtained one verse at a time. So, at the end of your life, the challenge is to be able to look back and have made it through the trials and troubles because the word of God was faithfully hidden away in your heart!

C. **An Evaluation.** Write out the two verses you have memorized as best as you can:

Matthew 4:4 _____

_____

_____

_____

Hebrews 10:25 _____

_____

_____

_____

_____

Date Lesson Completed _____ *Discipler* _____

KNOWING GOD
A Study of God the Father, the Son, and the Holy Spirit
Lesson Eight

Memory Verse: *Hebrews 10:25*   **Lesson Verse:** *1 Peter 1:8*

> *"Whom having not seen, ye love; in whom, though now ye see him not, yet believing, ye rejoice with joy unspeakable and full of glory."* **1 Peter 1:8**

I. Introduction

A. THEOLOGY! What an awesome subject: *the study of God!* Theology has long been called the queen of the sciences because it is the very foundation of what mankind can know, and it is the limit of what mankind can experience. All other sciences are somewhere in between, and are all relative to how man views and understands God.

B. This lesson will present a *brief* study of the one true God in heaven, in order for the new believer to personally know Who it is who created them, Who hears and answers their prayers, and Who it is that will be the final Judge in the future.

II. How Can We Know God?

A. The Bible says in John 1:18, *"No man hath **seen** _____ at any time..."* Yet, the same Bible says, God has revealed Himself to mankind in the following **three ways**: In His Creation, in His Word (the Bible), and by His Son, Jesus Christ.

B. We Find that God Has revealed Himself first **In His *Creation*.**

1. Psalm 19:1-3, tells us God's creation is constantly teaching and instructing every person on this planet that there is a Creator, and that HE is worthy of worship.

2. According to Romans 1:18-20, *"That which may be _____ of God **is** manifest"* - it is not hidden. We don't know *everything* about God, but what can be known is revealed because, God has made sure that it is shown "clearly" to all people by His "_____ *of the world".*

3. You find proof for the existence of a Creator in:

   a. DNA – biology – the fact that DNA has design and order and information;

   b. All the laws of the universe – physics – they are amazingly balanced;

   c. There needs to be an ultimate Creator for everything to come into existence – nothing "just happens" without something starting it or creating it.

   d. If you found a watch, you would easily know that someone MADE it and that it did not just appear out of random chances coming together. The same is true with all of life and the universe itself – someone had to make it!

4. None of the above proofs for a Creator are enough for anyone to know WHO the Creator is, but just enough to know that He does exist. Romans 1:20 concludes that people know enough about God and are *"without _____ "* because if they don't believe, they are simply rejecting the information God gave them to begin with, and will always come up with their own gods to worship in the place of the Creator!

5. The fact that the whole world attempts to worship a Creator, proves they know there is something bigger than the world that deserves worship. They just don't know who He is or how to find Him. But that is why God reveals Himself in more ways.

C. Secondly, God has revealed Himself **In His *Words*.**

1. Everything we can know about God is written in the Bible.
2. We will never know everything there is to know about God, but what we can know, we will find in the Bible (Deuteronomy 29:29).
3. The purpose of the Bible is to enable seekers to know God, love God, and enjoy God forever! Without the Bible, it is a blind exercise!
4. The gospel, the life and preaching of Jesus Christ, and the revelation of the mysteries of God are made understood by the "_____ *of the prophets*" (Rom 16:25,26), which have been "*made known to* _____ *nations!*"
5. If you want to know God, you will find Him in the pages of the Bible! Not in universities, laboratories, or test tubes.

D. Thirdly, God Revealed Himself **In His *Son*** (Heb 1:1-2; John 14:7-9; Matt 11:27)

1. The greatest revelation about God was found in Jesus Christ. A person can study science all their life and never know who created everything. A person can know all about the Bible, and yet never know its Author. So, God had revealed Himself best when He came into this world and spoke for Himself (1 Tim 3:16).
2. Jesus came not only to pay for our sin-debt on the cross, but to reveal the **Person** of the God who made each of us. Jesus told Philip in John 14:9 that "*he that hath seen me hath seen the* _____."
3. If God had not revealed Himself, man would not be able to ever know Him at all. But God *has* proven that He is very interested in man knowing Him *intimately!* In John 17:3, Jesus says, "*and this is life eternal, that they might know* _____ *(YOU) the only true God, and Jesus Christ, whom thou hast sent.*"

E. Do you WANT to know Him? The God who created you, and made everything there is, made it possible for you to know Him (Jer 9:23,24) if you really want to (Jer 29:13)!

III. What Can Be Known About God?

A. **We Can Know for sure that God Exists**

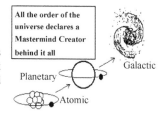

All the order of the universe declares a Mastermind Creator behind it all

Galactic
Planetary
Atomic

1. Psalm 19:1-3 tells us that all of creation declares that an intelligent Being created everything that there is. There has to have been a Mastermind behind all of this universe!

    a. A book requires an author to have written it.
    b. A program requires a programmer
    c. A poem requires a poet
    d. A design requires a designer
    e. An invention requires an _____
    f. When we see a painting, do we believe that the artwork created itself, or, is it self-evident that an ARTIST created it?
    g. So, All of Creation requires a Creator!
    h. Any other belief is Insanity. It is *insane* to believe that everything came about by mere *chance* out of nothing!

2. Only a _____ believes that there is *no God* (Ps 14:1).

B. **We Know that God has a Personality and Emotions**

1. God *grieves* at things (feels remorse, Gen 6:5,6) – especially at our sin.

2. God gets _____ (1Kings 11:9), and yet loves (John 3:16). These are two great contrasting emotions - and God possesses them to the fullest!

3. God can _____ (Prov 1:26), and even _____ (Zephaniah 3:17; Isa 62:5). There are some things that really excite God!

4. Our God is a _____ God (Deut 6:14,15). Look at the context - it is dealing with idolatry, and how that He is very jealous of His creation turning a blind eye to His love and work in their lives, and wasting their worship on idols, which really are satanic demons!

5. Therefore, all the emotions that a person experiences, God experiences - only in their purest form, because He is _____ (Psalm 99:9; 1Peter 1:15,16).

C. We Know that **God is perfect, and cannot sin, or fail, or stop being good!** (Mt 5:48) That is what makes Him God.

D. **We Know that God Created Everything**

1. Genesis 1:1 describes God creating…

    a. Time ("in the beginning")
    b. Space ("heaven")
    c. Matter ("earth")

2. He created everything visible (all matter) AND _____ (everything spiritual; Col 1:16).

3. The ONLY thing that has always existed, and always will exist, is God (Ps 90:2).

E. **We Know God is Greater than all His Creation**

1. He is *Creator* and *Sustainer* of everything. Without Him we can't exist.

    a. Gen 1:1 says, "*In the beginning God _____ the heaven and earth.*"
    b. John 1:3 says, "*All things were _____ by him and without him was not anything made that was made.*"
    c. Ephesians 3:9 declares that, "*God … created all things by _____.*" Not by evolution, or a "big-bang"!
    d. Colossians 1:17 "*And he is before all things, and by him all things _____*" (are held together)! Jesus is even the *glue* of the universe.

2. God is *Eternal*, "*from everlasting,*" and "*to everlasting*" (Ps 90:2)

3. He is three things all at the same time:

    a. All powerful (*omnipotent, Matt 28:18*)
    b. All knowing (*omniscient, Mt 9:3,4*)
    c. All present (*omnipresent, Ps 139:7-10*)

4. He exists OUTSIDE of all He has created – that means He is bigger and greater than everything He has made! So, the next time you look out at a starry sky, knowing how big our universe is, know that the God we worship is bigger still!

F. **We Know God loves His creation - He is the *Author* of Love (1 John 4:7-8)**

1. Everything that God created, was _____ in His sight (Gen 1:4,10,12,18,21,25,31).

2. God is not willing that any of His creation _____ (2Pet 3:9) – to be lost forever in hell.

3. God showed His love toward us by giving His only _____ _____, (John 3:16) who Himself took our place so that we could go free to heaven by faith in Him! Now, **that** is real love (1 John 4:10).

G. We know **there is only one God** (1Kings 8:60; Isaiah 45:6)

1. Many religions believe there are different *gods* that control various aspects of life, like a sun-god, a god of death, a god of lightning and thunder, and a god of harvest.
2. Each god has to be appeased and made deals with in order for things to go well.
3. But, there is only one, almighty, all wise God, that has already done everything so that anyone can be forgiven and made right in His eyes (2Cor 5:21).

H. **God is a *Three Part* Being** - Three Persons, Yet One God; not three different gods!

1. This is the concept of the God-head (Tri-unity, or Trinity).

   a. Notice how God said in Genesis 1:26, "*Let _____ make man in _____ image, after _____ likeness.*" (Same in Isa 6:8). The '**us**' is the trinity.
   b. Notice the Trinity in Jesus' baptism (Matt 3:13-17).
   c. Notice the Trinity in the Great Commission of Matt 28:19.
   d. The Trinity is listed in Paul's prayer in 2Cor 13:14.
   e. Jesus, the Father and the Holy Ghost are _____ (1John 5:7).
   f. All throughout creation, watch for God's triple signature: like the 3 states of water (ice, liquid, and vapour), the 3 dimensions, the 3 states of time (past, present, and future), 3 basic elements of matter (proton, neutron, and electron), three parts of man (1Thes 5:23), and so on.
   g. The concept of the Trinity is not made-up. It is *beyond* our understanding!

I. The Godhead (the Trinity) then is made up of **the** _____, **the** _____ (the Son), and **the Holy Ghost** (the Holy Spirit) – see 1John 5:7.

IV. Let's First Examine God as The Father

A. **God is a spirit!** God exists without any physical form or body. John 1:18 says, "_____ man" has ever seen the Father with their mortal eyes, because God is a _____ (John 4:24). He only exists as pure light (1John 1:5).

B. **God Has a Name.**

1. God the Father's true name is ***Jehovah*** (Ex 6:1-3) which means "the Lord, the promise keeper."

   a. Every time you see the word "**LORD**" as all capital letters in the King James Bible, it is the word **JEHOVAH** in Hebrew!
   b. It is a very holy name (Lev 19:12) – NEVER to be used flippantly or in vain!
   c. But at the same time, don't let the Jehovah Witnesses scare you away from that name. It truly IS God's name!

2. Another name God goes by is "*the I _____*" (Ex 3:13-15). Jesus called Himself by this name (John 8:56-59)! That's because Jehovah and Jesus are the same.
3. One final name you can use for God is "_____" which means 'Daddy' – a very humble, loving name that we can refer to God as (Ro 8:15; Mk 14:36)

C. **God IS the Father.**

1. God is referred to as **God the Father** because:

   a. He is the Father (the Begetter or Creator) of all things.
   b. Secondly, He is the Father of the Son of God, Jesus Christ (Psalm 2:7).

c. Thirdly because He is the personal Begetter of your salvation - you become His child by faith, and He becomes your Father, or "Abba," (means *Daddy*, Gal 4:6; Mk 14:36), who loves you and looks out for you as *His child* now!

2. God the Father is the authority of the Trinity. He is in charge of this universe whether we like it or not. That makes Him sovereign.

3. We are supposed to submit to the will and commandments of God the Father.

    a. Jesus submitted to the will of the _____ in Gethsemane (Mt 26:39).
    b. The Holy Spirit obeys the will of the Father (John 15:26).
    c. Certainly WE should submit!

4. Jesus said we are to pray to God the Father (Matt 6:9).

5. The title of "Father" is reserved only for three persons:

    a. God – Holy Father (John 17:11) – not a name for the Pope!
    b. Your earthly father (your parent, see Mt 19:5)
    c. And the "founding fathers" of your nation
    d. It is NOT for anyone else who may want you to call them 'father.' We are told to call NO ONE ELSE "*your* _____ " (Mt 23:8,9)!

D. The most amazing truth about **God the Father** is that the great Architect of all creation - your Creator - **wants YOU to personally get to know HIM!** The greatest purpose in anyone's life is to get to know God, start to love God, and always enjoy God in your life as you serve Him in "_____ *and in* _____ " (Jn 4:23).

V. Let's Next Examine God The Son, Jesus Christ

A. **Jesus is the Word of God** (John 1:1-3; 1John 5:7).

1. In the beginning the "_____ " always was (existed).
2. He was and is God. "*the Word ... was* _____" (Jn 1:1)
3. Even though He was God, He became _____ and dwelt amongst men (Jn 1:14)

B. **Jesus IS God** – The "Deity" (the *God-ness*) of Jesus Christ

1. The Bible calls Jesus GOD!

    a. Heb 1:8 has God the Father talking to His Son, and says, "*But unto the Son he saith, Thy throne O* _____..."
    b. 1Tim 3:16 says, "_____ *was manifest in the flesh...*" To be manifested means to be shown as real – God really became flesh. Most of the new bibles only say "He" inferring that only JESUS became flesh. We ALL believe THAT fact. But will we believe that GOD became flesh? That is the issue!

2. In Jesus was ALL of God (Col 2:9). The word Godhead means *trinity*.
3. As a Man, Jesus was separate but equal with God (Philp 2:5-7). Jesus took nothing away from God, by being God as well! Ponder that!
4. Notice His name in Matt 1:23, "*...Emmanuel, which being interpreted is* _____ _____ _____." (See Isaiah 44:6,8)!
5. So, *Jesus* is the manifestation of *Jehovah* God of the Old Testament (Ex 6:3).

    a. They both are called *Lord of Lord's* in Deut 10:17 and Rev 19:16.
    b. They both are called *Alpha and Omega* (the first and the last) in Isa 44:6; 48:12, and Rev 1:17; 22:13.
    c. They both can't be Gods (compare Isa 44:8 with John 20:28; 14:6-9) – they must be the same God!

    d. Psalm 68:17-18 says GOD, while Eph 4:7-10 says Jesus.

    e. Compare Ex 3:13,14 with Jn 8:56-59, and see Ps 90:1,2.

    f. Jesus is the ALMIGHTY! (Rev 1:8; Gen 17:1)

C. **Jesus is THE most prophesied person in the entire Bible** (Luke 24:27).

1. The Defeater of Satan (Genesis 3:15)
2. The promised Prophet like Moses (Deut 18:15)
3. The coming King of Israel (Isaiah 9:6,7)
4. The Suffering Servant of God (Isa 53:6)
5. The Substitute for sinners (Num 21:8; John 3:14-16)
6. The Rock of the Wilderness (Exod 17:6; 1Cor 10:4)
7. The Bread of Life – Manna from heaven (John 6:58)

D. **THE Most Wondrous Thing of all time happened... When God Became a Man – when the Word of God became the Son of God**

1. We call it Christmas!
2. God the Father did not birth another God. God the Word became a Man (Jn 1:14)
3. When He became a MAN, He became Jesus, **the Son**. God lived as a Son.
4. So, He is NOT just the Son of God, but God Himself, in the flesh. *Jesus* was really *Jehovah God* who had come in sinless flesh.
5. Jesus said, *to see and know Him* is actually to see and know the "_____" (John 14:6-9). Jesus was not just a man, or even "another God" (see Isaiah 43:11; 44:6). He was God the Father, in the flesh!
6. This is a great mystery, but is understood by the fact that Jesus was really God contained in flesh like you and me live (1Tim 3:16).

E. **Jesus is Eternal.**

1. Even though He was born, and had an earthly beginning, He has always existed. He was God before coming to earth.
2. John 1:1 "*In the beginning* _____ *the Word and the Word was with God and the Word was God*." The "Word" is **Jesus**, and the Bible says that He was both *in* the beginning, and *was* God Himself (Jn 1:14; 8:56-59; 1 Jn 5:7; Ex 3:13-15).
3. Jesus shared the glory of God His Father "*...before the world* _____." (John 17:5). He was not created – He is the *Creator!*
4. How many things were created by Jesus (John 1:3)? _____. So Jesus could not have been created since "*without* ____ *was not anything made that was made.*"
5. God talked with Jesus and the Holy Spirit when He made man in the beginning (Gen 1:26). God was not talking to angels, but to Jesus and the Holy Spirit. Note the "*Spirit*" in Gen 1:2.

F. **Jesus is the Son of Man** – Fully Human, AND Fully God

1. The supernatural Birth of Jesus was foretold **700 years** earlier (Isaiah 7:14)!

    a. Matt 1:18-20 tells us, "*for that which is conceived in her is of the* _____ _____. Jesus was NOT conceived by **Joseph!**

    b. Jesus was born of a _____ named Mary (Matt 1:23). She was not *just* a "young woman" like some of the Bibles say in Isa 7:14. God was doing something very supernatural!

2. Jesus' Life on Earth was truly supernatural, and **sinless**.

    a. Luke 2:40 *"And the child grew and waxed _____ in _____, filled with*
        _____: and the grace of God was upon Him."
    b. Jesus was "_____ *of the devil."* (Luke 4:1,2), and yet never sinned,
        because *"...in him is no _____."* (1 John 3:5)
    c. 1Peter 2:22 says that Jesus *"... did no _____..."*
    d. 2 Corinthians 5:21 tells you that He even *"... **knew** no _____."*
    e. So, with all of Jesus' sinlessness, He could have just STAYED separate from
        us, but instead, He came into our world, and went all the way on the cross to
        bring us back to God (Isaiah 53:4-6,10).

  3. Jesus grew up in a normal family. Jesus had _____ and _____
     (Mt 12:46-50; 13:55,56; Mk 6:3). Mary has more children after Jesus. They were
     actually half-brothers and sisters – not cousins.

G. **Jesus IS the Promised Messiah** – the Saviour of the whole world!

  1. His title "Christ" is the same as "_____" (John 1:40,41), which means, the
     "chosen One".
  2. It was prophesied that the messiah would:

    a. Heal the Jewish people (Malachi 4:2).
    b. He would save them from their enemies (Zechariah 9:8-10).
    c. He would restore the kingdom of David (Isaiah 9:7).

  3. But before He could do any of that, He had to suffer in the place of all mankind!

H. **Jesus is the Saviour of the Whole World** purchasing forgiveness for all!

  1. His very name 'Je-sus' means, *"Jehovah Saves"* (Mt 1:21).
  2. Jesus paid all man's sin-debt Himself, taking the place of all sinful men in death,
     providing full forgiveness for anyone who will believe (Acts 13:38,39).

    a. Rom 5:8 *"But God commendeth his **love** toward us in that while we were*
       yet _____ Christ _____ for us."
    b. 2Cor 5:21 *"For ___ (God) hath made ____ (Jesus) to be ____ _____ ____*
       who knew no sin; that we might be made the _____ of God in him."
    c. Only the blood of Jesus Christ can cleanse sin. Heb 9:22 says, *"...without*
       shedding of _____ is no _____," and 1 John 1:7 states, *"...and the*
       blood of _____ _____ his Son _____ us from all sin."

I. **Jesus has the victory** over death and hell giving us eternal life (Romans 6:23)!

  1. All other religious founders are in the grave: Islam (Mohammed), Buddhism
     (Buddha), Mormon (Joseph Smith), Jehovah Witness (their *Jesus* is dead), etc.
  2. After Jesus rose from the grave, He was seen by over _____ wit-
     nesses (see 1Cor 15:3-8).
  3. Acts 2:32 says, *"This _____ hath God _____ ____, whereof we are all wit-*
     nesses." Jesus did NOT stay in the grave!
  4. Jesus is now living and is seated at God's right hand (Heb 10:12), as our ONLY
     _____ (1Tim 2:5). He's our advocate/defence attorney!
  5. HIS life enables us to live and prosper in this life (Col 2:9,10; 1Cor 1:30,31)!
     Without Him, you will have no life (John 15:1-7).

J. **Jesus IS Lord** – that means He is in charge of your and my life (Philp 2:11).

  1. He is Greater than the _____ – over all the Laws of God (Mark 2:28).
  2. He is Greater than the Temple (Matt 12:6).

3. He is Lord of the weather (Mark 4:39-41).
4. He is Lord over all demons and even Satan (Luke 8:26-31).
5. He is greater than sin's grip over you (Matt 9:6).
6. He is able to conquer health problems and death (John 11:43-45).
7. He is King over all kings, and Lord of lords! He is actually the Boss over all bosses, Ruler over all rulers and the king over all kingdoms!
8. Why don't we do what He says? (Luke 6:46)

K. Jesus is COMING again!

1. He is coming to take us home to heaven (John 14:1-3).
2. He is coming soon (Mark 13:32,33) – when you are not expecting it!
3. He is coming _____ (Rev 22:12).
4. We should be looking for Him every day to come for us (Titus 2:13).
5. More about this in **Lesson 20**, when we study the Future!

VI. God The Holy Spirit, (the Holy Ghost)

A. The *Holy Spirit* is a **Person**.

1. He is the Third Person of the Trinity. The Holy Spirit comes from the Father, and is referred to as a Person – not just a Power. John 15:26 *"But when the* **Comforter** *is come, whom I will send unto you from the Father, even the* _____ *of truth, which proceedeth from the Father,* **HE** *shall testify of me."*
2. We say *"person"* because He is as much God as the Father and Jesus Christ. Just as He was active in creation, the Holy Spirit actively indwells the body of the Christian (1Cor 6:19), and empowers him for God's service.

B. The Holy Spirit IS **God**, just as the Father, and the Word are.

1. The Holy Spirit was with God in the beginning. Gen 1:2 states, *"...And the* _____ *of* _____ *moved upon the face of the waters."*
2. 1 John 5:7 *"For there are three that bear record in heaven, the Father, the Word, and the* _____ _____, *and* **these three are** _____.*"

C. The Holy Spirit is **All Powerful**.

1. He provided the power that Jesus relied upon to live perfectly (Luke 4:14).
2. It was the power of the Holy Spirit that _____ Jesus from the dead (Rom 8:11; see also Acts 2:32).

D. The Holy Spirit does some very important **work** in people's lives:

1. He *convicts* people – convinces them of their guilt before God (John 16:7,8).
2. He *regenerates* **us – gives us a new LIFE**. John 3:5 *"Jesus answered, Verily, verily I say unto thee, Except a man be* _____ *of water and of the* _____, *he cannot enter into the kingdom of God."*
3. He *indwells* the believer the moment he believes, therefore the believer's body is the Temple of the Holy Spirit. 1Cor 6:19 *"What? know ye not that your* _____ *is the* _____ *of the Holy Ghost* **which is in you**...?"*
4. He *fills* the yielding believer. Eph 5:18 *"Be not drunk with* _____ *wherein is excess; but be* _____ *with the Spirit."*
5. He *seals* the believer. Eph 4:30 says, *"And grieve not the Holy Spirit of God whereby ye are* _____ *unto the day of redemption."* That means **once saved, always saved.**

6. He **instructs** the believer, guiding him to maturity (Jn 14:26) through _____ (2Tim 2:15) and under Bible preaching. The Christian cannot grow without the Bible being the priority in their life (Mt 4:4; Job 23:12)!

7. He **empowers** believers to live beyond their human abilities (2Tim 1:7)!

8. He **bestows gifts** of ability to the Christian that enable him or her to serve God effectively.

9. He produces **fruits** in the life of the believer as well (Gal 5:22,23). These counteract the "works of the flesh" that our old nature does naturally (Gal 5:19-21).

E. The Holy Spirit gives Priceless GIFTS to believers:

1. There WERE nine **SIGN** gifts given to first century Christians as listed in 1Cor 12:1,8-11.

   a. **Word of** _____ - ability to know what people ought to do (wise actions) in tough situations (1Cor 12:8).

   b. **Word of** _____ - the ability to know something that is hidden in others (Mt 9:4).

   c. **Faith** - The ability to believe God for others even when they themselves just can't believe (Mt 17:20).

   d. _____ - The ability to miraculously cure diseases (Mt 10:1), and raise the dead back to life (Mt 10:8).

   e. **Miracles** - a supernatural ability to prove what you are saying is from God (Mark 16:20).

   f. _____ - the ability to foretell the future in addition to telling-forth what the Scriptures already say.

   g. **Discerning of spirits** - the ability to sense demonic activity in other people (Mt 16:21-23).

   h. **Tongues** - miraculously preaching the Gospel in foreign languages (Act 2:1-12; 1Cor 14:21,22; Isa 28:11).

   i. **Interpretation of tongues** - ability to translate what someone is saying in a foreign language so others can hear what is being spoken (1Cor 14:27,28).

   j. Some of these are available to us today (faith, and discernment) in an obviously limited way, but not like in the first Century. They all have passed away (1Cor 13:8-10) because they were special **miracles** to turn Israel's heart back to God (Mk 16:15-20). They were not for all Christians, nor for all time (1Cor 1:22; 14:22).

2. There are seven **SERVICE** gifts of Romans 12:6-8 given today that enable Christians to serve God by their life. _These was explained back in **Lesson 6**._

   a. _____ - the gift of **preaching**. It is prophetic because you KNOW the future from the Bible!

   b. _____ - the gift of **serving**, as "a minister"

   c. _____ - the gift of **teaching** God's word

   d. _____ - the gift of **encouragement**

   e. _____ - **giving** above normal, as the Lord gives you extra money because He knows you will give it away!

   f. _____ - the gift of **management**

   g. _____ - the gift of **comfort**

   h. Take a moment and note which one(s) you might have.

F. The Holy Spirit produces Priceless FRUITS in the lives of believers too!

1. The Holy Spirit plants **9** different fruits in the believer's life (Gal 5:22,23). They are far more important than any gift of miracles you may wish you had! Take time to discuss what each fruit means!

2. God in Galatians 5:22,23 says that *"The fruit of the Spirit is..."*

    a. _____ - unconditional love (1Cor 13:1-8) Only God produces this in and through the life of the believer. The ability to love all that God loves

    b. _____ - unending, always present. It is an attitude of the mind that over-rides circumstances and feelings.

    c. _____ - being at rest even in a storm (Mk 4:36-40)

    d. _____ - endurance, ability to put up with trouble

    e. _____ - compassion, even when you want revenge

    f. _____ - ability to do right when hard to do so

    g. _____ - ability to always believe God

    h. _____ - not drawing attention to yourself

    i. _____ - being under control; Holy Spirit-control

3. Here are some ways to get all the above fruits to grow in your life:

    a. Weed out any sins that can choke the fruit that God is trying to grow in you!

    b. Specifically feed the fruits, and not your flesh – with humility, and the Bible!

    c. Allow God to prune you as He sees fit – taking away people and things that are draining the life that He is trying to put IN you!

    d. Allow the fruits to be picked by, and spent on others. That's why God produces fruit in you – for others to use up! God will always replace them!

VII. Do You Want To Know God Better?

A. **Get to Know His Son.**

1. Trust Him to save you! You can go to church, be baptized, become head deacon, or even a pastor, and yet, if you do not know Jesus Christ as your own personal Saviour, you cannot ever know God - you can only fake it (John 3:3)!

2. Spend time with Him reading through the Bible, casting all your care upon Him.

B. **Get to Know His Word.** Once you are born again, and know God's Son Jesus Christ, you only know His saving power. The next step involves *studying* His word He left for you to read, love, memorize, and live in (2Tim 2:15)!

C. **Seek to Know His Will for Your Life** (Romans 12:1,2). Seeking to know God's will for your life (who to marry, what career path to follow, how you should use your spiritual gifts to serve the Lord, etc) will help you draw very close to Him. There is an entire lesson (**Lesson 12**) that will help you discern God's will for your life.

Date Lesson Completed _____   *Discipler* _____

PERSONAL WORSHIP
A Study of the Christian's Life and Attitude Toward God
Lesson Nine
Memory Verse: *Hebrews 10:25*   **Lesson Verse:** *Psalm 9:1,2*

> *"I will praise thee, O LORD, with my whole heart; I will shew forth all thy marvellous works. I will be glad and rejoice in thee: I will sing praise to thy name, O thou most High."* **Psalm 9:1,2**

I. Introduction

A. To the Christian, **God** has first-place. He is worthy of all our worship, all the time.

B. Yet most people believe worship is something only to be done in a church building, or only when everyone else is worshipping God.

C. Worship is how we personally honour God! It is not praying or sitting in church. It is actively giving God your best efforts, your sharpest thoughts, your deepest love, and your richest gifts. Worship is showing our love for God.

D. This study will examine how to develop and improve your personal worship of our God and Saviour, Jesus Christ (Rev 5:12,13), like we will in heaven!

II. The Purpose of Creation - To Honour and Glorify God!

A. Genesis 1:1 tells us that, *"In the beginning God created the heaven and the earth."* But WHY did God create everything? What is the biggest purpose of creation?

1. The answer is found in Revelation 4:11. *"Thou art worthy, O Lord, to receive _____ and _____ and power: for thou hast created all things, and for thy _____ they are and were created."*

2. Everything that exists was created to glorify the Creator - much like a watch is usually manufactured to adorn the wearer of it.

3. To **glorify** means to make beautiful, to praise, worship, or bring all good attention on someone you have lifted higher than yourself.

4. To **honour** means to esteem highly, to greatly respect, or to place great value upon something or someone.

B. Psalm 19:1 states that *"The _____ declare the **glory** of God..."* Did you know that all of creation automatically glorifies the Creator - it reflects Him, and praises Him by its order and beauty. But why don't humans? We are part of God's creation as well! The answer is found in our _____, where sin, self and Satan usually receive our worship instead of God (Jer 17:9).

C. God _____ us to worship Him (John 4:23,24).

D. For any part of God's creation to not honour Him as its Creator, and Lord and God, is the worst form of disrespect and contempt!

III. The Purpose of Salvation - to *enable* us to honour and glorify God!

A. Sin in us does NOT honour God! So, Jesus Christ came to deliver sinners from sin so that they might honour and glorify God once again (Eph 2:4-6; Eph 1:4-6,12).

B. When we were unsaved, we served our own pride and fleshly desires. But now we glorify the Lord. 1Peter 2:9 says we are a *"_____ generation, a _____ priesthood, an _____ nation, a _____ people; that ye should shew forth the _____ of him who hath called you out of darkness into his marvelous light."*

C. If you are saved, then show it!

IV. The Constant Attitude of the Believer Towards God is to be One of Praise!

A. The **attitude** of your heart and mind is most important, if you expect to bring praise and honour to the Lord by your life. With so much *pessimism* in our world, we must be careful to maintain a daily attitude of praise (not because things are good, but because our God is good). The flesh (our old sinful nature), and Satan are totally opposed to the Christian maintaining this type of attitude.

B. There are three kinds of attitudes a Christian can have towards God (Rev 3:15,16):

1. **Cold Attitude** - *unthankful, angry, hurt, bitter, rejecting.*
2. _____ **Attitude** - *uncaring, apathetic, unconcerned, numb!*
3. **Hot Attitude** - *rejoicing, thankful, passionate, and serving fervently.*

C. You have to re-train your mind to think on things that honour the Lord. Look at Philp 4:8. Think on the things that are "*true, _____, just, _____, lovely, and of good report.*" Concentrate on things that promote virtue, and PRAISE. The Christian should focus on these things! The act of godly worship is based upon your choice to have a right attitude! Make this a verse for you to memorize this week!

V. How To Develop Your Personal Praise and Worship of God

A. First, realize that **worship is not just for church time**. Praise is something that should be radiating from the heart of the Christian throughout each day (Psalm 33:1; 35:28; 71:8; 71:14). Even when times are hard, or not "in season." It should be something you do as naturally as breathing.

B. **Worship God spiritually** – with your spirit (John 4:24). The words you say are not nearly as important as the heart behind the words. To worship spiritually means:

1. Humble yourself – offer to God nothing but praise.
2. Be honest and real to God.
3. Don't worry about your surroundings – they do not make or break worship.
4. Worship whether anyone else is.
5. Bow your head and close your eyes – worship focuses on God, and nothing else.

C. **Worship God the way HE wants you to – the Bible way** (2Tim 2:15) – there is a right way! Most people worship any way they feel like. THAT is not acceptable with God (Psalm 19:14)!

1. "_____" in God's word daily – that means KEEP God's word in your thoughts and obey it throughout each day (John 15:7,8).
2. **Meditate on God's word** (Psalm 1:1,2; Josh 1:8).
3. **Live God's word daily** (Jam 1:22; Matt 5:16) – that is what faith is – trusting God enough to *obey* every word!
4. When our thoughts are filled with God's words, our heart will naturally worship!

D. **Learn to be Spirit filled** (Eph 5:18). A Christian is "sealed" (preserved) by the Holy Spirit from the moment of salvation, but can often be very empty of His power. The following are practical steps to having a Spirit-filled life:

1. Remember that the Holy Spirit is God, and is a Person that seeks a prominent place in your life (John 16:13)!
2. **Get saved** (John 3:3-6,12). You cannot be spiritually-minded unless you get the Spirit of God in you (John 4:24; 1Cor 2:14,15). There are SO MANY "christians" who never have been born again the Bible way, so they end up trying to be "spiritual" instead of "Spirit-filled!"
3. Be sure to **confess and forsake all sin daily** (1John 1:9; Prov 28:13).

   a. The Holy Spirit fills only clean "vessels," or bodies (2Tim 2:21).

b. So, have clean, wholesome thoughts. Your heart and mind cannot contain both spiritual and wicked thoughts at the same time (2Cor 10:4,5).

4. Learn to **ignore your *self* and your *wants* daily** (Gal 2:20), and focus on doing *Christ's* will according to His word (Mt 26:42). This is probably the hardest step for most new Christians – we don't know how to "let go" of what we are so used to carrying (grudges, bitterness, sorrow, anger, lusts, etc).

5. In prayer, **present your body (your hands, your mind, your plans, etc) to the Lord** as a living _____, for Him to use (Rom 12:1). Be ready to pay the price of serving Him! He is worth it!

6. "_____" to be filled with the Holy Spirit (Luke 11:9-13), so that you can minister to others. You have not, because you _____ not (James 4:2).

7. **Love God** (John 14:23). Sounds so simple, but it is the foundation for worship.

8. **Obey the Holy Spirit** when He directs you (Acts 5:32). Most Christians are unaware of His guidance, and very disrespectful when He gives it (Eph 4:30)!

9. Believe that the Holy Spirit will empower you to do what He has called you to do (Heb 11:6; Acts 4:29-31; 13:1,2).

E. **Maintain an attitude of gratitude.** Just become thankful for absolutely everything!

1. "*In every thing give* _____ *for this is the will of God in Christ Jesus concerning you*" (1Thes 5:18,19). A bad attitude of a Christian can "quench" (turn off) the work of the Holy Spirit.

2. Jesus died to conquer not just your sins, but your complaining too! It is THIS one thing that so limits God's work in our lives (Ps 78:36-42).

3. **So, constantly express your thankfulness**, verbally praising God with your lips, for all His care, His wonders and blessings (Ps 100:4; Col 3:15)! Our worship is often so empty because we *neglect* to praise and thank God.

F. **Enjoy personally worshipping God.**

1. Your time in prayer and in the Bible can be so full of joy if you try to *enjoy* it, instead of *endure* it (1John 1:4).

2. Enjoy worshipping alone, **and** in the presence of other believers - in singing, testimony times, and prayer times. When the preaching is good, say "AMEN," and "PRAISE GOD," even when it steps on your toes!

3. This is what the congregation did in the Old Testament at the reading and preaching of the word of God (Neh 8:1-6)!

4. And this is what we will be doing for all eternity in heaven (Rev 19:1,4-6).

G. **Worship God together as a Church** (Heb 10:25; Psalm 95:6).

1. Our personal worship should blend with other believers aas congregational.

2. Public worship is never a time to be ashamed, or to show off. It is a time of focusing ONLY on the Lord Jesus Christ, and worshipping Him!

3. God means for all believers in an area to gather together and worship God together so that they can live for God as a unified, assembled body in this world.

4. Our worship should be decent and orderly (1Cor 14:33,40).

5. So, make sure you and your family are faithful members of a Bible believing Baptist church, attending all services, and serving in various ministries so that any number of believers can worship God without distraction.

H. **Have Family Devotions.** Make worship a family affair!

1. Devotions are when you set aside time every day to worship (show your devotion to) God. Pray, praise, and give thanks to the Lord TOGETHER as a family by singing spiritual songs in the car or at home (Col 3:16), quizzing each other and honouring each other's spiritual growth in the word of God.
2. The best time to have family worship time is every morning, right after breakfast (make sure to have the whole family eat together – stop letting everyone eat when they want, and on their own)! You only need to set aside 15-30 minutes.
3. Have everybody get their Bible, and then read out-loud through a Book of the Bible (like Psalms, or Proverbs, or Matthew). Let each person read a verse, and help them understand what it is saying. Try to make the Scriptures apply to your family and the things you are going through.
4. Hold your family close during this time of worship.
5. After about 15 minutes, have someone bow their heads and pray about what you all have learned, asking God to help you all be like Jesus, and to do right throughout the day. Pray also for the needs of your family, and your church, and missionaries.
6. You can switch the time to right after your dinner, or just before bed. Whatever will work best for you and your schedule. Just make sure you set a time, and then do it EVERY DAY!

I. **Surround your home life with the right kind of music (Eph 5:19;** Cf Eccl 7:5).

1. Be very careful about what kind of music comes into your heart (Jer 10:2).
2. Listening to godly music will lift your heart to praise God (Ps 150). Worldly, carnal, lustful music (Rock Music, etc), will quench the Spirit, and will hinder and block your ability to worship the God of heaven!

   a. So, purchase a lot of good, godly music to listen to throughout the day.
   b. How do you tell the difference between good music and worldly music?

      1) The world's music emphasizes the rhythm and beat of the music.
      2) Godly music has no drums, and emphasizes the words of Scripture and Bible truths. In other words, you will mainly hear the words sung instead of the music performed.

   c. If you want to fill your home and mind with praise, you need to throw away all your worldly music, and buy as much Godly Christian music as possible!

J. **Fellowship with the right friends!** Maintaining good friends in the church will provoke you to praise and worship God more. God says in 1Cor 15:33 that "*evil _____ corrupt good manners.*"

1. When we hang around with "bad influences," it usually affects us for the bad.
2. So, be careful who you spend all your time with so that their filthy language, and wicked thoughts don't overtake all the work of the Holy Spirit in your life.
3. If we don't protect our walk with God, it just crumbles, because, God will just simply back away from your life if you so desire - He cannot totally leave you, but it will seem like He has when you push Him away (Psalm 35:22; 38:21).

K. **Just remember, you were saved to praise the Lord** (Psalm 9:1; 33:1; 34:1)!

Date Lesson Completed	Discipler

THE LORD'S SUPPER
A Study of Our Lord's Memorial to His Death on the Cross
Lesson Ten
Memory Verse: *Hebrews 10:25*   **Lesson Verse:** *1 Corinthians 11:26*

> *"For as often as ye eat this bread, and drink this cup, ye do **shew** the Lord's death till he come."* 1 Corinthians 11:26

I. Introduction

A. One of the memorials that Christ has instructed Christians to regularly practice is that of the *Lord's Last Supper* with His disciples.

B. This event is supposed to be regularly remembered by Christians as a Church, and is called an 'ordinance' or commandment (1Cor 11:2) – it is mandatory for Christians to honour and remember our Lord's death on the cross.

C. The purpose of this lesson is to acquaint the Christian with what the Bible teaches about the Lord's Supper, its importance, and the attitude with which it should be experienced, and conducted.

D. Before we go any further, read through two portions of Scripture: Matthew 26:26-29; and 1Corinthians 11:23-33.

II. The Importance of the Lord's Supper

A. The Lord's Supper powerfully focuses our lives back on what it cost for people to be forgiven - the substitutionary death of our Saviour in our place.

B. 1Cor 11:26 says that when a Christian eats the Lord's supper, *"...ye do shew the Lord's _____ till he come."* So, its primary importance is to **remind** us of the death of the Lord Jesus Christ. Luke 22:19 says, *"...this do in _____ of me."* It is intended to bring our attention back to what Jesus did for us on the cross.

C. This *Remembrance Supper* has many spiritual reminders that are supposed to affect our lives now that we are saved:

1. That Jesus Christ's death was <u>for us,</u>

2. That the price of our sin was Christ's suffering on a cross,

3. That Jesus submitted to the crucifixion because there was no other way to satisfy the justice demanded for the sins of the whole world,

4. That we should not now live the way we used to because sin has not only been paid for, but defeated on the cross!

III. The Elements of the Lord's Supper

A. It all started with the **Passover** Meal (Exodus 12:1-8)

1. God defeated the mighty Egyptian Pharaoh not with an army, but by His people simply trusting in the death of innocent lambs in their place!

2. If a household did not kill a lamb and put the blood of that lamb on the outside doorpost of their house, God's judgment would fall on that house and their firstborn would die!

3. But if a household believed God's warning, and put the blood of their little lamb on the doorposts of their house, God's judgment would PASS-OVER them.

4. That night, all of Egypt experienced judgment and death, while God's people, who had just put their faith and trust in a lamb, walked out free from slavery!

5. But that was not the end of the story!

6. The Passover lamb of Exodus chapter 12 pointed people's attention to a **future** Lamb who would take away the "_____" (John 1:29).

B. The Lord's *Remembrance Supper* is the fulfilment of the *Passover Supper*.

1. The Passover Supper had the following foods in it (Mt 26:20,21; Ex 12:18-20):

   a. Roasted lamb meat
   b. Bitter herbs – like horseradish
   c. A dish of sour vinegar sauce
   d. Unleavened loaf of bread. Plain, flat bread (like a tortilla) not white or fluffy
   e. Unleavened grape juice to drink. Plain, fresh tasting, **unleavened wine** – it was only grape juice, not alcoholic

2. The Passover supper focused everyone's attention on the lamb that gave its life so that God's judgment would "pass over" them.

3. Jesus came to be the _____ of God to take away the sins of the whole world through His death on the cross (John 1:29; Luke 22:7-20).

C. Why was everything unleavened?

1. In the Passover meal there was to be no _____ (yeast) used at all (Ex 34:25).

2. Why? Because LEAVEN is a picture in the Bible of _____ (1Cor 5:6-8), and Christ has no SIN in Him (1John 3:5).

D. At Jesus' last supper with His disciples, he took these **TWO** foods, and taught them to remember His death with them.

1. **The unleavened loaf of bread pictures His body**. We are told in 1Cor 11:24 that Christ's body was _____ for us. Not only are we to remember His death, but also His **suffering**. The breaking of bread in the supper **pictures** the breaking of His body! It does NOT *continue* the same sacrifice for there is NO further sacrifice needed (read Hebrews10:5-14; and John 19:30)!

2. **The unleavened cup of wine pictures Christ's blood.** The wine (grape juice, or new wine) pictures His _____ (1Cor 11:25), which cleanses us from our sin and saves our souls. His blood is **pictured** (not *recreated*) in the cup from which we drink during the memorial (Rom 3:24,25). It was shed for us for the remission of (the taking away of) our sins (Heb 9:22). So, fresh grape juice is used because normal fermented wine is *leavened* and alcoholic, while new wine (grape juice) has not fermented but only has the flavour of the grapes.

E. Some religions teach that the body and the blood of Christ are *really consumed* when eating the Lord's Supper, but that teaching is definitely not Scriptural.

1. Jesus taught an almost entire chapter on His body and blood being sacrificed for the sins of the whole world (John 6:27-35, 41,42, 47-63).

   a. The Jews had asked Jesus for literal *bread* to give them eternal life (6:34).
   b. So Jesus explained in John 6 that the manna God gave to the Israelites in the wilderness did NOT give anyone eternal life (John 6:49) , but that now God has given the world a *better* "manna" (6:30-34,50) – He gave Himself.
   c. Just as the Israelites accepted the manna in the wilderness as a gift from God, and gathered it and ate it to live physically, people now need to accept the Bread of Life to liver eternally!
   d. Jesus said His words are life giving and need to believed (John 6:47).

    e. Jesus knew however, that they would not believe His *words* (John 6:35,36) so He purposely turned them away with a parable since all they wanted was food for their belly, not for their soul (John 6:41-44,66).

2. When Jesus spoke of *"eating His flesh and drinking His blood"* in John 6:53-63, He was very careful to explain that He was NOT speaking literally.

    a. John 6:63 tells us that the words that Christ was speaking *"are* _____."

    b. People were not to eat *Him*, but rather partake of Him *spiritually*, which means accept His finished work on the cross like you would a free meal.

    c. The Jews were commanded **never** to eat _____ (Lev 17:11,12), for the life of the flesh is in blood. Only pagans ate blood in the worship of their false gods.

    d. So, what Jesus said confused all the Jews (John 6:52, 60) who were trying to understand what Jesus said literally and physically (eating His body) which was contrary to Scripture. Or Christ is teaching cannibalism!

    e. This was not the only time that Jesus used "figures," or examples, or word pictures to explain His work on earth:

      1) Jesus compared Himself to LIVING BREAD, and yet His physical flesh profits no one in any way (John 6:63).

      2) LIVING _____ (John 4:14,15; 6:35; 7:37-39).

      3) He also referred to Himself also as *"the* _____ *"* (John 10:7,9), and yet he was not a *literal* door with hinges, but the WAY through which anyone can get to heaven (John 14:6).

      4) When Jesus told Nicodemas to be *"born* _____ ", he thought Jesus was telling him to go back into his mother's womb and be born all over again *physically*! Yet Jesus was talking about another birth – a spiritual birth!

      5) So, many things that Jesus spoke about were not physical, but spiritual.

F. So, at the cross, there lays a GIFT (Rom 6:23), and that is all. There is no *flesh* and *blood* waiting to be eaten. But there is ***eternal life***, which needs to be *received* into your HEART (John 1:12,13) by faith (Eph 2:8,9) as if accepting a piece of bread!

IV. Who Can Participate in this Remembrance Ceremony?

A. The people Paul was writing 1 Corinthians 11:20-26 to were *believers*.

B. Lost people are not included at the Lord's table because they have never experienced the free gift of salvation that the Lord's table is *picturing*. The death and sufferings of Christ would have no real significance to them.

C. Not only is it restricted to true Christians, but to "clean" or "worthy" Christians who have confessed sins and things that are displeasing to God, since it was our sins that crucified Jesus (1Cor 11:27-34)!

D. That is why there is a time of deep reflection on our way of life, and any sinful habits that we may be holding on to, that will stop us from honouring Jesus' death!

E. It would be a mockery if someone tries and remembers an event that has no meaning to them - like remembering the day you got married, when you never got married!

F. Only for Christians who are worthy - serious about Jesus being Lord in their life

    1. Unworthiness - All of us are unworthy of God's love. But there are Christians who are "unfit" as servants of the Lord. Living for the world, and not for Christ

    2. When you treat Christ flippantly, or without fear, you are acting just like those who CRUCIFIED Him!

    3. God wants every Christian to participate - but not when they are not serious about their Christian life

4. Are you living a lie? Calling yourself a Christian, but not honest? not saved yet? Don't eat until you settle your own relationship to God!

5. Are you living in sin as a Christian? Rejecting what you know God has said, and holding on to something that you know is against God? Don't eat unless you are willing to turn away from it!

6. Are you serious about the Lord? Or, is He just a convenient Genie that you turn to for impossible situations? Become His servant!

G. But every Christian ought to use this time as an opportunity to get their life cleaned up right then and there, and then start fresh for this week - walking with the only God and Saviour Jesus Christ

V. How is the Lord's Supper to be Performed?

A. There are no explicit instructions on how to perform the Lord's supper other than presented in 1Corinthians chapter 11. No fancy rituals, or mystical sayings are involved. There is no transformation of the bread and wine! It is only a remembrance.

B. Simply, unleavened bread and unleavened wine (grape juice) are to be eaten and drank in the worship time of your local church (Act 2:42; 20:6,7) for the purpose of **remembering** Christ's substitutionary death *in your place* so you could be completely saved from the punishment of your sin!

VI. As a Christian, How Should I Approach the Lord's Supper?

A. **With fear and trembling**. Paul does rebuke the Corinthians for taking this event lightly in 1Cor 11:17-22. They had turned it into some kind of a feast for satisfying one's hunger rather than making it a time of remembering the Lord's death. This is a very sacred time, and should be approached with a sacred attitude.

B. **With desire**. Jesus Christ in Luke 22:15 _____ to eat the Passover with His disciples. Although the Lord's table should be approached with reverence, a believer should look forward to the Lord's supper as a way of bringing his attention back to what Christ had done for him.

C. **With a clean heart**. The Bible in 1Cor 11:28,31 tells us to _____ and judge ourselves when we partake of the Lord's supper. This self-examination is to make sure that our relationship with God is right. God chastises those that partake who do not forsake their sin (Prov 28:13). The Lord's supper is a *reminder* that our _____ was the reason for Christ giving His life for our salvation from sin, and God wants us to be clean spiritually when we partake of the Lord's supper.

D. **With good understanding**. There are **two** "tables" listed in 1Cor 10:20,21. One is a SACRIFICE to _____, and the other is a "communion" (10:16) or "fellowship" with Christians who regularly *remember* Christ's death. So many people in their 'churches' participate in a mockery of the Lord's Table, and are actually worshipping devils. No Christian has any business doing that.

VII. Comparing the Lord's Supper with the Eucharist

The Lord's Supper	The Roman Catholic Eucharist
Is a *memorial* of Christ's death	Is a **re-sacrifice** (Christ is killed again)
Uses simple unleavened bread	Uses a fancy 'graven' (**IHS**) wafer
Uses simple unleavened grape juice	Uses intoxicating, alcoholic wine
Presented by Bible believing pastors	Presented by Bible rejecting priests
Is a reminder of what saved us	Is part of the process of salvation
Called **communion**, and **Lord's Supper**	Called **the Mass**
A simple reminder	A fancy ritual and ceremony

Date Lesson Completed _____	Discipler _____

Section TWO Test
Fellowship With Other Believers

NAME: _____ DATE: _____

(Each mark = 2 points) SCORE: _____

Congratulations on completing Section TWO of the **First Principles** Bible Study Course! This test will help you evaluate how much you learned in your study time. Please take your time, and think about each question so that you remember what the Bible taught!

1. According to the Bible, in 1 Corinthians 6:19,20, a Christian's _____ is the temple of God.

2. The New Testament church can be best described as _____ _____

3. Write out word-perfect Hebrews 10:25 _____ _____ _____ _____

4. The final authority of the church is? _____

5. According to the Bible, what is a Bishop? _____ _____

6. What is a *deacon* in a church? _____

7. A church meeting is mainly for: **worship, preaching,** or **prayer**? (circle one)

8. Not only does Christ have His church, but so does whom? _____

9. List a way that a person can identify false religion _____ _____

10. Bible study is incomplete if a person is only a hearer of the word and not a _____ _____

11. When memorizing Scripture, make sure that you memorize not only the words of the verse, but also the _____

12. *Theology* is the study of _____

13. List the three ways that God has revealed Himself to humanity: 1) _____, 2) _____, 3) _____

14. List the location of a verse that teaches that God is a tri-part being (a trinity) _____

15. The name JESUS means _____

16. The name EMMANUEL means _____

17. Jesus was born without a human _____

18. Throughout Jesus' entire life, He never _____ at all!

19. According to 2Cor 5:21, God made Jesus Christ to be _____ for us.

20. Not only did Jesus die, and get buried, but also _____

21. 1 John 5:7 says that there are three that bear record (stand together in testimony) in heaven: the Father, the Word, and _____

22. There are nine fruits of the Holy Spirit in the life of the believer. Name three: 1) _____, 2) _____, 3) _____

23. The primary purpose of a person's salvation is to _____ God

24. There are three kinds of attitudes that a Christian can have toward the Lord: Hot, _____, and Cold.

25. Instead of being filled with **wine**, the Christian is to be filled with _____

26. In order for the Christian to best serve the Lord, they are told in Romans 12:1 to present themselves a living _____

27. God's will is summed up in 1 Thessalonians 5:18, that in everything we are to give
_____

28. Describe what Family Devotions are: _____
_____

29. Is there a difference in the kinds of music a Christian should listen to, as opposed to what the world listens to? _____

30. What is a church *ordinance*? _____

31. Name the three ordinances: 1) _____, 2) _____,
3) _____

32. When a Christian participates in the Lord's supper, they are remembering what event? _____

33. The breaking of bread pictures the breaking of Christ's _____ at the cross

34. What kind of bread is to be eaten at the memorial of the Lord's Supper?
_____

35. What kind of wine is to be drank in the Lord's supper? _____

36. The important thing to have when participating in the Lord's supper is a clean what?
_____

How are you doing?

Have you been born again? **Yes, No.** When? _____
Have you been baptized? **Yes, No.** When? _____
Have you read your Bible all the way through yet? **Yes, No.** What Book are you reading currently? _____
Have you memorized the two memory verses listed so far? **Yes, No.**
How many Scriptures have you memorized so far? _____
Are you faithful in church (every Sunday possible)? **Yes, No.**

Well Done!

You have now completed Section TWO, and its test. Hand this test in to your Discipler, and it will be quickly graded. The results will only be known by you, your Discipler, and the Course Administrator. Its results will not be made available to ANYONE else. After going through this test, knowing what you don't know, and maybe don't understand, you may want to go back over certain portions of the Course before going on to the next Section. Otherwise, press on, and keep growing!

SECTION THREE

This Section of your Discipleship study will establish you in

The New Testament Church

Memory Verse:

> *"Now ye are the body of Christ, and members in particular."* **1 Corinthians 12:27**

Some QUESTIONS:
1. WHO is the body of Christ? _____
2. To be a member of that body would imply what? _____
   _____

In this Section, you will study the following subjects:

- **Prayer** - Walking with God!
- **Finding The Will of God** - Discovering God's Plan for your life
- **Fighting Spiritual Warfare** - Dealing with sin and temptation
- **The Christian Family** - Developing a godly home
- **Handling Finances** - Managing your money and your priorities

   MY NAME: _____

PRAYER
A Study of the Christian's Walk With God
Lesson Eleven
Memory Verse: *1 Corinthians 12:27*   **Lesson Verses:** *Psalm 116:1,2*

> *"I love the LORD, because he hath heard my voice and my supplications. Because he hath inclined his ear unto me, therefore will I call upon him as long as I live."* **Psalm 116:1,2**

I. Introduction - How Important is *Prayer* in my Life?

A. Someone once said a Christian is only as strong as his prayer life is. Think about that... because it is true!

B. Your personal relationship with the Lord Jesus Christ... your spiritual maturity and stability... cannot grow without the proper reliance upon God that prayer enables.

C. Leonard Ravenhill writes, "Poverty-stricken as the church is today in many things, she is most stricken here in the place of prayer. We have many organizers, but few agonizers; many players and payers, but few prayers; many singers, few clingers; lots of pastors, but few wrestlers; many fears, few tears; much fashion, little passion; many interferers, few intercessors; many writers, but few fighters. **Failing here, we fail everywhere.**"

D. You were created to need God, and prayer is the only way to get every need met!

E. The purpose of this lesson is to acquaint the believer with a powerful prayer life so he or she can effectively _____ *"with God"* (Gen 6:9).

II. Prayer Defined - Hebrews 4:16

A. Prayer is seeking God. *"When thou saidst, _____ ye my face; my heart said unto thee, Thy face, LORD, will I _____."* (Psalm 27:8) To seek God's face means, to seek His attention, like you would want someone to look right at YOU when you are talking to them.

B. You seek God by simply talking with Him, sometimes for brief moments, and sometimes for extended periods of time. When you are reading the Bible, God is speaking to you; when you are praying, you are speaking directly to God.

C. Prayer is the soul of man offering up the desires and burdens of his heart to God with humble confidence that we shall obtain the help we need because of Jesus (Heb 4:16).

D. Prayer is our *worship* of God the Father, in the authority of the name of His Son, Jesus Christ, by the power of the Holy Spirit (John 16:23; Rom 8:26).

E. Finally, prayer is our source of confidence in God. By praying, we will know that we already have the answer to our need (Mt 6:7,8; 1John 5:14,15)!

III. What Prayer Is!

A. Prayer is God's appointed way for Christians to get the things they need (Jam 4:2).

1. God urges all believers to pray all the time for absolutely everything they need (Luke 18:1; 1Thes 5:17; Philp 4:6; 1Tim 2:1; Eph 6:18).

2. God already _____ what you need (Matt 6:7,8)

3. But God often waits for you to come to Him for those things by praying for them, instead of you just *expecting* things to happen in your favour.

4. We won't get everything we ask for, or we would be spoiled brats.

5. We won't get all the things we think we need.
6. But if we ask according to God's _____, we will receive it (1John 5:14,15).

B. Prayer is part of the process that God uses to give Christians the fullness of _____ (John 16:24). Just praying accesses the joy that Christ has!
C. Prayer is the Christian's way out of all trouble, and the cure for all worry and anxious care (Philp 4:6,7; 1Pet 5:7).
D. Prayer is the only way to get the power of the Holy Spirit in your life for God's work (Acts 4:31; See also 2 Chron 7:14).
E. Prayer accomplishes **five** things:

1. Through it, we fight the spiritual warfare we are in (Eph 6:11-18)
2. It is a spiritual watchdog against _____ (Matt 26:41; 1Cor 10:13)
3. It _____ God (Heb 11:6).
4. It changes the person praying! How?

   a. By changing your focus of attention – from your need to your Supplier!
   b. By changing your worry into faith and trust
   c. By changing your goals – you may seek to change your situation, but when you pray, you will start to allow God to decide the outcome of every situation, even if it ends up hard on you. The goal will be to do the will of God, instead of YOU making God **do** the will of YOU! Ponder that for a moment!

5. It moves the heart of God. Prayer not only moves us when we pray, but it also does cause God to respond to our need, and can do all the following (Eph 3:20):

   a. Move any _____ (Matt 17:20).
   b. Heal any disease (Psalm 103:3).
   c. Turn the heart of _____ and despots away from doing evil (Prov 21:1).
   d. Freeing believers from prison and persecution (Acts 12:5-7).
   e. And save the most sinful person (1Tim 1:15)!

IV.The Place of Prayer - Where Should a Christian Pray?

A. **Privately most of all!** Christians are *not to pray as a public show*, but rather in a "_____" (Mt 6:5,6). The principle is, have a special place of prayer in your home (the *closet* is as good as any), as well as everywhere you go, but not for show!
B. **Pray in church** (Matt 21:13; Acts 12:5), with other believers in the meetings.
C. **Everywhere** (1Timothy 2:8). Don't limit your prayer life to the church house only! Wherever you are, if you have a need, or are thankful, pray!

V. How Does a Christian Pray?

A. Pray like you were speaking *face to face* with your best Friend (John 15:15,16)!
B. Pray with the following ingredients:

1. **Praise** – Start off with worship and adoration of the Lord God of heaven and earth, just worshipping who He always is (Ps 95:6; 34:1). Prayer starts with loving God and worshipping first!
2. **Repent.** Repent from every known sin (Ps 32:5). Make a list and agree with God about them (confess them to Him alone) so that you can actually get right with the people you have sinned against right after you have prayed!

   a. Be *humble before God* (2Chr 7:14). Pray as a nobody, with no means of making God do what you want Him to do. Trust He will do right (Gen 18:25)

    b. Pray *honestly*. Be totally real before God. He knows you through and through, so make sure you thoroughly repent of any and all sin in your life before asking God for anything (Psalm 51:1-4). And then you can talk straight with God!

3. **Believe**. Pray *believing* (Heb 11:6)! You have to believe God can and will answer your requests! Know that God hears you, and **believe** He will answer you.
4. **Ask**. It sounds obvious, but a lot of people forget to ASK for what they need! Jesus said you can *"ask what ye will and it shall be done unto you"* (Jn 15:7)! Jesus uses three words to describe HOW to ask in prayer for what you need (Matt 7:7,8):

    a. *Ask* - never *demanding*, but just *"asking"* (John 16:24; Matt 21:22).

      1) Never be afraid to ask God for things that you believe you need.
      2) Be *specific* about what you need. If you want God to answer your needs specifically, then you need to be specific with Him about your needs. So, give God all the details, burdens, and needs.
      3) Never use "vain _____" (Matt 6:7) which are prepared prayers that people repeat over and over thinking they will be heard if they just keep repeating themselves! Well, it won't help! Just ask for what you need from the heart, using only the words as you feel like saying.

    b. *Seek* (Heb 11:6). Seeking is when we LOOK for the answer to come from God instead of from our parents, our friends, or from the government. Be fully committed to getting GOD to supply your need (Jam 1:5-8).
    c. "_____" (2Cor 12:7-9). It often seems like the door to God is closed when we pray. So Jesus invites us to be persistent and to keep knocking on heaven's door until we know God has answered us (Luke 11:1-13; 18:1-8)! If at first God does not seem to answer your request, keep "knocking" on heaven's door, asking until either He answers the need, or tells you NO, or tells you to WAIT. All three are good answers!

5. **Listen**. Pray *listening* (1Kings 19:11,12). This is VERY important! When you pray, every once in a while STOP, and be quiet – let God calm your heart when you are anxious, and then see if He speaks to your heart right then and there!
6. **Yield** - Accept God's will in the matters you have prayed about (Jam 4:13-15). *Accept* God's answer. This is very important! God always answers us when we pray, but sometimes He answers with a YES, sometimes with a NO, and sometimes with a WAIT. So, two-thirds of all God's answers are hard to accept!
7. End every time in prayer being _____ (Philp 4:6). Even before you have received your request. Just trust that God is going to take care of the need!
8. **Always**. Pray *all the time* (1Thes 5:17). At every opportunity.

C. Now, List those eight things above, and try to memorise them in order:

    1. _____   2. _____
    3. _____   4. _____
    5. _____   6. _____
    7. _____   8. _____

VI. What Should You Always Pray For?

A. *Wisdom* – ask God for the ability to make right decisions (Jam 1:5).
B. For *courage* to be bold as a Christian in the world around you (Acts 4:23-31).
C. Pray for *all people in authority* over us (1Tim 2:1-3), that they obey God.

D. For *people who are serving the Lord, that they would be greatly used of God and always protected.* People like *your* Pastor and his family, Missionaries, Bible Teachers, Deacons, and people who volunteer in your church to serve others.

E. For *every need* you know about (Philp 4:6; 1Pet 5:7; Ps 34:6; 55:22)

1. It is okay to pray for things YOU need. Just not the whole time!
2. A Christian is someone who has discovered they are totally dependant upon the Lord for everything! There is nothing too big, or too small to pray about.
3. Pray for the needs of others – starting with your own family!

F. Think… What if all you get tomorrow depended upon what you pray for today?

VII. There are Eight Important Conditions for Answered Prayer

A. You have to be a child of God (Prov 15:29), and you have to be right with God.

1. God answers the prayers of His children first! All religions pray, but prayers are vain unless they come from believers in Christ.
2. Make sure you are not in rebellion to any of God's commands or will for your life (1John 3:22; Ps 66:18).
3. Is there any _____ (sin) in your life that you won't let go of (Ps 66:18)?
4. These two things stop almost ALL prayers from ever getting heard in heaven: people being *unconverted*, and being *ungodly*.

B. Get rid of any unforgiving attitude towards others. You must make sure that you first _____ others their sins against you before you ask God for things (Mark 11:24-26). Do you have such an attitude? Do you have wrong attitudes (constant anger, hatred, bitterness, disrespect, etc) towards others like your wife, or your husband, or your parents, or your employer, or your pastor, or other Christians, or even your enemies (1Pet 3:7; Eph 4:26,27; Col 3:19)?

C. Seek God's _____. Ask for things according to God's _____, and not yours (Matt 26:39). Are you asking _____ (i.e., for the wrong things, James 4:3)? Do you have only selfish reasons for praying and not for others?

D. Pray in _____, believing (Mark 11:24; Heb 11:6; James 1:6,7) – not flippantly. How is your confidence in God's sufficiency? Are you uncertain, or hesitant about what you are praying for? If so, you are hindering it's answer.

E. _____ with Christ (walk with Him throughout each day) as opposed to only coming to God when you are in trouble or in desperate need (John 15:7).

F. Make sure you pray to the right Person… Pray to God the Father, with the help of the Holy Spirit, in the _____ of Jesus Christ (John 16:23,24). You cannot approach God and make requests without *Authority* - **Jesus** is our Authority for getting everything!

G. Is your life over-scheduled – prioritize your time putting God first. If you don't, then God feels no obligation to answer your prayers right away!

H. Are you lazy? Make every **effort to pray** instead of complain, or get upset!

I. If after you have evaluated all these things, nothing happens, then God actually HAS answered – just not the way YOU wanted Him to: He has just said 'No', which is just as good as if He had done what you thought needed done.

VIII. Will you right now make a promise to God that you will spend **at least 10 minutes** in heart-to-heart prayer *every day* before the throne of God, and then walk with Him throughout each day, always leaning upon Him for every need?

Date Lesson Completed _____   *Discipler* _____

THE WILL OF GOD
A Study of the Will of God for the Christian
Lesson Twelve

Memory Verse: *1 Corinthians 12:27*   Lesson Verses: *Romans 12:1,2*

> *"I beseech you therefore brethren, by the mercies of God, that ye present your bodies a living sacrifice, holy, acceptable unto God, which is your reasonable service. And be not conformed to this world: but be ye transformed by the renewing of your mind, **that ye may prove what is that good, and acceptable, and perfect, will of God."** Romans 12:1,2*

I. Introduction

A. A famous preacher once said, "a successful man is one who finds out what **God** wants him to accomplish with his life, and then fulfils it." Therefore, the true measure of a person's success is not in social status, bank account, influence, or fame. It simply is doing what God wants him or her to do.

B. This lesson will acquaint the Christian with how to find what God's will is for them, as revealed in the Bible, so he can begin to live the abundant Christian life in the centre of God's perfect will!

II. Understanding The Will of God - Let's first understand some things:

A. Most people are *self*-willed by nature. They do what they do because they want to. The Christian's actions however, are not to be driven by *self*, but by God. Take a look at Galatians 2:20, and ponder whether that verse is true in your life yet or not.

B. God created you for *His* glory and _____ (Rev 4:11), and therefore, not for yours only (1Cor 6:19,20). That may come as a surprise!

C. There are two kinds of wills God has for a person - His *general*, all encompassing will for people everywhere; and His *specific will* for each individual.

    1. Before God reveals His *specific* plan to an individual, that individual must be submitted to God's authority over his or her life. Every person must want to not only find God's plan, but already be willing to do it no matter what it happens to be! Why try and tell someone specifically what to do with their life, when you know they won't do it?

    2. The key rests in whether you are truly interested in not just *knowing* the will of God, but more importantly, interested in *DOING* it (Romans 8:5; James 1:22)!

D. There are always THREE stages to the will of God

    1. **First**, Doing what God says in the Bible – not the whole Bible, but a general set of clear instructions for every man, woman, boy, girl! Just be faithful doing the "little" things God has shown you in His word (Luke 16:10).

    2. Then, **AS** you are doing those things, God will show you His perfect will for your life – sounds great, but listen to the last stage…

    3. Thirdly, There will always be a **delay** before you actually experience living in that BIG, perfect will of God for your life – as Illustrated by David:

       a. When God found David, David was already doing God's will in small things (i.e., taking care of his father's sheep)

       b. Then God anointed him to be king

       c. Then it took 7 years before David was finally crowned as king!

III. God's *General* Will is Found in His Word, the Bible

A. You will never discover God's will without the Bible, because God has given seven foundational instructions/plans for all mankind to live by.

B. God's general will for all of mankind is to:

1. Be _____ (1Tim 2:3,4; 2Pet 3:9)! Everyone must begin here!
2. Be **saturated**/filled with the _____ (Eph 5:17,18). A surrendering of your life to the work and authority of God over your will and plans.
3. Be **satisfied**/thankful in _____ things (Eph 5:19,20; 1 Thes 5:18)
4. Be **submissive** servants in everything you do (Eph 6:5-8), remembering "*ye serve the* _____ _____" (Col 3:23,24). This includes submitting to all the laws of the land (1Pet 2:13-15).
5. Be **sanctified** (1 Thes 4:3-7). Sanctification means we separate ourselves from sins and evils so we can be holy and clean objects in God's hands (2Tim 2:21). This involves every Christian coming away from all the activities and influences that hinder us from serving the Lord with our whole heart (2Cor 6:17,18).
6. Be ready to sometimes _____ (1Pet 3:14-17; 4:19).
7. Be a **soul-winner** (Mt 28:19,20; Acts 1:8)

C. All the above will make you so that you are **so much like the Lord Jesus**! All Christians are designed by God to ultimately become *conformed* to (just like) the image of God's Son, Jesus Christ (Rom 8:28,29).

D. If you are not currently obeying God's clearly revealed will for your life (the above list), then God can never reveal His specific will to you because the one builds upon the other (Matt 25:21).

IV. Finding God's Specific Will For Your Life

A. The specific will of God for your life is just an extension of the general will of God for all mankind. The will of God for your life will not violate His general will - there are no "exceptions to the rule." God's will never contradicts His word.

B. Finding God's specific will is referred to as "proving" it, to yourself and to the world (Rom 12:1,2). Whatever you discover, will have to be proven as being God's will for you. God expects you to *live* His plans. This requires you to "sacrifice" your plans and goals, and replace them with His!

C. Let the word of God "speak" to your heart. God speaks directly to you through the Bible (Like Gen 12:1 where Abraham is told to leave his family and go to a place that God would lead him to). You must therefore be saturating your mind with Scriptures so that God can "talk."

D. One of the main purposes of the Holy Spirit in your life is to guide you in your decisions (John 14:26; 16:13; 1Cor 2:9,10). When making decisions, especially ones you are unsure of yourself, pray, and seek wisdom (James 1:5), and the confirmation of the Holy Spirit before proceeding (Rom 8:14).

E. Wait for God to "open doors" of opportunity. Sometimes, when we just "push ahead," we find ourselves forcing through blocked "doors" that God intended for us to keep out of (like marrying the wrong person, or working at the wrong job). The Apostle Paul sensed God blocking his path several times so that he would ultimately find the right path (Acts 16:6-10). Learn to accept circumstances as guideposts in the direction of God's leading. Just make sure you "_____" in all the steps of the Lord (Ps 37:23).

F. Finally, make sure that in your decisions, you "_____ *in the Lord with ALL thine heart; and lean not unto thine own understanding*," (Prov 3:5,6). God's will does not always make sense - but it is always best! Therefore, when you find God's will, you will have _____ (Psalm 37:37), because He knows best! Your attitude must be to let God's "_____" be done, not your own (James 4:13-15).

V. Some Discussion

A. Work through the following issues in life, and discuss how you would go about finding God's will in the various situations. Think of some additional helpful Scriptures that would guide you in finding God's will for each issue.

B. What do you think is God's general will for your life right now? What of the above seven things are you in need of working on? Tick each one that applies to you right now.

Key Truths about God's Will
❖ It will never contradict His written word!
❖ It will cost you to live it.
❖ It is built upon the seven general wills for all mankind - you cannot shortcut those to do what you want to do.
❖ It is found through prayer, and getting counsel from mature Christians and your pastor.

☐ Be Saved?
☐ Be **saturated**/filled with the Holy Spirit?
☐ Be **satisfied**/thankful in all things?
☐ Be **submissive** servants in everything you do?
☐ Be **sanctified** / separated from sins and bad habits?
☐ Be ready to sometimes **suffer**?
☐ Be a **soul-winner?**

C. What do you think is God's specific will for your life?

1. To ultimately be an... Astronaut, Fireman/Firewoman, Pharmacist, Builder, Architect, Politician, Policeman/Policewoman, Chef, Plumber, Engineer, Electrician, Computer Programmer, Artist...? _____

2. What dream possibly has God placed in your heart? _____
_____

3. What about marriage?

   a. If you are single, do you believe God wants you to be married? Yes / No
   b. What are the qualifications God has for you to choose from (2Cor 6:14; Deut 10:12). Ask yourself, Is the person saved? Are they faithful in seeking God's will, or only self-centred? Are they mature, or childish? Have you sought wisdom about your desires from your parents?

4. Are you working a job? If not, shouldn't you be working a job? (2Thes 3:10)

   a. What would be important for a Christian to look for in a job, and how would the Christian know it is the right one for him or her? _____
   _____
   b. What kind of job is acceptable to God? _____

5. Should you be a part of a Gospel ministry in your church? Yes [_] No [_]

   a. How do you find my ministry that the Lord has for me?
   b. Is God looking for talent or availability (Philp 4:13,19; 1Cor 15:58)?
   c. Am I worried about people's impressions of me, or pleasing God?

6. Could God actually Call you to Preach/Pastor/be a Missionary? (Mt 9:35-38; Lk 14:16-24; Act 13:1-4; 2Tim 4:1-4). Are you willing to be whatever HE asks?

Date Lesson Completed _____ Discipler _____

SPIRITUAL WARFARE
Dealing With Sin, and Your Spiritual Enemies
Lesson Thirteen
Memory Verse: *1 Corinthians 12:27*   **Lesson Verse:** *1 Corinthians 10:13*

> *"There hath no temptation taken you but such as is common to man: but God is faithful, who will not suffer you to be tempted above that ye are able; but will with the temptation also make a way to escape, that ye may be able to bear it."*
> **1 Corinthians 10:13**

I. Introduction - "How Do I Overcome Sin in My Life?"

A. When a person becomes born again, they become a "new creature" (2Cor 5:17). But there is a problem. They still have an "old creature" around called "the old _____" (Col 3:9,10). These two do not get along in the Christian's life, but instead, are *at war* against each other! They each want to dominate your life!

B. This lesson is intended to equip you to fight a good warfare against sin and temptation in your life. This is an unpleasant study for the Christian that is only looking to serve the Lord comfortably, because some of the things discussed here may be in *your* life, and you may not see them as wrong. The challenge is to see what the Bible teaches, and submit to it, since only then will a Christian have <u>real</u> freedom and joy!

II. Dealing With Sin - Recognizing the Enemy, and Conquering Him!

A. **What is all the fight about? Let's Realize** *Why* **You Sin**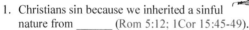

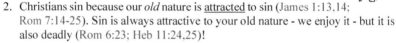

1. Christians sin because we inherited a sinful nature from _____ (Rom 5:12; 1Cor 15:45-49).

2. Christians sin because our *old* nature is <u>attracted</u> to sin (James 1:13,14; Rom 7:14-25). Sin is always attractive to your old nature - we enjoy it - but it is also deadly (Rom 6:23; Heb 11:24,25)!

B. **Let's Realize How God Views Your Sin**

1. First, your sin has already been judged and paid for back at Calvary (2Cor 5:21)! He views all your sins as being in the past, and forgotten (Heb 10:17)!

2. Yet, sin can still hinder your effectiveness as a Christian (Heb 12:1)! It hinders (besets) by weighing you down, and pulling you off the course He has for you.

3. It causes God to have to **chastise** you (Heb 12:6) like a parent does his child. To chastise means: _____.

4. It causes you to reap what you have sown (Gal 6:7,8). God cannot save you from experiencing the pains and scars that sin leaves in your life. He died to save you from eternal punishment in hell.

C. **You Must Battle Against the Temptation to Sin**, or you will by nature "give-in" to its dominion over your life (Eph 6:12; 1Tim 6:12; James 4:7).

1. **Decide that <u>your</u> sin is <u>your</u> fault, not anyone else's.** You must accept responsibility for your sin, and start not only taking the blame, but taking steps to keep from giving in anymore. You will never correct anything until you face your responsibility (Prov 28:13).

2. **Know your real enemies:** The <u>external</u> enemy is *this world*; the <u>internal</u> enemy is *your own flesh*; and your infernal enemy is *the devil*! As a soldier, know who your enemies are, and be equipped to defeat them!

3. **Protect your mind!** Don't allow sinful thoughts to control your mind (2Cor 10:4,5). The TV can destroy you spiritually (Ps 101:3), as can wrong music (Eccl 7:5)! So, STOP watching ungodly TV programs, and QUIT listening to ungodly music stations! Get advice on where to get access to some good, godly Christian music to listen to.

4. **Don't make "provision" for the** _____ (Rom 13:14). Don't provide for ("feed") the desires of the flesh. Stay away from things that you know will get you into trouble! Don't place more opportunities to sin in your path than are already there!

5. **Look for a way of** _____ out of temptation to sin (1Cor 10:13). God promised to get you through every temptation, if you want to!

6. **Judge your sins *yourself*** (1Cor 11:31,32). When you do wrong, and fail spiritually, think through <u>why</u> it happened! Don't *justify* yourself - instead, take responsibility for your part, get back up, and do better next time! You CAN if you will decide to work at it with God's help (Rom 8:12-14)!

7. **Confess your sins to God daily,** trying to do it immediately after you sin (1 John 1:9). Be specific, and determined not to fail again.

8. **Hide God's ____ in your heart** so you can use it like a sword against sin and temptation (Ps 119:11). Jesus Christ overcame temptation by quoting specific Scriptures that related to each temptation (Mt 4:1-11).

9. **Trust God's promises to cleanse you,** and to fight your battles for you when you give Him the authority to do so (2Cor 7:1; 1Jn 3:1-3; Heb 4:15,16)

10. **Walk daily in the power of God's Spirit** – it's like plugging in a light – only when plugged in will it shine!

    a. You can either obey the _____, or God's _____ (Gal 5:16-25)!

    b. Your flesh, and God's Spirit can never get along (Rom 8:1-8)!

    c. The reason why it is so hard to live godly is because both the flesh and the Holy Spirit fight against each other's desires, and YOU have to decide who wins each day!

III. Dying To Your Self (Romans 6:1-11) - *Your biggest enemy is your own self!*

A. Jesus Christ truly died for **all** your sins, as well as the sins of the whole world, providing forgiveness. When a person receives Jesus Christ as Saviour, they receive that same forgiveness of all their sins that was accomplished back at the cross (Rom 6:10; 1 John 2:2).

B. When Jesus died, the _____ of your sin died also on that cross because He took away sin (Rom 8:1).

C. When you as a Christian sin now, its judgment is transferred back to the cross automatically. Since sin's power was severed, it can no longer affect your eternal destiny!

D. Therefore, "reckon" (understand) yourself to be ____ unto the sin that tempts you (Rom 6:11)! To be "dead" means, "*not to respond to it like you used to.*" Now that you are born again, you no longer *have* to give-in to sin. Your flesh will still want to sin, but the Spirit of God in you is greater than your flesh (1John 4:4), and if you so choose, you can put-off (ignore) the desires of your flesh, and give-in to the desires of the Holy Spirit (Eph 4:22-24).

E. Paul wrote in 2Tim 3:1-5 how that people in the last days would be "*lovers of their own* ___..." Everyone seems to have **ME, MY, & I** as priority. The world's psychology is increasingly stressing "*self esteem,*" and it is increasingly creeping into Christian churches.

F. Notice Matthew 10:38-39. Verse 39 says, "*He that findeth his life shall* ___ *it: and **he that loseth his life** for my sake shall* ___ *it.*" What do you think Jesus meant by "losing his life?" ___

___

G. Read Philippians 2:3-8. Notice that verse 7 says that Jesus made himself of ___ ***no reputation.*** Verse 3 says that we should esteem others better than ourselves. It is evident that godliness does not promote **self,** but rather *the death of self.* Could it be that <u>self</u> is what hinders us from becoming Christ-like after we are saved from the judgment of our sin?

H. Look at what Paul said about *his identity* before salvation (Philp 3:4-8). He said I count all of it but "___". Is that how you feel about *your identity*?

I. After salvation, Paul said in Gal 2:20 "*I am* ___ *with Christ...*" Who was living *through* Paul? ___! Jesus can live through you too!

IV. Separation Issues (James 4:4) - The Christian MUST separate from sin!

A. The principle is: **Keep yourself out of situations where you know that your flesh is tempted to sin.** This is called *Separation,* and it is good! It is not negative, but rather positive since you are separating FROM ungodly things, UNTO *godly* things - so that you can live godly (Tit 2:11,12)!

B. **Some things to be separated from (2Cor 6:17):**

1. Places where the *flesh* is in control and not the Holy Spirit, like pubs, liquor stores, Discos, Night Clubs, *Secretive* Societies, Dance halls, gambling halls, etc! This means don't allow yourself to just watch anything that is on TV!

2. Places where people are *exposing a lot of their bodies,* or drawing attention to their bodies (like beaches that are packed with almost naked people). No Christian needs to be a hermit, or ugly looking in order to be spiritual. But a Christian is to show off the "___ *man*" by a godly life (1Pet 3:1-4).

3. Stay away from anything that causes you to lose control of your will - like bad friends, drugs, drink, and anything else that stops you from choosing to do right.

4. Things that ___ (ruin) your body and health (1Cor 3:16,17).

C. **Definite Areas of Separation Between Christians and Non-Christians:**

1. In ___ (2Cor 6:14; Amos 3:3). You can fall in love with anyone. Make sure that it is the Lord who brings you two together, and not your own lusts!

2. Stay clear of all works of darkness (2Cor 6:14), and demonic worship (2Cor 6:15), and especially ___ (2Cor 6:16). Don't toy with *Ouija* boards, *Tarot* cards, "crystals," and horoscopes (Lev 19:26; Dt 18:10-12) which are all Satanic. They are NOT of God.

3. Stay out of friendships with the unsaved when they become wrong - i.e., they make demands on you that go against God (Acts 5:29) and try to pull you back into sin. Always be a witness though, and love them as Jesus did. "*Speaking the truth in* ___." (Eph 4:15).

4. Stay far away from False teachers (1Tim 6:3-5), "*...from such* ___ *thyself*" (1Tim 1:3,4; 4:7; Gal 3:1) and heretics (2 John 9-11) - Those that teach things contrary to clear Bible truths (like Jehovah's Witnesses, Mormons, etc)!

5. Because, to ___ this world is very dangerous (1 John 2:15,16)!

D. Some Basic Rules to Follow:

1. *Decide to*:

   a. NOT love this _____, neither the things in it (1John 2:15,16)!
   b. Seek guidance from God in prayer and Bible study regarding a particular issue that you don't understand (James 1:5).
   c. Make sure that anything you are about to do glorifies God, and honours Jesus Christ (Col 3:23).
   d. Use common sense - If you have doubts about something, then **don't do it**! Most Christians disregard warnings and guilt, and just go ahead thinking they have "liberty" not remembering our adversary, the devil is a lion seeking only to _____ (1Pet 5:8).
   e. Do only things that you know Jesus Christ Himself would do if He was in your shoes (1Pet 2:21).

2. *Separate yourself from:*

   a. Anything designed to overthrow or cast doubt upon your faith in God (Rom 14:23), like false science (1Tim 6:20), and evolution.
   b. Anything that would destroy your testimony, or debase your morals and lead you to sin (Heb 11:24-26).
   c. And finally, anything that would harm your body - physically, mentally or emotionally (1Cor 3:16,17; 6:18-20).

3. *Separate yourself unto:*

   a. A life of service for our Lord (1Cor 15:58; Gal 6:9)
   b. A life of holiness and purity (Titus 2:11,12)
   c. A life for others (Matt 28:19,20) - Soul-winning!

Date Lesson Completed _____ *Discipler* _____

THE CHRISTIAN FAMILY
A Study of God's Greatest Reflection of Himself
Lesson Fourteen
Memory Verse: *1 Corinthians 12:27*   **Lesson Verse:** *Genesis 2:24*

> *"Therefore shall a man leave his father and his mother, and shall cleave unto his wife: and they shall be one flesh." Genesis 2:24*

I. Introduction - *No Greater Challenge Than Having a Godly Family!*

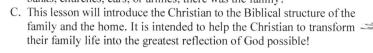

A. The Biblical type of family is the most fundamental unit in a society! Without strong, godly families, a nation is doomed (Ps 9:17)!

B. When God made this world, He completed His creation with a *man* - but He did not create him to be <u>alone</u> (Gen 2:18). God created man to exist <u>as a family</u>. Before there were cities, thrones, space programs, banks, churches, cars, or armies, there was the family!

C. This lesson will introduce the Christian to the Biblical structure of the family and the home. It is intended to help the Christian to transform their family life into the greatest reflection of God possible!

II. The Family Unit - What is a Family?

A. When the world tries to define a "family," it constantly has to change and adapt its definition to fit people's changing attitudes. Yet God has given us a perfect, never changing pattern for us to adapt to: the example of *Himself*!

B. Notice God's titles: the _____, the Word (became *the Son*), and the Holy Ghost (1Jn 5:7). These three "Persons" exist as *one unit*. So is it to be in a human family, because mankind was designed like God is (Gen 1:26,27)!

C. Every human has three "parts": a body, _____, and spirit (1 Thes 5:23).

D. Every family has three "parts": the father, mother, and children. *There are only three.* The exceptions are when a person is not married (when a person is single, he or she is still part of the family that they were born into), and when there are no children in a relationship. These are "exceptions" - not the norm!

E. Either you are single and under your parents, or are married and have your own children (or at least wish you could have children).

F. Both of these places are right, and a blessing to be in. Don't let the world try to mould you to *its* definition of life, family, and so-called happiness (see Prov 17:1; 15:17; 21:19).

G. The family unit is being attacked viciously today by the areas of homosexuality, and promiscuity (sexual immorality between men and woman who are not married). Both are wrong (1Cor 7:1,2; Lev 18:22; 20:13; Rom 1:26-27), and can only be resisted if God's design for men and women is understood and protected!

III. Are You Single? *God will take care of you* (Heb 13:5)

A. If a person is single, they should not _____ to be married, but seek to honour and glorify God FIRST by their life (1Cor 7:27; Mt 6:33), trusting He will direct their path to the person they should marry (Ps 37:4) as He did Adam (Gen 2:18-23).

B. Being single is best, but is not for everybody.

C. Don't be discouraged if you feel too old to be married, or *past your prime*! God brought a wife to Isaac when he was ___ years old (Gen 25:20)!

D. Singleness is not a time of only waiting, but a time of **doing**. Your life doesn't start when you get married – it started the moment you got saved (John 10:10)!

IV. The Confusion about Homosexuality

A. **Jesus said it is okay to not be interested in getting married (Mt 19:10-12). It is called being a _____.**

   1. It is a scientif fact that NO one is born a homosexual, bisexual, or transsexual.
   2. But some are born with no interest in sex.
   3. And some decide to stay single, so that they can serve God without any distractions (1Cor 7:32-34)
   4. Everyone else is fine with getting married and having children.
   5. This section of the study on the family will explain God's purpose for all three attitudes towards sex.

B. **God designed adult men and women for each other sexually.** We are specifically designed to have sex with a marriage partner.

   1. A man and a woman are marvellously designed by God in every way (Ps 139:14), and that means in *every* way.
   2. Marriage joins a man and a women together physically (Gen 2:21-24; Matt 19:5,6).
   3. There is nothing wrong with sex **in** the covenant of marriage (Heb 13:4).

C. **Men and women are supposed to marry, and have children.** That is the general design and natural expectation of all adults, male and female (1Tim 5:14; Ps 127:3).

   1. The apostle _____ was married (Matt 8:14,15).
   2. Joseph and Mary were married, and they had more children after the birth of Jesus (Matt 13:54-56), so they were a normal family – unlike the idea that Catholics have of Joseph's relationship with a perpetually virgin Mary.

D. **But there are some exceptions to being married.** Those exceptions are often confused and twisted into homosexual and lesbian concepts that ruin God's design, and especially confuse children, leading to their abuse.

E. **Jesus explained the exceptions** (Matthew 19:12)

   1. A 'eunuch' is someone that either does not want to have sex with their marriage partner, or cannot have sex.
   2. Three Biblical attitudes towards being single:

      a. Jesus said, Some people are _____ eunuchs – unable to have sexual intercourse for whatever reason. These are not interested in getting married or in having sex. And that is perfectly fine.
      b. Other people are forcibly **made** eunuchs by men – when men are physically castrated, for whatever reason, they have been "*made into a eunuch.*" The Ethiopian eunuch in Acts 8:27 was forcibly made that way so that he could be trusted with the Queen's treasury, and this was a common occurrence up until recently amongst many government civil servants all over the world.
      c. Some people **decide** themselves to be a eunuch – they do not want to be married and are fine being single and are able to serve God without distractions (1Cor 7:32). They do not seek sex with anyone. As Christians, they just live for the advancement of kingdom of God! The Apostle Paul was single all of his adult life, and wished more people would stay single (1Cor 7:8). They may later on in their life decide to get married, which is fine as well. In other words, if a young man, or a young woman does not seek to be married, that is fine. And if they change their minds, that is fine as well.

3. So, if a young woman is not interested in "guys", that is perfectly fine. It does NOT mean they are a lesbian. And if a young man is not interested in "girls", it is perfectly fine too. They are not queer. Not unless they have become influenced by the pressure of the homosexual culture that is wrongly promoted by society today!

4. But if you are naturally interested in sex, then by all means, marry (1Cor 7:1,2,8,9)!

F. **Anything beyond those four attitudes towards sex is wrong according to God, and will be judged (Heb 13:4; Eccl 12:13,14).**

1. The Bible calls homosexuality "_____ *affections*" (Rom 1:26)

2. It is "_____ *nature*" which means it goes against how we were designed as male and female (Gen 1:27)

3. Homosexuality is a lust for someone you cannot have – like adultery and pornography is – "*the men, leaving the _____ use of the woman, burned in their _____ one toward another; _____ with _____ working that which is unseemly*" (Rom 1:27). Unseemly means, unwatchable, because it is so dark and wicked.

4. God warns that homosexuals are destined to receive "*in themselves that recompence of their error which was meet*" (Rom 1:27) – referring to God's specific judgment upon THEM for that specific sin.

G. **Homosexuals and Lesbians CAN be saved, and CAN become "straight"** (1Cor 6:9-11) – but they have got to <u>want</u> to be saved from their sin (Matt 1:21).

1. How does Paul describe homosexuals in those verses? "*such ____ some of you.*"

2. Homosexuals, just like adulterers, fornicators, liars, and drunkards need to repent towards God for the awfulness of their sin, and get saved before too late!

3. If you have confusion about sexuality, that is normal in this day and age. So many movies and music stars are pushing homosexuality into every relationship. God commands us to get counsel, and seek forgiveness for our wrongdoings, and start following Jesus. Jesus can straighten anyone out!

H. **Final thought. Do not just expect that young men and women are pure in heart and desire** – they need to be talked with and taught and humbled about any sexual sins and any abuses in their past before they ever embark on marriage so that their marriage is wonderful, and lasts like God designed it to (Heb 13:4).

V. **Preparing For Marriage - Courtship and Marriage for Christians**

A. **God's Purpose in Marriage - *Study these!***

1. **Companionship** (Gen 2:18) - Throughout creation, God balanced everything out - He created two of everything (to everything, there is a positive, and a negative; a true and a false; a light and a darkness; an up and a down; a male and a female, etc). When He created Adam, He was not finished, but knew Adam needed companionship (ie, someone that he could intimately relate to - who was just like himself). He created someone who would think like Adam, and understand Adam. None of the rest of creation could relate to Adam (Gen 2:19-23).

2. **Completeness** (Gen 2:18) - God did not give Adam a "buddy" or "friend", but a "completer" (someone who matched Adam's needs like a glove does a hand). Eve was not to be another *Adam*, but to be what Adam was NOT, and to "compliment" his needs as he does hers! She was called a _____, meeting his needs.

3. **Enjoyment** (Heb 13:4) The marriage relationship is the most enjoyed of all relationships because of the intimacy of companionship and completeness! Marriage is not a duty but a thrill, and it never gets dull when based upon God's pattern! The key is the couple must operate within God's limits so trust is always maintained.

4. **Children** (Gen 1:28; 9:1; 1Pet 3:7). The natural result of human intimacy will usually be children! Adam and Eve discovered this (Gen 4:1). Believe that Children are always a blessing, and a gift from the Lord (Ps 127:3-5) to a husband and wife.

5. **Protection** The purpose of a godly relationship is for the benefit of the people *in* the relationship. Adam needed Eve at times, and she supplied that need as she protected his weakness. Eve needed Adam at times, and he was to supply that need as he protected her weakness (Eph 5:25-29; Eccl 4:9-12)

6. **Representation** - The Christian marriage relationship is to present a living example of the loving relationship between Christ and believers (Eph 5:31-33).

B. How God Sees Marriage

1. **As good.** *"Whoso findeth a wife findeth a _____ thing, and obtaineth favour of the Lord."* (Prov 18:22). Marriage is not outdated, or old-fashioned. It is the greatest relationship, and is honoured by God!

2. **As pure.** In marriage, the bed is _____. (Heb 13:4) – being married is wonderful, and a blessing, and just what God designed it to be. It is not to be a place of fear, or of wickedness, but of joy, and blessing (Prov 5:18,19; Song 7:7-12). If it is not honourable, it is not a marriage.

3. **As enduring.** *"The Lord, the God of Israel saith that he hateth _____."* (Malachi 2:16). Only by seeing how God hates adultery and divorce can we see the seriousness of marriage (Mt 19:3-6)!

4. **As meeting each other's needs** (1Cor 7:3-5; 32-34). The one person who is best able to meet your needs is the one who knows you best! The purpose of marriage is not to "obtain" but to "supply," knowing your own needs will be provided for in the process!

5. **As built upon friendship, and communication** - not on requirements, and expectations. The marriage relationship starts with friendship, and is built upon **trust**. If a person's mate is not their best friend, then the foundation of the marriage is flawed, and can collapse (Song 5:16)

6. God sees marriage **as a covenant** (a binding commitment) that makes their relationship the priority human relationship in life (Gen 2:24). Marriage is **not** an experiment! It is a total <u>commitment,</u> and a total <u>sharing</u> of the total person with another until death. This most wonderful of relationships both confines and yet fulfils the human heart!

C. Courtship or Dating (Psalm 34:3) – How to find a mate for life

1. Most people try so very hard to find the love of their life by using the feel-good methods of dating, drinking, and discos.

2. God has a much better method that has worked from the very first day! It is called Courtship.

3. What is Courtship?

   a. Courtship is a relationship between a man and a woman in which they seek to determine if it is God's will for them to marry each other. Under the protection, guidance, and blessing of parents or mentors, the couple concentrates on developing a deep friendship that could lead to marriage, as they discern their readiness for marriage and God's timing for their marriage. (See Proverbs 3:5–7)

   b. Courtship is a choice to avoid temptation and experience the blessings of purity. It is a choice to not emotionally give away your heart, piece by piece, to many others through casual dating relationships and instead to ultimately give your whole heart to your life partner.

   c. Courtship is a choice to **wait** for God's best for your life. It is a decision to trust in God, honour others above yourself, and believe God will do good to you, all because He is love. (Ps 9:10; Rom 12:10; 1Jn 4:8)

4. Understanding and applying the following guidelines will result not only in a marriage pleasing to God, but also one that will be the most rewarding for ourselves. It provides the foundation for winning the world for Christ.

5. The concepts presented here are helpful guidelines to consider, but the list is not exhaustive. Each person, along with their parents or other mentors, must seek God's direction for the specific steps of their courtship.

6. Let's compare Dating and Courtship – *read each row, from left to right*:

What Dating Is...	What Courtship Is...
Dating is mainly for having Fun (not really serious, but wanting to just "look around").	**Courtship is mainly for finding a Family.**
Starts as soon as possible (these days dating starts around 12 years old or so).	**Starts only when spiritually ready and serious about marriage.**
By your own choice.	**By the wise advice of parents and godly Christians, especially the pastor.**
Defined by the world – almost anything goes when on a date.	**Defined by the Scripture** (see below).
Letting the "flesh" decide what is right or wrong to do on a date.	**Letting God's Holy Spirit define** what is right and wrong to do, and obeying Him!
Lots of trial and error (which leads to loads of disappointments).	**Following careful steps**, leads to fewer disappointments.
Lots of temptation, and guilt.	**Very little temptation**, yet great joy for obeying God, and finding His will.
Based on how you feel about the other person.	**Based on how God is directing your life** for His glory, to the person you should be with.
Usually ends in massive heartache and ultimate distrust, and even divorce.	**Usually ends with a life-long mate.**

   a. As a young person, it is a good thing to have fun with people of the opposite sex, as long as you have your parent's permission, and as long as it is when you are in a group and not alone. God does not ask you to live as a monk or a nun. But He does expect us to keep ourselves pure from fornication and from sexual temptation (1Thess 4:3)

   b. Therefore, it is not a good thing to just "hang around" the opposite sex without a Godly purpose, and without Godly supervision. It will usually lead to sinful thoughts and sinful acts that you will regret.

7. So, Have the Right Focus (Col 3:17; 1Cor 10:31) - in marriage, as well as every other area of life, our purpose is to glorify _____.

   a. If something is contrary to the will of God, then we must reject it, and lose it (Lk 9:23,24) – reject it as dead!

    b. Your desire ought to be to have the RIGHT marriage partner, that GOD gave you - not just marry the next available person!

8. Seek The Right Person (Gen 2:18)

    a. God specifically created a _____ for Adam that was suitable for him.

    b. Two people are not equals (God created Adam and Eve, not Adam and Steve) but rather complements; i.e., each possessed mutually affirming gifts, strengths and insights. Each was incomplete without the other. Each person had qualities that the other needed to fulfill his duties before God.

9. Get The Right Counsel (Pr 23:22; 20:18)

    a. Dating is a modern substitute for wise counsel and lots of prayer!

    b. Too many parents do not really know their children because by the time that their kids become teenagers, they have spent virtually no time with them compared what others have spent.

    c. But if parents have fulfilled their Biblical role faithfully, they should know their children better than anyone else in the world. They should have 20-odd years of experience with their children, know their moods, tempers, gifts, and weaknesses. They are providentially equipped to advise their children about what kind of person they should be courting. When a child reaches the age where courting is now appropriate, parents and child should sit down and do a frank analysis of both themselves and potential partners.

10. Have A Right Mind (Philp 2:1,2,5)

    a. The first thing to have is a right MIND (right way of thinking) – don't follow your heart or emotions, or do just what everybody else may be doing.

    b. The mind of Christ seeks to not only find fulfilment and happiness, but enjoys making other people happy, and serving them as Christ taught us to

    c. Your MIND must be in charge of the relationship, over-ruling your heart because when only you heart is in charge, it will get you in trouble (Jer 17:9).

    d. So, always THINK as you love – don't get carried away!

11. Develop The Right Heart (Philp 2:3-4)

    a. The goal of any relationship is *ministry*, not manipulation. We are not to seek to have our own needs met, but rather meet the needs of others. Yet usually marriages are made because young people think that a certain person will meet their "needs." Instead, we must see life as a process of giving up rights, and taking on responsibilities.

    b. A single person MUST learn how to be "other-oriented" in their thinking. Otherwise they are only going to be a taker in the relationship, and a destroyer of the relationship!

    c. Selfishness is the cause of most marital disasters.

    d. Both man and woman must make genuine sacrifices to make a godly marriage. If one or both of the people are not ready or able to make those sacrifices, then they are not suitable marriage partners.

        1) Husbands must be willing to give themselves up for their wives. Husbands don't just need a wife in order to succeed, they succeed first by sacrificially ministering to their wives!

        2) Wives **must submit** themselves to their husbands. You had better make sure your husband is worthy of submitting to!

12. Meet the Qualifications (Eph 5:22-31; Prov 31:10-31; 1Pet 3:1-7)

   a. The best indicator of future performance is past performance. If you want to know what a person is going to be like in the future, just take a long, hard look at where he or she has been. Now it is so true that God transforms sinners. Yet, when deciding who is or is not suitable as a mate for our children, the past is a great indicator of what you can expect down the road.

   b. In generalities, the future mate should pass the following test:

     1) Are they truly saved? And do they live like they are? (Matt 7:20-27)
     2) Is he or she strong in their trust in the Lord? (Prov 3:5,6)

       a) Do they trust God, pray about their needs, and rest in the Lord's answers, or do they fret and worry and panic?
       b) Do they praise God a lot, or do they find fault, and complain?
       c) You should seek someone who is more spiritual than you are, and loves God more than you do!

     3) Is he or she yielded and submissive to God's will for their life (Acts 9:6)? Do they know their calling and are they working diligently at it?
     4) Is he or she consistent, or does he or she change their mind constantly, and do things impulsively (Prov 24:21)? Are theye ever happy jusy where they are at, or always complaining?
     5) Do they truly love you, or do they really only love themselves? (Eph 5:25; Titus 2:4)
     6) Are they trustworthy? Do they exhibit integrity? Do they keep their promises? (Psalm 7:8; Prov 11:3)
     7) Are they a hard worker? Both the woman and the man must love hard work, or they will pull the relationship apart with their laziness (Gen 3:19; Prov 20:4; 2Thes 3:10).

   c. When looking for a potential husband:

     1) Look for a man who possess leadership ability. Someone who wants to lead his family, and be an example of serving, instead of just being lazy and letting the wife make all the important decisions!
     2) Look for a man who works very hard. Make sure that he can save and manage money and thus financially provide for the family (1Tim 5:8).
     3) The Bible asks:

       a) Is he good FATHER material (Col 3:19-21, Eph 6:1-2)?

         1. Look at his own father for insights as to how he will handle frustration, anger, fear, etc.
         2. Does the young man's father trust his own wife, love her (Eph 5:21-25), nurture and care for her (Pr 31:11), granting her honour as a equal heir (1Pet 3:7), understanding her and being gentle with her (1Pet 3:7)?
         3. The way the young man's father treats his mother is likely the same way he will treat you or your daughter.

       b) Is he A ONE-WOMAN man (1Tim 3:2) or has he had lots of previous entanglements that could come back and haunt you both?

    c) Is he sensible (Tit 2:6) and does he possess the general godly charac-
ter qualities of an elder / mature Christian (1Tim 3:1-7)? If not, then
no matter how friendly, charming or attractive, look somewhere else.

  d. In the same way, potential wives should be:

    1) Submissive in spirit (Eph 5:21-22) and respectful in their attitude and
demeanour. Most women are extremely assertive because of the training
of the feminists!

    2) Sensible, looking forward to working at home, kind, loving their hus-
bands and children (cf. Tit 2:3-5).

    3) They are able to do good to their husbands because they are industrious,
charitable, skilled in their work, well-dressed (modestly so), good man-
agers of resources and, of course, they must fear God (1Tim 2:9-10; 1Pet
3:3,4; Pr 31:22,30).

    4) If a woman lacks the qualities necessary for any of these before marriage,
there is no way of knowing if she will ever develop them afterwards.
Therefore, parents ought to make it a point to examine potential mates
according to objective, Biblical criteria. If they don't meet the qualifications, then no matter how attractive they are, they are not suitable for
marriage.

13. Keep The **Right Distance** (1Cor 7:1-5; Gen 2:24) – VERY IMPORTANT!

  a. If all the other issues are dealt with, then this issue will be easy. If the heart
is not submissive to God's way, then no amount of warnings, and walls will
stop two people from committing fornication.

  b. There is a right amount of distance that must be maintained between two
unmarried people (Pr 6:27-29) – no touching. Touching, clinging, cleaving
to each other is for when married – period!

  c. If you start to violate this principal, no amount of determination and repent-
ing will stop you from God's judgment (Heb 13:4)!

14. Conclusions

  a. Parents must teach, and nurture these truths into their young children.

  b. Young men and women need to evaluate just how much they are willing to
"wait" until marriage, and to let God prepare them for this most important
of all life's treasures – a family!

  c. The fruit of living godly is eternal. The pleasures of sin, are only for a season
(Heb 11:24,25)!

D. **Principles of a Happy Marriage**

1. **Make _sure_ both persons are** _____ (Mt 7:21-27; John 3:3,7;
2Cor 6:14; Amos 3:3)! No Christian should ever think that they can be happy
married to someone who doesn't care about Christ! It is next to impossible to
change a person after marriage!

  a. A woman marries a man, hoping he will change, but he doesn't.

  b. A man marries a woman hoping she never changes, and she does!

2. **Give 100%!** The marriage life is _NOT_ 50/50, but rather 100/100% of each partner! You no longer are two persons, but _____ (Gen 2:24)!

3. **Delete from your vocabulary words like: _hate, divorce, mine, yours!_** Don't
remain angry, or vengeful with you mate (Eph 4:26,27), but rather take the time

and talk the problem through until it gets settled! This takes prayer, and humility on your part (Pr 16:32)! Study **1 Corinthians 13** together, and implement each phrase into your relationship!

4. **Have a LOT of grace (tolerance) with each other** (1Pet 4:8; Heb 12:28)!

5. **Both must agree to submit** to the Biblical pattern for their home as found in the word of God, with the husband as the loving head of the home, the wife as the help participating in decisions, yet not forcing her way, and the children in nurtured obedience. The husband must be in submission to the word of God (1Cor 11:3).

6. **Look forward to _____.** Focus your energies no longer on yourselves, but rather on raising *God's* heritage (Ps 127:3). Don't spend time worrying about affording children, but on loving them!

7. **Burn the bridges back to your single life!** Your mother should not "*keep your room,*" and you should destroy all the letters and notes you may have from old lovers! You cannot serve ____ masters (Mt 6:24)!

8. **Realize that your marriage and your family is your FIRST ministry**, before your job, your church, or even your *self*! This is the hardest task! And yet the most enduring, and rewarding!

9. **Have family Bible-time** (Deut 6:6-9)! This means a time where you and your family sit down together and read out of the Bible for about ten or fifteen minutes, and then you pray for each member of the family. Have different members of the family pray each time. Sometimes, act out what is being taught in the Bible. Always make it a special time. The goal is to develop a godly home atmosphere all day!

10. **Romance your mate regularly** (Gen 26:6-8; 1Cor 7:1-3). *Continue* to date each other, admire one another, woo each other's attention, read the Song of Solomon together; purchase your wife flowers! Do crazy things just to show each other how crazy you still are for them!

11. **Listen to one another** (Eph 5:21), without grudging (Eph 4:31,32)! There MUST be specific time set aside for each other, just where you talk and listen to each other's heart concerns, gripes, dreams, etc.

12. **Purpose to have times of fun with just your family, weekly!** This is so important to their emotional health! It lets them know that they mean something to you, and that you really find joy with them, instead of only out of the house!

VI. The Dangers in Marriage. Marriage by nature can be full of problems because there is more than one flawed human being in the relationship! But God has balanced that out thankfully, when He is invited to be the focus of the relationship.

A. **Wrong Expectations** (Mt 11:7-9, 16-19). This is the source of the majority of problems in marriages. People naturally expect things of each other, and when those expectations are not met, problems arise (Ps 62:5; 37:4; Pr 11:7). **How to defeat wrong expectations:**

1. Learn from Christ what He wants of YOU! Focus on becoming what Christ intended for *you* to be, instead of what you think He meant for your mate to be! Surrender your expectations to the Lord, and love your mate as a gift from Him.

2. Begin to nourish and develop your spouse into the best that they can be -- not brow-beating, or nagging them, but encouraging, and equipping them with what they need to be their best!

3. Communicate. Tell your mate what you need, and listen to the needs of your mate. Learn about each other. Don't just demand!

4. Then start meeting your spouse's needs, instead of so desperately wanting him or her to meet yours!

B. **Stubbornness** - not yielding - not allowing God to change you in any way BY your partner. God put the two of you together NOT because both of you were already perfect, but because each of you, when combined, made a stronger team than any one individual could have ever been! God wants BOTH people in a marriage to affect each other for good (Jam 4:6). Both partners MUST allow the other person the authority to help mould and shape them (1Co 7:4; Eph 5:21; 1Pet 5:5).

C. **Over-sensitivity.** Intimacy naturally means *vulnerability*. And vulnerability oftentimes results in *hurt* (Ezek 16:45). Extreme emotional hurt must be given to God (Isa 53:3,4). Don't take it upon you to revenge any hurt you may receive from your partner. You must learn to take the situation as God's way of getting you to rely on Him to handle the "pay-back." He assures us He will do a very good job of it (Rom 12:17-21). In other words, suffer _____ (1Cor 13:4), and endure some _____ (2Tim 2:3), and develop the ability to love and be _____ when the other person does not deserve it (Eph 4:31,32), simply because that is how God treats you!

D. **Complacency.** Your relationship with your spouse is a living, and growing relationship - it never sits idle. It is either growing closer, or farther apart, based upon your efforts. The lack of effort by BOTH people will result in decay setting in. Vigilance must be maintained. There is never a time that a person can just sit back and say, "I got it made. Everything is perfectly under control." This is not to say that you should be happy with a relationship *out of control* (1Cor 14:40). In other words, work hard at your relationship. Don't just take it for granted, and draw from it, while not investing into it! Both of you must work at this!

E. **Being focused on short-term gratification.** This is where evolution has taught 99% of all married couples that they are in a relationship only to *get*. And instant gratification turns into demand. And demand creates slavery. And slaves revolt! Maturity is required in the heart and desires of each partner so that gratification is found in supplying the others' needs before themselves (1Cor 7:33,34; Acts 20:35). At the start of any marriage, it is expected that the two people will not automatically know how to give more than they get, but over time, this attribute should fully develop!

F. **Disrespect.** This is vital to conquer (Eph 5:33; 1Pet 3:1-7)! Honour each other, and _____ each other _____ than themselves (Phlp 2:3)! Disrespect is formed by *distrust*. Therefore, have very short memories about past failures, and always completely forgive each other when asked (Lk 17:3,4; Heb 10:17). This will allow you to maintain respect and praise for your mate even though they are imperfect. Keep your love and respect **fresh** (like God does, Lam 3:22,23). Both of you are commanded to work at earning and maintaining each other's trust! If the other person has problems with you, then try and fix those problems to the best of your ability (Mt 5:23,24)!

VII. Dealing with Hurts in the Home

A. What Offends You?

1. Has anyone physically Bullied you? Yes / No
2. Has anyone said unfair words and actions against you? Yes / No
3. Has anyone ever taken you to court? Yes / No

4. Were any of the above a close friend, or your husband, your wife, your parents? Yes / No Name one person:

_____

5. Who was also rejected, bullied, hurt? Isaiah 53:3; Psalm 55:12-14

_____

B. **How easily do YOU take offense?** (Prov 18:19)

1. Some things ARE clearly offensive – physical abuse, pornography, sexual abuse
2. But MOST things should NOT be offensive / upsetting to the Bible believing Christian! Why? Because we trust in the Lord, and not in people's goodness towards us. (Psalm 119:165)
3. Some people live as if they are entitled to being constantly offended… to being upset all the time! Ask yourself if YOU are constantly upset.
4. Do you feel that you have to 'defend' yourself when somebody says something you take personally, and so you usually take offense?
5. Why do people take offense? Usually because we feel an injustice against US. And we feel we MUST bring "balance" back to our lives through an equal response!
6. Most people feel weighed down with past offenses against us:

   a. All the HISTORY of abuses and hurtful words said, and destructive things done against us can haunt us all our lives
   b. All the HURTS… INJUSTICES… All the BAD MEMORIES…
   c. But each offense that we hold onto WILL become our own chain and prison if not released / or let go of!

7. Jesus works backwards to what you would think about handling offenses

   a. Our natural reaction is to TAKE control – be in charge of bringing about justice concerning our lives – because we believe no one else will!
   b. But Jesus says to get control of your life, you have to LOSE it (Luke 9:23-25)
   c. RELEASE it! And leave it to who? _____ (Romans 12:19)

C. **Handling Past Offenses**

1. Forgive the Person in the same amount that YOU have been forgiven (Eph 4:32)

   a. God has given us THREE Great Examples of Forgiving

      1) _____ (Gen 45:1-5) forgave his evil, uncaring brothers
      2) _____ (Lk 23:34) forgave ALL those who had just beat Him and whipped Him, and nailed Him to the cross and left Him there to die!
      3) _____ (Acts 7:59,60) forgave those who were stoning him!
      4) All of them were intensely hurt and offended and abused, and great injustices were done against them! And yet they forgave without hesitation! Even though their enemies first asking to be forgiven!

   b. So, it is **mandatory** of a Christian to Forgive –it is actually commanded (Matt 18:21-22), NOT SUGGESTED.
   c. Forgiveness must be absolute and total (Matt 18:23-27)

     d. Unforgiving-ness is a WICKED SIN (Mt 18:28-35) to get out of your heart!

     e. There is NO forgiveness for you without you forgiving others! (Mk 11:25,26)

     f. It Must be Total, or it is NOT Forgiveness (Psalm 103:2,3,11,12; 85:2)

     g. You are NOT forgiving their SIN against you (only GOD can forgive sin); but you ARE forgiving THEM of sinning against YOU!

2. Forbear the Justice (Eph 4:2; 6:9; Col 3:13)

     a. To forbear means to hold off getting even

        1) Whoever hurt you, did wrong.

        2) But by God's amazing grace, you can put off getting even, and leave the vengeance to God to take care of (Rom 12:19).

        3) David put off repaying his enemy king Saul, for all the injustices against him (1Sam 24:16-19).

     b. God forbears/puts up with US - is longsuffering towards us (Rom 2:4; 3:25)!

     c. If He has been slow to act against YOU, then, YOU must become SLOW to act against those who have hurt you as well! VERY SLOW (James 1:19)!

3. Now you can Forget the Offense – each of them, one by one

     a. Holding onto every memory of every hurt, and every reason why someone cannot be trusted, and every reason why someone ought to be punished, will only kill the spirit of your mind! It will burn you out; twist your thinking; drain your spirit and your joy.

     b. You were not made to carry all those memories and hurts (1Peter 5:7).

     c. So, Forget some things of your past on purpose (Philp 3:12-14).

        1) You can leave behind, ALL your past failures

        2) And ALL the Hurts against you – how? By forgiving them all!

        3) All the failed parenting, relationships, marriages, decisions and debts!

        4) Even ALL the disasters that seemed to ruin your life – trusting instead, that GOD was actually in control and making everything work together for "_____" (Romans 8:28) – like Joseph trusted!

D. On-Going Offenses – if there are ongoing offenses...

1. Confront the Person – don't just ignore what people do to you. Tell them they hurt you / or did wrong towards you. Be respectfully honest with them.

2. Forgive the Person – right on the spot. See all the above!

3. Expect the Person to do right. Tell them they should take responsibility for what they did against you.

4. After that, you must go ahead and love them anyway – bless them – pray FOR them (Matt 5:43,44).

E. Getting Counsel

1. Not everyone can do the above (Rom 12:18).

2. If you find all this hard, then get counsel / spiritual help, so YOU can do right, whether anyone else does or not.

3. Beware of holding grudges (Lev 19:18; James 5:9).

4. Your family, your home, and your future is at stake!

F. Fear What Anger is Doing to Everyone in Your Home

1. First, see YOUR anger for what it is – a way for the _____ to take over your heart, and our home (Eph 4:26,27).
2. Remember what God did with ALL His anger towards YOU!
3. Repent of staying angry instead of forgiving offenses
4. Then, replace the anger with the RIGHT way of thinking about offenses against you! Replace it with forgiveness, love and dependency on God.
5. If another person is the one full of anger, they need to work through this section of Discipleship. If they are unwilling, then YOU need to pray and fast for their heart to be broken and softened and made like Christ's!

G. Overcoming Anger – Let the word of God change the way you handle anger!

1. Write down what the following verses say about **THE WRONG WAY** to handle anger. You are handling anger in a sinful and unbiblical manner when you:

    a. Ephesians 4:26,27:   *Refuse to admit that you are angry. Clam up and pretend nothing is wrong. Make this your normal way of dealing with anger.*

    b. Proverbs 17:14:   *Pick a fight as soon as you can. Be as nasty as you can.*

    c. Proverbs 29:11, 20: _____

    d. Matthew 5:21, 22: _____

    e. Ephesians 4:31: _____

    f. Proverbs 26:21: _____

    g. Proverbs 15:1: _____

    h. Colossians 3:8: _____

    i. Romans 12:17, 19: _____

    j. 1 Peter 3:9: _____

    k. 1 Corinthians 13:5: _____

    l. Philippians 4:8: _____

2. Can you see yourself doing ANY of the above when YOU get angry? Yes / No
3. Now write down what the following verses have to say about THE RIGHT WAY to handle anger. Some of these are repeats of above Scriptures, but now you are looking for instructions on the RIGHT way to respond to offenses,

    a. Romans 12:19-21:   *Never take your own revenge; turn the matter of punishment over to God; seek to help your enemy in specific ways.*

    b. Ephesians 4:26:   *Acknowledge that you are angry and seek to solve the problem immediately. Don't allow unresolved problems to pile up.*

   c. Ephesians 4:29: _____

   d. Ephesians 4:32: _____

   e. Matthew 5:43, 44: _____

   f. Proverbs 19:11: _____

   g. Proverbs 15:1: _____

   h. Proverbs 16:32: _____

   i. Proverbs 25:28: _____

   j. Proverbs 14:29: _____

   k. Proverbs 29:11: _____

   l. Galatians 5:16-23: _____

   m. 1 Thessalonians 5:18: _____

4. All of the above is God's way of looking at your anger and how YOU now need to see it and manage it.

VIII. The Role of The Husband/Father (Prov 17:6) – To Be A Team Leader!

A. A husband is to _____ his wife (Eph 5:25) as he loves his own _____ (Eph 5:28,33). Men are the main problem! God directs most of His words at men because men are stubborn and rebellious, and need the most encouragement to do right!

B. The pattern for this kind of love is to be as _____ loved the _____ (Eph 5:25) when He died so we could live! A wife will only thrive spiritually when her husband loves her beyond everything else!

C. This love will be shown by a husband accepting his responsibility to be the _____ of his wife and family (Eph 5:23). The Husband is the head of the home *positionally* (1Cor 11:3), leading, and making the important decisions with his wife's input (he is not dictator). The head of the man is _____! Therefore, how can a man expect his wife to be in submission to *his* decisions, if he himself is not in submission to God's word?!!!

D. The purpose of a husband's love is shown in how Christ gave Himself for the church that He might _____ and _____ it with the washing of the _____ (Eph 5:25,26). Therefore, the husband is responsible for maintaining the wife's purity and love for God, by not damaging her emotionally, physically, or spiritually! He is to care for, and nurture his wife and family like a farmer does his soil and plants!

E. According to 1Peter 3:7, a husband must:

   1. *Dwell* with (live with, spend time with, get intimate with, but not dominate) his wife according to _____ - i.e., he will work to know her needs, and weaknesses, and strengths, and seek to build her up and strengthen her.

2. Give "_____" to his wife (only in Biblical Christianity is the woman elevated to that of royalty). Do this in public! *That's an order!* Listen to your wife! Include her in the decisions, and allow her to be right!

3. He will recognize that she also is an _____ of the grace of life - she is just as important, and as much a beneficiary of God's gift of children, and family, and life itself as the husband is!

F. If a husband loves his wife, he will not allow himself to get _____ against her (Col 3:19), and will work to keep her from getting bitter against him! But remember, the two of them must work together at this!

IX. The Role of the Wife

A. God made the woman as an _____ meet for the man (Gen 2:18).
Define *help*: _____
The word '*meet*' means *match*, or fitting to his needs (Mt 3:8; 2 Tim 2:21).

B. God made the woman _____ the man (1 Cor 11:9).

C. A woman is to _____ herself to her husband. (Eph 5:22).

1. A wife is supposed to be subject to her husband in _____ (Eph 5:24). If she is not married, then she is still subject to her father while at home.

2. One exception to this is that we ought to obey _____ rather than _____. (Acts 5:29). The wife is to disobey when the husband gets abusive or directs her to go against the word of God.

3. A man will not respect a woman who does not respect and obey God more than she does him. And for sure, a woman will not respect a man who does not respect and obey God more than his selfish wants!

D. The wife is also to _____ her husband (Eph. 5:33). She is to honour her husband as she should honour Christ.

E. According to 1 Peter 3:1,2, a woman should have a chaste _____ (her life and language should show forth purity) coupled with _____, *not disrespect*. The woman should not live in fear of her husband, but in fear of falling short of God's design for her and her husband.

F. A woman should have a _____ (soft) and _____ spirit (1 Peter 3:3,4). She needs to refrain from a loud, clamorous, demeaning, and nagging attitude (Pro 21:9, 19).

G. God said to the first woman (Eve) that her _____ would be to her husband and that he would _____ over her (Gen. 3:16). This is part of the curse that Satan brought into the world, but it also is part of the way that God designed the Christian woman to defeat Satan by his own devices

X. Children - *The MOST intensive (and rewarding) part of a family's energies*

A. **What are Children as far as God is Concerned?** In marriage, "*children are an _____ of the Lord, and the fruit of the womb is his _____*" (Ps 127:3). Therefore, they are an opportunity for Christians to raise up a Godly generation! Why is it that Christians want all of God's blessings, except for children? Children are God's **greatest** blessing! *Remember the blessing of being HIS children!*

B. **Establishing A Child's Proper Relationship with God.**

1. A _____ can and should trust Christ at a young age (2 Tim 3:15)!

2. Fathers are not to _____ their children, but bring them up in the _____ (tender training) and _____ (encouragement) of the Lord (Eph. 6:4). Therefore, it is the responsibility of the father to instruct

his children in *spiritual* things - it is not the church's, school's, or the Government's job! Provoking children (yelling at them) only _____ them (Col 3:21)

3. A parent should teach the word of God _____ unto their children (Deut. 6:6,7). That means with a lot of time and effort!

4. List the four areas that a child should mature and develop in, according to Luke 2:52 (*note: it is the parent's job to develop these areas*)

   a. _____ - Bible learning and general education
   b. _____ - by healthy eating and exercise for growth
   c. _____ - pleasing to God – living by faith
   d. _____ - being a blessing to others – hard working

C. **Disciplining Children - The orderly and controlled manner of training** (Titus 2:1-4; Eph 6:4) "*Bring them UP...*"

1. **In their thoughts.** Have a Bible-centred home, with lots of Scripture and good books surrounding them. Also, HAVE DAILY DEVOTIONS!

2. **In their daily walk.** Help them choose good friends, work on their composure, as well as to be clean, and look clean.

3. **In their talk.** Develop their manners (to be courteous and say "*please*," and "*thank you*," and "*may I*").

4. Children are <u>commanded</u> to _____ their parents (Eph 6:1), and not just in a few things but in _____ things (Col 3:20). *Teach them this!*

5. Parents are God's representatives to their children. The fifth commandment **commands** children to _____ their parents (Exodus 20:12). The home is the training ground for the children, and there must be a consistent, spiritual atmosphere there for them to be able to see *how to live*, and *what is expected of them.*

6. Learn from *your own* _____ (Prov 13:1; 6:20)! Don't waste your life trying to prove you know better! Talk to them, and listen to them!

7. Our example of this is the Lord. "*Whom the Lord _____, He* **chasteneth**" (Hebrews 12:6) which means, "corrects" not punishes!

8. Is chastening supposed to be pleasant? _____ (Heb 12:11)

9. God chastens us as His children in order for us to be partakers of His _____ (Hebrews 12:9,10). That is the purpose of parental correction - to mature a child, and develop in them godliness!

10. The pattern in discipline - note that the Bible emphasizes *correction*, and not just punishment (Prov 22:15):

    a. Set down <u>clear</u> and understandable rules in your home! Let your children know what is expected of them, and what will happen if they disobey. They don't need to live in fear of you!

    b. Identify each violation - they have to know <u>what</u> they did wrong. Give patient and clear instructions when the child does wrong.

    c. "*Chasten thy son while there is _____*" (Prov 19:18). Don't get into the habit of letting them "slide" by in their disobedience. It will come back and haunt you later!

    d. Never yell or threaten! Speak firmly and exact the punishment right away (Eccl 8:11)! Don't repeat commands, and *don't count!*

    e. Use a "rod." Not the hand, or a board, or a belt. A **Rod** is a small branch off a tree that *stings **but does not bruise**.*

    f. **Love** your children after each time of chastening. <u>This is a must!</u>

11. Don't be afraid to have rules in your home. Not too many, but loads of them are just fine. Change the rules as the children grow older.

12. Never let the children think they have their own privacy. You must always have access to their emails if they have them, and their mobile/cell phones.

13. Reasons why a parent should discipline their children

    a. Correction delivers the soul from _____ (Prov 23:13,14)

    b. Correction establishes righteousness. "_____ *is bound in the heart of a child, but the* _____ *of correction will drive it far from him.*" (Pr 22:15)

    c. "*A child left to himself bringeth his* _____ *to* _____ " (Pr 29:15)

    d. Correction provides _____ for the parent. (Prov 29:17)

14. Some tips for disciplining children:

    a. There is a certain method God gives parents to use in discipline. "*Thou shalt* _____ *him with the* _____." (Prov 23:14) The corrective use of a small "stick" is not being abusive.

    b. He that loveth his children chastens them _____ (Pr 13:24). This means *early* before their character is formed, and over and over (not just on occasion).

    c. Should a parent withhold discipline when a child starts to cry? _____ (Prov 19:18). The child is smarter than you think!

    d. Recognize children do not become perfect with one spanking - discipline is a long term process.

    e. Never withdraw affection and love from your children.

    f. Never spank in anger or out of embarrassment (Eccl 7:9)!

    g. Never compare children with other children - this crushes them!

    h. Don't ridicule or make fun of their weaknesses or handicaps.

    i. Allow children to express their viewpoint, keeping avenues of communication open. Let them know they are important to you!

    j. Admit mistakes when you make them. Live honestly and humbly.

    k. Give them nothing they cry for, and only that which they ask for politely. Don't be afraid to say "**no**" to your children when they want things they do not need.

    l. Be creative in your discipline - as they grow older:

        1) Restrict (ground) them from activities
        2) Give additional chores – this is always great!
        3) Restrict them from the telephone or other important items
        4) Remember making rules to protect them is your job! Don't be shy!

XI. **Lastly, Enjoy Your Children** – Make sure they know you love and enjoy them!

A. When everything is said and done, rules and discipline without love only hurts a child.

B. The greatest thing that God ever did for this world was LOVE it (John 3:16)! So make sure that everything you do, you do in great love for your children!

Date Lesson Completed _____ *Discipler* _____

FINANCES
A Study of The Stewardship of Money and Possessions
Lesson Fifteen
Memory Verse: *1 Corinthians 12:27*   **Lesson Verse:** *Philippians 4:19*

> *"But my God shall supply all your need according to his riches in glory by Christ Jesus."* Philippians 4:19

I. Introduction

A. The main emphasis in the Bible is not placed upon the mere *possession* of money, but rather on the *responsible use* of it! There is a big difference. You may be surprised at just how much the Bible has to say about "money." Money means "control," and "control" is the *real* name of the game. In other words, are you in control of your money, or is your money, and desire for possessions *controlling you*?

B. This lesson deals with maintaining a proper attitude toward money, material possessions, and the importance of financial freedom from debt.

II. The Responsibility of Stewardship

A. **What is Stewardship?** The Bible refers to the Christian not only as a child of God, but as a _____ of what God gives us (1Cor 4:1,2).

1. A steward is "One who manages, or oversees another's property, finances, or other affairs." We are dealing with the control and management of money and possessions *for someone else* - not just our own! Examine the example of young Joseph in Genesis 39:1-6.

   a. Who was Joseph's "master?" _____

   b. What was Joseph in charge of? _____

   c. Therefore, stewardship means <u>responsibility</u>. The issue for the Christian then is, "to whom are *we* responsible, and for *what*?"

2. God who owns _____ things (Psalm 24:1)! We may possess some things in this life, but then again, it is we who are born and will die, while God remains. Therefore, when we take up "ownership" of something, we really are taking up *stewardship* of something that first belongs to God!

3. As stewards, we must remember that really, everything is a _____ from above (James 1:17), and that just as the Lord _____, He also can and does _____ _____ as He did with Job (Job 1:21).

4. *Spirituality* cannot be measured by *abundance* of material possessions or its *lack*. God doesn't condemn anyone for simply having money. Nor does He condemn anyone for *not* having money. Instead, God is concerned with us maintaining a *right attitude* towards money. It is not money itself that is evil, but the _____ of money (1Tim 6:10).

5. Stewardship involves _____ (1Cor 4:2) over the things God has given us, including money. We are to be faithful with what we now have, and not worry about what we don't have (Matt 25:21).

6. Stewardship is not grievous, but rather an enjoyment. 1Tim 6:17 says "*God... giveth us richly all things to _____.*" God never wants us to idolize money and seek after riches, but to seek first the _____ of God and His righteousness (Matt 6:33). He wants us to learn to be content, no matter where we are economically (Heb 13:5).

B. **God's Four Purposes for Money** - To provide for:

1. The needs of you and your family (1Tim 5:8) - **Main Purpose**
2. The needs of others (1Tim 6:17,18; 1 John 3:17) - **Compassion**
3. The operation of the government (Rom 13:1-8; Mt 22:17-22) - **Taxes**
4. The operation of your local church (Mal 3:10) - **Tithes and Offerings**

C. **The Problems With Money**

1. People end-up trusting in money instead of trusting in God (Mark 10:23-27; Prov 11:4, 28), to supply all their needs (Philp 4:19).
2. It is easy to start loving earthly possessions instead of heavenly ones (Matt 6:19-21; Col 3:1-4; Pr 30:7-9).
3. There is a great danger in thinking God's blessings can be measured by a person's material possessions (**Luke 12:15**; 1 Sam 16:7).
4. Beware when your life's objective becomes earning as much money as possible (Prov 23:4; Eccl 5:10-12).

Truths About Money
❖ To love money is the beginning of the worst nightmare anyone could ever have!
❖ All your money belongs to God - it is only yours because God first gave it to you.
❖ You owe God the tithe of every pay-check - if you hold back, then be ready for God to get you!
❖ A cheerful giver is the happiest person alive!

D. **Things Money *Cannot* Buy**

1. _____ (Prov 16:16)
2. A righteous life (Prov 28:6)
3. A good night's sleep (Eccl 5:11,12)
4. The word of God (Ps 119:14,72,127)
5. Good health (Luke 8:43)
6. Quietness, peace (Eccl 4:6; Pr 15:16; 17:1)

E. **Personal Achievement and Ambition**

1. Ambition is the drive to obtain, or accomplish something beyond yourself. Ambition is definitely not bad. What you seek to possess, when it becomes your "god," is where the problem comes in. Every Christian needs ambition - or else no one would be getting up in the morning to go to work!
2. It is not wrong to achieve success. God desires that we have the desire to be a success in everything we do. The issue is HOW we achieve it (Ps 1:1-3; Josh 1:8). God wants us to achieve success the right way, which is always the Bible way (1Cor 9:25; 2Tim 2:5).

F. **How to Evaluate the Lack of Money**

1. When you experience a perceived need, the following are the possible reasons why you may not have the money for it.

   a. You may not need it. God may be saying, "Forget about it for now."
   b. You may have already misspent it. You may have already over-spent yourself on things that you did not need (new TV, phone, tablet), so that now you cannot obtain things that you do need (food, clothing).
   c. God may be testing your faith (Jam 1:2-8). Sometimes God wants to see if you will wait upon Him to provide the funds instead of getting impatient, and making the "thing" your "god" (Ps 27:14).
   d. Your perception may be all wrong - you may have the wrong attitude about what are your *needs* and what are your *wants* (Luke 12:15)!

III. Steps to Financial Freedom

Many people are in financial bondage. They owe the bank, credit card companies, friends and relatives. You may be facing great personal pressure in your home and marriage because of these debts. Here are some wise steps from God's word that you can take to become financially free.

A. **Transfer Ownership**. You are owned by _____ (1Cor 6:19-20; Col 3:23-24). Give everything over to God for His control. This encourages you to be faithful with what you currently possess - so you don't squander or waste it (Mt 25:14-30).

B. **Become Free from Debt** (Rom 13:8). Realize that it is a priority (Pr 22:7)! Here are some helpful steps to getting, and staying *current* financially.

 1. *Start with a written budget* (Prov 27:23-24). Record all your expenses and income in a monthly budget. Write out a basic budget below:

Write Out Your Budget by Percentage of Income (no matter how small) Monthly GROSS INCOME: _____			
EXPENSE	Avg	Your Expense	Percent
Firstfruits to God (the tithe)	**10%**	_____	___%
House Rent or Mortgage (incl insurances)	23%	_____	___%
Groceries	18%	_____	___%
Auto/Travel Expenses (Fuel, Repairs)	10%	_____	___%
Household Needs and Clothing	8%	_____	___%
Electricity, Heat, Water	8%	_____	___%
Savings	5%	_____	___%
Entertainment (Birthdays, dining out)	5%	_____	___%
Telephone	5%	_____	___%
Miscellaneous (Snacks, Newspapers)	8%	_____	___%
Other _____	0%	_____	___%
Total	**100%**	_____	___%

  a. This helps you know where you are financially.
  b. **Bind yourself** to living within the budget, and don't "cheat" on it.

 2. **<u>WORK</u>** *to obtain money, and to get ahead of debt*. It takes work (Pr 10:4)! Money is not a God-given right. Work, not money builds your confidence, develops character and discipline (2 Thes 3:10-12). Work was designed as a lifestyle for man even before Adam and Eve sinned (Gen 2:15), and hard work is part of the curse God placed upon life *because of* Adam's sin (Gen 3:17-19).

 3. *Determine the difference between "needs" and "wants"*. Example: When you need a car. You may <u>want</u> a new BMW. But your <u>need</u> can be satisfied with a used *Ford*. Quit demanding only what *you want*!

 4. *Begin to eliminate non-essentials*.

  a. Avoid *costly* _____ (Prov 21:17) - every TV channel available!
  b. Utilize individual skills by "fixing and doing things yourself".
  c. Get rid of non-essentials in your life that only drains your pocket.

 5. *Think before buying* (Prov 24:3). Every purchase should be evaluated:

  a. Is it a necessity? Have I checked whether it is a *need*, or a *want*?
  b. Does this purchase reflect my Christian values? Is it questionable?
  c. Is it the very best buy? Or is it just convenient on credit cards?

 6. *Discontinue Credit (and Overdraft) Buying.* If you are in debt from the misuse of credit cards, or your **bank overdraft**, then stop! <u>**Totally Stop Using Them!!**</u>

You will have to sacrifice some of your wants and desires in life to get current, or you will only get deeper into debt.

7. **Practice _Saving_.** Save part of the money you obtain, even if it is only a little a month (Prov 21:20). Don't spend everything you make (Lk 15:11-16)! Prepare for the future (2Cor 12:14; Pr 13:22). How to save:

   a. Have sales resistance. Follow common sense and not your feelings when it comes to "sales" (beware of covetousness).

   b. Don't be guilty of *presumption*, where you assume the money you spend will show up somewhere, sometime later (Ps 19:13) - i.e., charging it when not having the money to pay it off right away

8. **Pray.** When we have done our best, then we can confidently ask God to meet our daily needs and be thankful for the way He provides (Matt 6:11). Learn to trust God (Heb 13:5,6).

B. **Practice and learn the blessing of giving to others** (Philp 2:4; Lk 6:38). Jesus said in Acts 20:35, "*It is more blessed to give than to _____.*" He was the best example of this when He gave himself on Calvary.

C. **Maintain a Clear Conscience** (Pr 28:13, Mt 5:23-24). Do all business dealings with a pure heart. Remember that you will give an account to God, so "*provide things _____ in the sight of _____ men*" (Rom 12:17).

IV. **What About _Tithing_ - The Giving of the Firstfruits of Our Resources**

A. According to Mal 3:8-10, the Lord is very serious about the Christian making sure that *money* does not become our "god." And the way He helps us to remember HIS first place, is by requiring us to keep *Him* in first place with our finances. This remembrance is called the **tithe.**

B. How much is a *tithe*? _____ of your income (Lev 27:32).

C. Tithing was normal for who? _____ (Heb 7:1,2).

D. In the Old Testament, tithes and offerings were presented *where*? (Dt 12:5,6; Mal 3:10) _____

E. In the New Testament it is to be gathered where? (1Cor 16:1,2) _____

F. *On what day of the week* should we tithe? (1Cor 16:1,2) _____

G. Why tithe to my local church?

   1. The giving of tithes and offerings to your local church is God's ordained way of supporting that ministry. There is no other way for a church to get money from the people who gather together there.

   2. So that your local church can be self-sufficient - not dependent upon the government, bazaars, or bake sales. And so that the pastor can be full time for serving the Lord (1Tim 5:17,18).

   3. Because we seek to obey Him! Faithful stewardship of our possessions involves designating the "_____" of our increase to God (Prov 3:9,10).

   4. Because we love God! Tithing is the payment of our *firstfruits* to God simply out of obedience to His word, and because we love Him (2Chron 31:5)!

   5. We tithe, NOT because God needs our money (Ps 24:1), but rather, because we need to learn how to manage our resources so that we can obey God - not just "survive" from pay-check to pay-check!

V. **Giving More than a Tithe?** *The Proof of Our Love for God!*

A. Christians do much more than just tithe out of obedience – **we give!**

B. **Why _Give_, When I Already Tithe?**

1. The tithe is an <u>act of obedience</u>, but giving above the tithe is an <u>act of love</u> because you are giving *above* what is required (Luke 17:10). The principle is, you have not *given* until you have paid what is owed!
2. Giving proves the _____ of our love - is it only out of duty (as with the tithe), or is it heart-driven (2Cor 8:1-8; 9:7)?
3. Giving above the tithe develops an attitude of **grace** (2Cor 8:6,7; 9:8), and dependence upon God. Remember, God *first* gave (John 3:16)!
4. Giving provides us the opportunity to make *eternal* investments (Philp 4:15-17; Mt 6:19-21). The more invested, the greater the return.
5. Giving allows God the opportunity to give back to us over and above what He already gives us (Luke 6:38)!

C. **What are the things a Christian should invest their giving in?**

1. Sending missionaries to preach the Gospel (Rom 15:24; Philp 4:16)
2. Gospel preaching and evangelistic efforts
3. Special church projects and need that your pastor may bring to your attention
4. All of these and more are things you need to prayerfully and obediently consider giving to above your tithe.

D. **Who are you actually giving to when you give?** (Pr 19:17; Mt 25:40)

E. **How Should I Give to the Lord?**

1. Give **Sacrificially** (2Cor 8:1,2). It is not always easy.
2. Give **Faithfully** (1Cor 16:2) - consistently!
3. Give **Cheerfully** (2Cor 9:7)! It is a privilege to be able to give!
4. Give **Willingly** (2Cor 8:3-5, 11, 12)! It is up to you!

| Date Lesson Completed _____ Discipler _____ |

Section THREE Test
The New Testament Church

NAME: _____   DATE: _____

(2 points each mark) SCORE: _____

The following questions will help you identify how much you have learned in your Bible Study time. Answer as many as possible, and take your time so that you can think and remember the answers. Most answers are obvious. Some questions however will be hard. All questions come from the material in the **First Principles** Study Course. God bless you as you examine what you have learned, and become confident in knowing and growing in God's wondrous word!

---

1. Prayer is simply talking with _____.
2. Jesus said that God hates what kind of prayers? _____
3. Prayer is the only way to get the power of *what* in your life? _____
4. There were three places of prayer in a Christian's life. Name one of them: _____
5. There are three ways to pray given in Matthew 7:7,8, one of them was "asking." What were the other two? 1) _____, 2) _____
6. To get an answer from God, you must pray according to whose will? _____
7. List one hindrance to God answering your prayer: _____
8. What is God's measure of success in a person's life? (concerning the will of God) _____
9. A Christian's actions are not to be driven by self-will, but by _____
10. It is not as important to *know* God's will for your life as it is to _____ it!
11. Will God's will for your life ever contradict His word (*His revealed will*)? ____
12. According to Proverbs 3:5,6, list the most important thing you must do to find God's will daily? _____
13. According to Colossians 3:9,10, our old nature is referred to as _____
14. Give a reason why a person still sins even after they have become a Christian? _____
15. How does God view sin? _____
16. How does God view a Christian's sin? _____
17. Whose fault is it when a person sins? _____
18. Romans 13:14 says that we are not to make _____ for the flesh to sin.
19. Psalm 119:11 commands us to do *what* with God's word so we won't sin against God? _____
20. Every person has three parts. Name them: 1) _____, 2) _____ 3) _____
21. List one of the God's five purposes of marriage (one was for us to be "fruitful and multiply"): _____
22. Describe God's view of marriage: _____
23. Instead of *Dating*, what is the godly approach to finding a marriage partner called? _____
24. Give one of the principles of a happy marriage: _____
25. What is the most important role that a husband and father has _____ _____

---

26. What is the most important role for the wife and mother: _____
_____
27. What are children (according to Psalm 127:3) _____
28. Can a child be saved at an early age? _____
29. Children in Ephesians 6:1 are commanded to _____
30. Who is our example of how to correct and train our children? _____
31. Is chastening supposed to be easy and pleasant? _____
32. Biblical correction will deliver a child's soul from what? _____
33. What is the root of all evil? _____
34. God has designed four purposes for money. Name one: _____
_____
35. Name a problem with money: _____
36. Name something that money cannot buy: _____
37. Tithing is the giving of our _____ to God.
38. Is tithing by our choice or by God's command? _____
39. How much is the tithe? _____
40. When a Christian does not tithe, what are they really doing to God? _____
_____

How are you doing?

Have you been born again? **Yes, No.** When? _____
Have you been baptized? **Yes, No.** When? _____
Have you read your Bible all the way through yet? **Yes, No.** What Book are you reading currently? _____
Have you memorized the three memory verses listed so far? **Yes, No.**
How many Scriptures have you memorized so far? _____
Are you faithful in church (every Sunday possible)? **Yes, No.**
Are you praying every day (**Yes, No**), Is God answering your prayers? **Yes, No.**
Is your home life developing, and becoming more Christian? **Yes, No.**
Are you tithing? **Yes, No.**

Well Done!

You have now completed Section THREE, and its test. Hand this test in to your Discipler, and it will be quickly graded. The results will only be known by you, your Discipler, and the Course Administrator. After going through this test, knowing what you don't know, and maybe don't understand, you may want to go back over certain portions of the Course before going on to the next Section. Otherwise, press on, and keep growing!

SECTION FOUR

This Section of your Discipleship study will establish you in

The Ministry of Christ

Memory Verse:

> *"Not slothful in business; fervent in spirit;*
> **serving the Lord."** Romans 12:11

In this last Section, we will study:

- **Personal Evangelism** - getting people to trust Christ
- **The Use of Wine and Strong Drink** - Is it right to drink?
- **My Job and Employer** - how to be a Christian at work
- **Creation and Evolution** - which is "scientific?"
- **The Future** - What is ahead for this universe?
- **Discipleship** - Learning to disciple!

MY NAME: _____

PERSONAL EVANGELISM
A Study of How to Turn Hearts to God!
Lesson Sixteen

Memory Verse: *Romans 12:11*   **Lesson Verse:** *Mark 16:15*

> *"And he said unto them,* **Go** *ye into all the world,*
> *and* **preach the gospel** *to every creature."* **Mark 16:15**

I. **Introduction.** What are *your* responsibilities in taking the Gospel to the world?

    A. In order for *you* to get saved, someone was <u>responsible</u> for taking the time to bring the saving message of the gospel to you. Make no mistake about it - no one just "becomes" a Christian. They must be urged to repent, and trust only in Christ as it is declared in the Bible (see Acts 26:17,18).

    B. That responsibility of *"preaching the Gospel"* was then passed *upon you*, so that others around you might be saved! That responsibility does not rest only with preachers, and pastors, but with every Christian!

    C. As Christians, we are commanded by the Lord to do *our* part in evangelising the whole world with the gospel (Matt 28:19,20; Acts 1:8).

    D. This lesson will focus on equipping you with the key Scripture verses that you can use to lead someone to Christ, as well as practical ways to make the Gospel clearly understood by the hearer.

II. **The Need for the Soul-Winner (Romans 10)** - Someone who persuades people about their need for Christ's saving power.

    A. The Soul-Winner is needed because of **the Condition of the World** (Rom 10:1-3) Everyone who is not saved is LOST and without hope.

        1. Everybody is "religious" (Jew, Gentile, heathen, civilized) - working their way to God and heaven! But _____ are saved (Mt 7:13,14).

        2. Everybody is born _____ (Eph 4:17-19). They are blind and incapable of getting to heaven. It is not "in them" to know how to come to Christ! By nature they are *"the children of _____"* (Eph 2:3).

        3. Everybody is _____ - hell-bound (Mt 23:33) - In need of being saved!

    B. The Soul-Winner is needed because of **the Power of the of Truth** (Rom 10:4-8)

        1. God's Truth makes a person _____ from the condemnation of this world (John 3:18, 36; 8:32).

        2. God's Truth directs a sinner to the Saviour - It stops them from trying to get to Christ their own way - they must come God's prescribed way!

        3. God's Truth can be possessed by anyone, anywhere, right in the palm of the hands, and even on the tip of the tongue (Rom 10:8).

    C. The Soul-Winner is needed because of **the Simplicity of Salvation** (Rom 10:9-13). A person must:

        1. Believe what God says about their condition - that they are a **sinner**.

        2. Accept Christ's crucifixion as sufficient to pay-off all their sins.

        3. Submit to Christ's Lordship - allowing Him to be Master of their life.

        4. Confess (testify, and then live) the true testimony of this Bible.

5. Never be ashamed of God's plan - You can confidently live now that you have heaven for sure!

6. It is all wrapped up in a person simply "*calling upon the Lord and asking Him to save them from their deserved punishment of hell!*"

7. The idea is that a person needs to see themselves as someone who has broken God's laws, and are like a man who has been caught by the police, and are standing before a judge and about to be judged for their crime, and they have NO way out! Only to find that Someone steps into the courtroom, and offers to take their place in the punishment, and if they will admit their own guilt, and then accept His offer, they can go free! It couldn't be easier!

D. The Soul-Winner is Needed Because of **The Lack of** _____ (Rom 10:14,15; Luke 10:1,2). It has never been a popular job!

1. How will people call on Someone they don't _____ in?
2. How will they believe on Someone that they never _____ about?
3. How shall people hear without some sort of a _____?
4. How shall they preach without other Christians sending them? Supporting them as they go freely - as missionaries, church planters and soul-winners?

E. The Soul-Winner is needed because it **is the Only Way that Works** (Rom 10:16,17). Truly, not everyone who hears will believe the gospel. But there is no better way! Faith is all that God is looking for (Heb 11:6; Eph 2:8)! And faith ONLY comes by hearing the presentation of the word of God - not through miracles and visions, and gifts!

III. The Work of the Gospel

A. God's Part

1. As a Christian, you must realize that you yourself cannot "save" another person's soul, nor can you by your own power draw that person to the point of salvation - you can't force people to respond.
2. The Son of God had to first completely pay for their sins through His sacrifice on the cross (2Cor 5:21), as the Lamb of God.
3. The Holy Spirit must _____ them of their sin (John 16:7-11). People must realize that they are guilty before God (compare 2Tim 4:2).
4. The Father must _____ them to the point of salvation (John 6:44)

B. **Your Part.** While salvation can only be done by God alone (John 1:12,13), it is the Christian that God has chosen to use as a tool to bring about a person's salvation!

1. In Matthew 13:3-8, we are the _____ that sows the seed of the word of God in the hearts of hearers (Mt 13:18-23).
2. 2 Corinthians 5:17-20 states that we are _____ that must reconcile man to his Creator through salvation
3. We are to open people's _____ (Acts 26:17,18) - takes a lot of effort!
4. Patiently *chip away* at people's misunderstandings (2Tim 2:24-26)
5. **Here are some thoughts:**

   a. Make sure that you pray before you go and present the Gospel. Let God cleanse you from personal sins, and then empower you to do this most miraculous work! Also, try and always have a partner with you who can pray while you witness, or who can witness while you pray.

   b. Use well-written Gospel leaflets! Make sure that everyone gets a Gospel leaflet so that they can read it later if they don't get saved right then.

    c. Use your own testimony of how *you* got saved.

    d. Have a New Testament with you. Mark the important verses (i.e., Romans 3:10, 23; 6:23; 5:8, 10:13, 17; John 1:11,12; etc.).

    e. Keep your breath clean - use breath-mints!

    f. Bring current events into the conversation in order to get them to realize that life is short and that they need a Saving God, not just a *religious system*!

    g. Have set times to go - Participate in church-wide soul-winning. If you don't make time for this, it will never get done, and you are in disobedience to our Lord's greatest command to the Christian!

C. Their Part. What every person on this planet must do to be saved

1. They must believe (Acts 16:30,31; John 3:16) of their own free will.
2. They must repent (Mark 1:15) – turn away from their sin unto God (Acts 20:21).
3. They must accept God's conclusions about them as true and right (that they are lost and sinful and without hope if they don't get born again, John 3:3). There is no negotiating with the Lord Jesus Christ. He is the only way of salvation (John 14:6), and if not done HIS way, then the person WILL die in their sins (John 8:24).
4. They must choose to follow Jesus and live as HE lived now (Matthew 9:9).

IV. The Presentation of the Gospel

A. Work Through The Following Stages of Soul-Winning

1. Conversation/Current Events - Look for ways to get the Scriptures into the conversation (like Jesus did with the woman at the well in John 4).
2. Convincing - Convince them that the Scriptures are **truth** (Romans 3:4)
3. Convicting (Making Guilty) - Work the Scriptures into their situation so they can be convicted of sin. Get them to _____ the Scriptures (John 5:39) to see that their own good works and their religion have failed them (Titus 3:5).
4. Conversion - Press them for a decision, and wait for Conversion (John 3:3,7) - This is a work only the Holy Spirit can do (John 16:7-11).
5. Confession- Encourage public Confession (Rom 10:10,11; Jn 12:42,43), announcing their new faith in Jesus Christ alone!
6. Commitment - Get them to realize that Christ is committed to them, and therefore, they should now be totally committed and loyal to HIM, at the cost of everything else (John 6:66-68; Mt 10:37,38)!

B. What the Hearer Must Realize

1. A person must realize that he is a _____ (Rom 3:10,23).
2. A person must understand that _____ died for him while he was still a _____, and NOT after he got his life cleaned up (Rom 5:8).
3. A person must come to God with genuine, godly *repentance* (Rom 2:4; Acts 20:21; 2Cor 7:10). Emphasize the meaning of *repentance*:

    a. More than just sorrow. It is MORE than just being sorry.

    b. But to change your life's direction because you realize you are UNgodly (currently going against God's laws), and are headed for judgment.

4. A person must believe he can only be *justified* (i.e., made righteous in God's sight) by trusting the blood of Jesus Christ to have paid for all his sins (Rom 5:9; Eph 1:7). God guarantees complete forgiveness to all who come to Him by faith!

5. A person must above all understand that it is *his faith* in the shed blood of Jesus Christ that saves him, and not any additional good works (Rom 3:25,28).

6. A person must call upon the Lord Jesus and ask Him specifically to save them (Rom 10:9,10,13). God cannot do it without their request!

C. **A Sample Presentation** - Get the conversation going

"If you died today, wouldn't you like to know that you would be in heaven?" "If so, let me show you out of the Bible..."

THE ROMAN'S ROAD TO HEAVEN

Who is good? Rom 3:10-12 says "*There is _____ righteous, no not one.*"

Who has sinned? Romans 3:23 says, "*For _____ have sinned, and come short of the glory of God.*"

Do you realise the eternal cost of your sin? Romans 6:23a states, "*For the wages of sin is _____.*" Your sin is THAT bad!

Nothing you DO can save you. Romans 3:20a says, "*Therefore by the _____ of the law there shall no flesh be justified in his sight.*"

God's love has made a way! Romans 5:8,9 declares, "*But God commendeth his _____ toward us, in that, while we were yet sinners, Christ died for us. Much more then, being now justified by his blood, we shall be saved from wrath through him.*"

You need to turn from your sin to God now! Repent! Be more than just sorry that you have sinned; you need to turn away from your sin. Fear it, and hate it all.

And then place all your faith in Jesus Christ alone. Romans 10:9 explains, "*That if thou shalt confess with thy mouth the Lord Jesus, and shalt believe in thine heart that God hath raised him from the dead, thou shalt be saved.*" And verse 13, "*For whosoever shall call upon the name of the Lord, shall be saved.*"

That is ALL you have to do – God has done all the rest!

D. **The Five Facts of Life**

Always remember that there are five basic truths that a sinner needs to realize. Make sure the following facts are well understood by everybody you meet:

1. You are a sinner in the eyes of God.
2. Unless something changes you, you will die as a sinner.
3. You will be judged by Almighty God as a sinner – not as a pretty good person.
4. You will be condemned to hell as a sinner.
5. Your only hope is in accepting what the Lord Jesus Christ did for you.

V. **Hindrances to the Presentation of the Gospel**

A. **Your Life not Being a Good Example** - When your walk does *not* match your talk. You may be the only Bible that your co-workers, and family will ever read (2Cor 3:2). Therefore, don't give anybody an excuse from being saved because your "walk" is no different than theirs (2Cor 6:17)! Live what you preach (Rom 2:21-23)!

B. **Watch Your Surroundings**

1. Get away from disturbances (turn off the TV, radio).
2. Have your partner occupy the attention of any children, or the spouse if they are present in the room.
3. Get somewhere where you can comfortably open the Bible so it can be seen by both you and the other person.

Date Lesson Completed _____ *Discipler* _____

Answers From Scripture to Show People How to be Saved

A Christian should be familiar with as many verses of Scripture as possible that deal with sin and salvation, and should be able to use these verses responsibly and convincingly. You should be able to quote most of these from memory to anyone at anytime, while others you should at least be able to find in the Bible to show someone.

The Necessity of Absolutely Believing

John 1:12 "But as many as _____ him, to them gave he power to become the sons of God, even to them that _____ on his name:"

John 3:16 "For God so loved the world, that he gave his only begotten Son, that whosoever _____ in him should not perish, but have everlasting life."

John 3:18 "He that _____ on him is not _____: but he that believeth not is condemned already, because he hath not believed in the name of the only begotten Son of God."

John 3:36 "He that _____ on the Son hath everlasting life: and he that believeth _____ the Son shall not see life; but the wrath of God abideth on him."

John 5:24 "Verily, verily, I say unto you, He that heareth my word, and _____ on him that sent me, hath everlasting life, and shall not come into condemnation; but is passed from death unto life."

John 11:25-26 "Jesus said unto her, I am the resurrection, and the life: he that _____ in me, though he were dead, yet shall he live: And whosoever liveth and believeth in me shall _____ die. Believest thou this?"

Acts 16:31 "And they said, _____ on the Lord Jesus Christ, and thou shalt be saved, and thy house."

Our Good Works Can't Save Us

Romans 4:5 "But to him that worketh _____, but believeth on him that justifieth the ungodly, his _____ is counted for righteousness."

Ephesians 2:8-9 "For by grace are ye saved through _____; and that not of yourselves: it is the gift of God: Not of _____, lest any man should boast"

Titus 3:5 "Not by _____ of righteousness which we have done, but according to his mercy he saved us, by the washing of regeneration, and renewing of the Holy Ghost;"

Galatians 2:16 "Knowing that a man is _____ justified by the works of the law, but by the faith of Jesus Christ, even we have believed in Jesus Christ, that we might be justified by the faith of Christ, and not by the _____ of the law: for by the works of the law shall no flesh be justified."

Repentance

Acts 17:30 "And the times of this ignorance God winked at; but now _____ all men every where to repent:"

2 Peter 3:9 "The Lord is not slack concerning his promise, as some men count slackness; but is longsuffering to us-ward, not willing that any should perish, but that _____ should come to _____."

Mark 6:12 "And they went out, and _____ that men should repent."

Hell

Matthew 13:42 "And shall cast them into a furnace of _____: there shall be wailing and gnashing of teeth."

Luke 16:23 "And in _____ he lift up his eyes, being in torments, and seeth Abraham afar off, and Lazarus in his bosom."

Matthew 25:41 "Then shall he say also unto them on the left hand, Depart from me, ye cursed, into _____ fire, prepared for the devil and his angels:"

Revelation 20:15 "And whosoever was not found written in the book of life was cast into the lake of _____."

Eternal Security

John 10:28-29 "And I give unto them _____ life; and they shall _____ perish, neither shall any man pluck them out of my hand. My Father, which gave me them, is greater than all; and _____ man is able to pluck them out of my Father's hand."

Answers From Scripture to Against Religions and Cults

Scriptures to answer the questions of Roman Catholicism.

1. Final authority being ONLY the Bible (Matt 4:4; Rom 3:4; John 17:17; John 8:31,32,36)
2. Mary needed a Saviour (Luke 1:46,47). She was a sinner - not sinless (Rom 3:10,23)
3. Jesus had brothers and sisters (Matt 1:24,25; 12:46-50; 13:55,56; Mk 6:3; Gal 1:19)
4. There is no need to pray through Mary, or any saint (1Tim 2:5)!
5. Religion ends up substituting the tradition of men in the place of the commandments of God (Mark 7:7,10)
6. Salvation is NOT by works (Eph 2:8,9; Tit 3:5; Isa 64:5), at all!
7. Watch out for anyone who <u>forbids</u> people to *marry* or to eat *meats* (1Tim 4:1-3)
8. Pastors are to be married as a general rule (1Tim 3:2). Peter was married (Mt 8:14)
9. Baptism is NOT important to our salvation (1Cor 1:17) - it is only for after salvation.
10. Jesus hates the Rosary (Matt 6:7), and any other repetitious prayer!
11. There is no purgatory (2Cor 5:8; Heb 1:3; 9:27; Rom 8:1) - either heaven or hell!
12. A person is justified only by faith alone in Christ Jesus (Rom 1:17; Gal 2:16)
13. Jesus finished paying for ALL of my sins on the cross (John 19:30)

Scriptures relating to Protestantism (Many issues are the same as with Catholicism)

1. Self righteousness is the worst sin (1 John 1:8,10; Rom 10:3)
2. Thinking *"My church is better than others"* is not what matters with God (John 3:3)
3. If someone says *"I keep the 10 commandments"* – show them that is impossible (James 2:10; Tit 3:5). Everyone must repent and be born again to be forgiven.
4. Thinking *"I am part of the elect"* is only true if you are a Jew (Isa 55:6,7; 1 John 2:2)

Scriptures To Deal with a Jehovah's Witness. These people are really confused.

1. Jesus is God in the flesh (Mt 1:23; 1Ti 3:16; Isa 7:14; Ro 9:5; 1Jn 5:20; Heb 1:8)
2. Jesus is the Jehovah of the Old Testament (Isa 40:3 & Matt 3:3; Dt 10:17 & Rev 19:16; Ps 68:18 & Eph 4:8-10; Ex 3:14 & John 8:56-58)
3. Jesus is equal with God (Philp 2:6-9; Isa 43:10,11; 44:6,8)
4. Jesus is eternal (Micah 5:2)
5. The trinity concept is Scriptural (2Cor 13:14; Gal 4:4-6; Gen 1:26)
6. There is a heaven full of mansions (John 14:1-3) awaiting Christians
7. The 144,000 witnesses of Revelation 12 are real Jewish male virgins (Rev 14:1-5)
8. If a prophet ever makes a false prediction, that person is to be stoned with stones, and disregarded (Dt 18:20-22)
9. When Jesus does come back, every eye shall see Him (Rev 1:7)
10. The Holy Spirit really is a real person (John 16:13)
11. Hell is literal and eternal (Matt 23:33; Rev 14:11; 20:10; Luke 16:23-31)

Scriptures to Deal with a Mormon about salvation.

1. An angel cannot present another Gospel than what is already in the Bible (Gal 1:8)
2. Exclusivity of Jesus Christ to salvation (John 14:6; Hos 13:4)
3. You can know that you have eternal life right now based upon the sole authority of the written word of God (1 John 5:11-13)
4. Baptism is not important (1Cor 1:17)
5. Decide the final authority issue (Rom 3:4; John 17:17; John 8:32,36; Matt 4:4)
6. God has no body, but rather is a spirit (John 4:24)
7. Jesus is God come in the flesh (1Tim 3:16)
8. God has always been, and always will be - never created (Ps 90:1,2)
9. Only Satan teaches that man can become like God (Gen 3:5; Isa 14:13,14)
10. The blood of Jesus Christ cleanses the sinner from SIN (1 John 1:7)
11. The Gospel is the death, burial and resurrection of Jesus for our sins (1Cor 15:1-4)
12. The true church of Jesus Christ never disappeared (Matt 16:18)
13. Disregard genealogies and fables (1Tim 1:4)

WINE AND STRONG DRINK
A Study of the Curse of Drink and the Christian's Response
Lesson Seventeen
Memory Verse: *Romans 12:11*   **Lesson Verse:** *Proverbs 20:1*

> *"Wine **is a mocker**, and strong drink is raging: and whosoever is de-ceived thereby is not wise."* Proverbs 20:1

I. Introduction

A. The Bible has never been unclear about the important issues in life. The problem is always that people play ignorant instead of taking the time to *"search the Scriptures"* (John 5:39) for **the right answer** about how to live, and what is **right** to do. This is true with what we are about to study.

B. Wine, and strong drink have plagued mankind from the time of Adam and Eve's fall in Genesis 3 up to today. It has affected even the best of people - see Genesis 9:20-22, where *"Noah began to be an husbandman, and he planted a vineyard: And he drank of the wine, and was **drunken**; and he was uncovered within his tent. And Ham, the father of Canaan, saw the **nakedness** of his father."* So began the sad tale of alcohol's influence!

C. This study will show that the correct use of wine and strong drink is not to be "in moderation" but **only as a medicine** - it is definitely not for social entertainment or pleasure -- *"He that loveth pleasure shall be a poor man: he that loveth **wine** and oil shall not be rich"* (Proverbs 21:17).

D. From the very start of this study, let the Scriptures make it very clear that *"Wine **IS** a mocker, and strong drink **IS** raging: and whosoever is* deceived *thereby is not wise."* (Proverbs 20:1). It is not an issue of whether wine can "become" a mocker when abused, but that its very nature IS mockery to the Christian life, and that **it deceives all who think they can handle it!**

E. This study is designed to present *God's view* of wine and alcoholic drink. You will need to fill-in the answers to the questions from the Scriptures presented. Please study **all** the Scriptures presented, and then fill in the blanks.

II. Study Outline on Alcoholic Drinks

A. The Different Kinds of Wine and Alcoholic Drinks

1. Did you know that there are **TWO** types of "wine" in the Bible?

   a. _____ - squeezed from the grape. Simple grape juice (Lk 5:37,38)
   b. _____ - fermented - alcoholic grape drink (Lk 5:39).

   The word "wine" in the Bible can refer to either **fermented** (alcoholic), or **un-fermented** (pure) grape juice. The word 'wine' is a general term. The surround-ing context of each verse tells you *which kind* of wine God is talking about.

2. There is also a drink referred to as "_____ *drink*" (Prov 20:1).
3. Let's look in detail at each of these three drinks:

   a. The Fruit of the Vine - called, "New Wine" - Juice of the Grape.

      1) It is not found in the "vat" but in the "_____" (Isa 65:8). It is fresh from the grape - simple juice with nothing added!
      2) God's people **never** drank alcoholic wine (Dt 29:5,6; 32:14)!

3) God's blessings are found in "_____" wine (Pr 3:9,10), not in fermented drinks. We will study fermentation a little later on.

4) Wine is compared to *"blood"* in the Bible, and God's people are supposed to only drink the "_____ *blood of the grape"* (Dt 29:6; 32:14). There should never be anything added.

5) New wine is a refreshing beverage not intoxicating drink (Ps 104:13-15)

6) Jesus drank "_____" wine at His last supper (Mt 26:29). **Jesus never drank alcoholic wine, or any strong drink!**

b. Fermented Wine - called "Old Wine" - what we call *'Liquor'*

1) Old wine is made by man. It is not natural. Let's look at how fermented wine is made, and what makes it "old":

a) It must be allowed to "decay" or spoil (the natural starches in the juice are allowed to break-down into sugars and alcohol).

b) The temperature, and sugar content must be regulated. If the decaying process is not carefully controlled, then it will sour, and be bitter, and therefore not enjoyable.

c) Yeast ("*leaven*" in the Bible) is added to enhance the decaying process. This is referred to as "mingling" wine with additional ingredients. Mingled wine may have sugars and other seasonings added during the fermentation process to enhance the flavour (Pr 23:29,30) for "special meals"

d) When kept under pressure, the resulting *carbon dioxide* from the fermentation is retained in the liquid until opened, producing a "pop" and resulting in carbonated bubbles, as well as the "head" on beers.

2) Old wine in the Bible is only used **as a drug**, not a refreshing beverage (1Tim 5:23; Luke 10:33,34).

3) It is referred to as an "intoxicating" beverage because it has the power to render someone senseless, or with less sense. Paul tells Timothy to "____ *a little wine*", not **drink** a little wine. Use it like you would a modern medicine. Old wine cleanses cuts and bruises, and can be used to purify water under extreme circumstances. People kept it around for "using", not drinking. You would NEVER take glass-fulls of medicines, yet people do with alcohol, and they do it to their hurt!

4) Fermented wine is only the beginning of a path that leads to stronger liquor! Alcoholic drink is never satisfying (Hab 2:5)!

5) Old wine is only permitted to be drank in the following situations:

a) When about to _____ - to not worry, and be able to ignore pains and past haunting memories (Pr 31:4-7).

b) As a medicine, alcoholic wine could be used as:

i) A psychological drug (Prov 31:6,7) to calm the overburdened mind - like using a sleeping tablet.

ii) A physical drug (1Tim 5:23; Lk 10:34) to ease pains, and clean out wounds.

c) **Important note** – there are so many better medicines today than the use of alcoholic drink, that are designed to address pain, or infection, and are controlled in their dispensing so that people can't easily abuse them like they can drink!

      d) So, unless you are living on a deserted island somewhere with no med-
icines except alcoholic drink, there is no need for alcoholic drink in
your home or life – period!

    6) The love of *old wine* is wrong (Prov 21:17), and is therefore a fleshly lust
that "_____ *against the soul*" (1Peter 2:11) - it keeps the person from
ever conquering sin and self, and being able to be filled with the Spirit
(Eph 5:18).

  c. Strong Drink

    1) Strong drink (like whisky and rum) is harder drink than alcoholic wines
and beers. These drinks have been referred to as "spirits" due to all the
"extra" alcohol that is added to them for a greater "punch."

    2) Hard liquor is a picture of God's **wrath** and judgment on a nation (Ps
75:8; Mt 26:39; 18:11; Rev 14:9,10). **It is NOT a blessing!**

B. The Results of Drinking

1. If you drink *New Wine* - It refreshes, and makes a person's heart and health good
(Ps 104:15, "*And wine that maketh **glad** the heart of man*"). Grape juice is good
for digestion, variation (variety is the spice of life), supply of vitamins, natural
sugar and extra energy intake.

2. If you drink *Old Wine* or *Strong Drink*:

  a. It numbs the brain making the person "think" that things are great. It is Satan's counterfeit of new wine, and of the joy of the Lord that comes from
enjoying natural foods.

  b. It impairs your ability to make right decisions (Pr 31:4,5).

  c. Liquor and **immoral sex** always go hand in hand (Gen 9:20-24; Hab 2:15,16;
Lam 4:21). It enhances the *domination* of the flesh!

  d. Liquor and **violence** go hand-in-hand (Hab 2:5,17).

  e. Watch how the Lord in **Proverbs 23**, describes the life of someone who
spends their time enjoying a few drinks (Prov 23:29-35):

    1) They have troubles (woe), and _____, and arguments (conten-
tions) - (Prov 23:29,30)

    2) They don't make sense when they talk (they babble, 23:29).

    3) They have wounds from fights they don't remember (23:29).

    4) They look terrible - not healthy and robust (23:29)!

    5) Alcoholic drinks have a *hypnotic* affect when you stare at it for a while
(23:31).

    6) Ultimately, the drinker finds himself in all sorts of trouble:

      a) **Bitten** with *addiction* to its poison (23:32)! Its effect is disastrous,
not beneficial!

      b) **Lustful, and remorseful** for all the things you end up doing and say-
ing when you drink (23:33)!

      c) **Physically sick**: dizzy and unable to stand or walk straight (23:34).

      d) **Emotionally sick**: blaming everything and everyone around you in-
stead of blaming yourself (23:35)! You will wish it was all a bad
dream!

      e) **Addicted** - dependant upon it, and not able to escape its hold on you!
(23:35)!

f. Liquor and **self-centeredness** go hand-in-hand. Drinking has the habit of becoming more important than even the welfare of your own children (Joel 3:3) - people will end up selling almost anything in order to get a drink!

g. Liquor and *religion* go hand-in-hand (Isaiah 28:7,8) - almost all the world's religions use either drugs or alcoholic drink to enhance their "spirituality" in the worship of their god.

h. Drinking in moderation *is possible*, but rarely maintained, and *always* ends in disaster! Just as with anything, it IS possible to do something, and it not hurt you (1Cor 6:12). But that is not the way to tell if you should do it or not! We have to do what is RIGHT by God's standards, and not what we can get away with!

i. Drinking liquor drives you away from your _____ and family (Hab 2:5) because it never can satisfy the emptiness of the heart!

j. Drinking liquor is usually pushed upon people (Hab 2:15). People don't normally go after the drink unless it is greatly advertised and pressured upon them (see any conversation at a pub between those who are drinking and those who are just sitting at the bar).

C. What about Beer?

1. Beer is made using basically the same process as that of wine, except, instead of using grapes, barley grain is used.

2. The purpose of drinking beer is the same as that of wine - to help a person "*relax, and unwind*." A Christian does not need a beer or a glass of wine to help them end a day, anymore than a child does. An adult who looks to ANY drink for help at the end of the day (to relax) is only looking for a cheep substitute to prayer and fellowship with God. **They are carnal, and backslidden, and need to repent!**

3. Even though the alcoholic content of beer is low, that is not a reason to drink it - *most people who do drink beer, drink a lot of it* - not just a sip or two. At the end of the evening, the beer drinker is full of alcohol, and is usually unfit to drive - **and is unfit to be a Christian!**

D. Biblical Warnings about Liquor:

1. Drink is like a "god" to some people (Isa 5:11). **They live for it!**
2. Drink is made out to be a proof of <u>manhood</u> and strength (Isa 5:22).
3. Drink is not to be a social event in your home or anywhere (Hab 2:15).
4. God says wine and drink will make a mockery out of you (Prov 20:1). In other words, the person who drinks, is **dumb, dumb, DUMB!**
5. **Drink is not a disease,** but an act of the will against God (Pr 23:35)!

E. The Usual Reasons for Drinking - why people drink intoxicating liquors:

1. <u>To forget troubles and heartaches</u> - Sometimes God **wants** you to have your troubles, to get you to see you are only "*reaping what you* _____" (Gal 6:7,8). To try to remove God's payback for your sin is to ignore God, and to reap more troubles. Then there are the times when you are called upon to suffer for being in the right (Philippians 1:29). Who would run to a bottle to "cope" with God's blessing (Mt 5:11,12)?

> **For a Christian to try and use anything other than *Christ* to cope with problems, is like a married man running to a *harlot* to help him cope with his life's problems! *It is just as wicked in God's eyes*!**

2. Because they don't have anywhere else to turn

   a. All humans are sinners by nature - we sin naturally. The core of our being is sinful in God's eyes. We are not pure, and holy.

   b. Our sinfulness is the source of our emptiness, and lustful desires for wrong things.

   c. The desire for Drink, is just one of many many sins that can take over a person's life.

   d. So many have been presented with *religion* as the answer to their sins, and sorrows, only to find it too is empty. So they turn to drink. But **only Christ** will satisfy when we turn to Him for the real help we need (Isa 53:4-6; 55:1,2).

3. Because they would rather **take the risk with drink,** than with drugs - Don't take *either* risk, since there is sure help with Christ (Jn 10:10)!

4. Because of pressure - friends and family are too important to you if THEY can pressure you into doing what God condemns (Mt 10:37)! What if they talk you into stealing, or lying - it is all the same - **you have no excuse, no matter how much pressure you feel!**

5. Because people think there is no other way to have a good time.

F. **The Lie about Drinking in "*Moderation*"**

1. Nobody can "handle" fermented liquor in moderation unless the following conditions can be met:

   a. You have to first *give* a person a drink, which violates Hab 2:15. Read it and see that it is wicked to give a friend a drink!

   b. The person has to first drink "to excess" to find out where their limit is - this then violates the first rule of "drink" because you have to get yourself "drunk" to know when enough is enough!

   c. The person then has to *keep drinking* in order to develop and maintain their tolerance of drink, so that they can handle more and more without getting drunk.

All of this is just a balancing-act that God never intended the Christian to get into. The Christian stays clear of things that can hinder their ability to serve their Lord!

> *"Abstain from all **appearance** of evil."* (1Thes 5:22)

2. *Moderation* is anybody's guess because a person does not usually know when they have exceeded their own personal limit of drink until someone else sees it, or they kill someone on the highway!

3. Alcoholic drink affects a person's **alertness**, and yet the apostle Peter says in 1Peter 5:8, *"Be _____, be vigilant; because your adversary the devil, as a roaring lion, walketh about, seeking whom he may devour"*

4. God expects a Christian to **stop drinking** completely at salvation:

> *"Know ye not that the unrighteous shall not inherit the kingdom of God? Be not deceived: neither **fornicators**, nor **idolaters**, nor **adulterers**, nor **effeminate**, nor **abusers of themselves with mankind**, Nor **thieves**, nor **covetous**, nor **drunkards**, nor **revilers**, nor **extortioners**, shall inherit the kingdom of God. And such WERE some of you: but ye are washed, but ye are sanctified, but ye are justified in the name of the Lord Jesus, and by the Spirit of our God."* (1Cor 6:9-11)

5. None of the listed people are "Christian" in their actions at all! The thing to ask yourself as you re-read the list is: *Can I do ANY of those things, IN ANY AMOUNT and it be right with God?* (Read this question again and again until you get the meaning!)

   a. **Fornicators** - Fornication is sex before marriage. If we can drink in moderation, then it is ok when we commit fornication in moderation! **NO!** Fornication is wrong from the start!

   b. **Idolaters** - Idolatry is completely wrong. A person cannot be a Christian and still have just a few idols (1Cor 10:14)! Neither can a Christian hold onto just a few drinks (as we shall see).

   c. **Adulterers** - Adultery is sex with another partner besides your spouse and is completely wrong - No Christian is right with God if they even commit adultery ONCE (Heb 13:4)! They must repent, confess, and FORSAKE the sin - not just "reduce" it!

   d. **Effeminate** - Being effeminate is when a man acts like a female, and is beginning down the road to homosexuality. God says that it is wrong for a man to stop being masculine, and says acting like a woman even in moderation is wicked!

   e. **Abusers of themselves with mankind** - This is homosexuality, and is not condoned in the slightest! It is an abomination to God (Lev 20:13; Rom 1:26,27)!

   f. **Thieves** - Thievery is wicked, and wrong even in the slightest amount for a Christian (Eph 4:28)! You cannot separate petty theft from big-time stealing. Stealing is wrong in all amounts!

   g. **Covetous** - Covetousness is the desire to have something that is wrong for you to have. It is not okay for the Christian to be a little covetous just as long as they don't let it take control of their life - it is just completely wrong (Ex 20:17)!

   h. **Drunkards** - Most people when they come to this verse read all the above descriptions correctly, but when they get to the word "*drunkards*" they only imagine that God does not want a Christian to get "plastered" drunk, and that it is OK if they drink *a little*. Sorry! Just as with ALL the other words, **God has no tolerance for the Christian even dabbling in any of this sin!** God considers a person who drinks even "in moderation" the same as a person who gets drunk. To "take" just one item from a store brands you as a "thief." To kill just one person brands you as a **murderer!** To drink just ONE alcoholic drink identifies you in God's eyes (maybe not in people's eyes), but in God's eyes as a **DRUNK!**

   i. **Revilers** - A reviler is a bad tempered man or woman, and God says that the Christian is NOT to lose their temper *at all!*

   j. **Extortioners** - Extortion is the illegal gain of money. A Christian is never to obtain money illegally, even in "moderation!"

6. None of the above people "*shall inherit the kingdom of God.*" And so the Bible continues, "*And such _____ some of you: but ye are _____ (cleansed from the sins), but ye are _____, but ye are justified in the name of the Lord Jesus, and by the Spirit of our God*" (1Cor 6:11). Christians in Corinth had at some time in the past been sinful in one or more of the above areas, but **NOW**, because of Jesus Christ saving them, they are different - they surely WERE that way, but are NOW washed, sanctified, and justified by Christ - and

they were not supposed to try and "cut back" on adultery, idolatry, thievery, homosexuality, or drunkenness. They were supposed to **stop all of it completely**, and live for Jesus Christ - the One who saved them "_____ *their sins*" (Mt 1:21), not saved them to be able to remain IN their sins.

G. **Questions from Other Scriptures** - Here are some verses that people quote to prove drinking in moderation for a Christian is permissible:

1. **Ephesians 5:18** The question is, whether the "*excess*" is in being **drunken** (which is usually thought), or in the **wine** itself (see Pr 20:1)?

   a. Look at 1Peter 4:4. Is it ok if a Christian does just a "little" rioting, as long as it is in moderation? NO! The *riot itself* is excessive, just like *wine itself* is excessive!

   b. The Christian has been *converted* at salvation from sin's power to the power in the life of Jesus Christ, and therefore, the person's **desires** have been converted - they have been changed from seeking satisfaction in wine, money, rebellion (riot) and pleasures, to seeking the things of God, and especially the Holy Spirit!

   c. Most "Christians" only dabble in yielding to the Holy Spirit because they want to continue to "dabble" in yielding to the desire for wine, beer and strong drink! God help us to get on one side or the other. Jesus said in Rev 3:15,16, "*thou art neither cold nor hot: I would thou wert cold or hot. So then because thou art _____, and neither cold nor hot, I will spue thee out of my mouth.*"

2. **1Timothy 3:2,3** The question here is whether "*given*" can only mean "intoxicated" or "addicted" to something. Look at verse 2 where "*given to hospitality*" is not intended to mean "intoxicated" with it, but open, and welcoming it to happen in your daily life. **The Christian is commanded NOT to welcome drink into their life**, nor to be open to drinking AT ALL! In other words, don't even desire it!

3. **1Timothy 3:8** "*...not given to **much** wine*" is referring to *home use* where you CAN use old wine in medicinal uses, but the Christian is to be careful not to get used to having it in everything you eat and drink. People can abuse a drug that was meant to aid medicinally, and end up getting addicted to it - like modern kids "sniffing glue!" Glue is good to have around your home - but make sure that you don't find yourself buying loads of it to sustain someone's "habit!" The wine here is like the wine of Romans 14:21, ("*It is good neither to eat flesh, nor to **drink wine** , nor any thing whereby thy brother stumbleth, or is offended, or is made weak*"), where the Deacon must be above question, and careful not to allow in his home what would cause others to stumble, including even grape juice. Remember, the same kind of "bottles" that held intoxicating wine, also would at other times hold fresh, grape juice. The problem would be for the new believer to discern whether "deacon so and so" was drinking alcohol, or new wine (the bottles weren't probably labelled).

4. **Titus 1:7** It is the same thing as 1Tim 3:3, but especially notice the words "*not _____ to filthy lucre*" - if we can drink to moderation, then, as long as we are moderate about it, we can partake of filthy *lucre* (money obtained wrongfully)! The Bible is its own interpreter. The words "*not given to*" means "***not desiring it, and not open to it.***"

5. **Titus 2:3** "*not given to **much** wine*." See 1Tim 3:8 above. The problem here is whether a person is allowed to drink as long as "much" is not consumed. No -

The command is that the older women of the passage were to resist the constant pressure of the day to turn to wine, and to teach the younger women GOOD things, to be SOBER, holy - **not how to drink!**

6. **Acts 2:12,13** *"drunk with new wine"* - Those who doubted the supernatural nature of the events of Pentecost came up with some illogical conclusions about why it was happening:

    a. Some said this was "crazy" (saying this event had no meaning).
    b. Others thought they were **drunk** with "_____ *wine*," which is only a derogatory statement. Nobody can get drunk on NEW wine because grape juice does not have any intoxication. It is like saying they were *drunk* because of drinking buttermilk - being unable to handle anything more than milk. The world just brands things that they don't understand as crazy, or immature. That's how they treat most of history, and the Bible.

7. **1Peter 4:3** *"excess of wine"* - This implies that as long as you don't get caught up in drinking wine "to excess" (where you get drunk), then you are right with God. According to Ephesians 5:18, the excess is IN the fermented wine to begin with - it is built into wine. The thing that Peter points out in this verse is that these Christians were no longer caught-up in the excess of wine - they had been saved, and their thirst for liquor had been converted to a thirst for God and His Holy Spirit! For further proof, look at verse 4, where the excess is found IN the *"rioting"*! Things that by nature are excessive include: ***riot, murder, rape, and drink!!!***

8. **John 2:1-11** *"the water that was made wine"* - This is usually where everyone refers to when they want to justify their desire to drink alcoholic wine, never imagining for one moment that the wine these people were drinking might actually be just fresh grape juice!

    a. Can you imagine Jesus showing up three days into a drunken binge, and offering them MORE liquor? Go on, think about it! Jesus would be violating His own rules if He gave His neighbour alcoholic "drink" (Hab 2:15).
    b. Jesus made extra special tasting pure grape juice that was enjoyed by all the members of the wedding party because they still had their discerning senses even though they had been drinking "wine" for three whole days! They were not drunk with fermented alcoholic liquor, but were enjoying refreshing grape juice!
    c. Jesus never drank wine that was mixed with anything else (Mk 15:23), but was always, only fresh from the vine (Mk 14:25)!

H. **How To Overcome the Addiction, and Attraction to Liquor** - The following is a list of basic things a person has to do to win over the addiction of alcohol - for a more thorough study, contact your pastor.

1. **Accept** the fact no one is "born an alcoholic," but rather **we are all born sinners** (Rom 3:23), and therefore sin - some by drinking, and others by thieving, etc. Without the salvation that Christ purchased on His cross, there is no victory available over drink or any other sin in your life!

2. **Get saved** (Mt 1:21; 11:28,29). You cannot win over addiction without the victorious power of Christ in your life! This cannot be over-emphasized: an alcoholic must not seek to become sober, or become a better husband, or anything but a defeated sinner who surrenders to the saving power of Jesus Christ (Rom

6:11; 10:13)! You must come to the living SAVIOUR, and only then will you find rest in your SOUL!

3. **Surrender** your entire life over to the Lordship of Jesus Christ (Mt 7:24-27) - Let HIM be the authority that tells you how to live your life - no longer live for your own appetites! Don't be a *slave* to your habits - instead, be a *prisoner* of Jesus Christ from now on (Eph 4:1)!

4. **Repent** of drink as a wicked and evil sin against both God, and the temple of the Holy Ghost, which is your body (1Cor 3:17; 6:19,20). This means more than being sorry - it means forsaking the sin of drink, and replacing it with the Holy Spirit of God (Pr 28:13)!

5. **Replace** the drink with the Holy Spirit (Eph 5:18). Fast and pray through the struggles of depression, anxiety, and nervousness that got you dependant upon drink in the first place! Seek God's Holy Spirit to fill each of those holes in your life that you used to try and fill with alcoholic drink! Progressively saturate your life with God's word in study, and with God's work, as you yield to right living! Remember, sin (even drink) "*shall not have _____ over you.* (Rom 6:14)"

6. **Become accountable** to a mature Christian who will help you through the times you used to rely on the liquor for. **This is a must**. You at least need a godly, Bible-preaching pastor to whom you can rely upon for straight biblical counsel, and rebuke when needed. You also need good friends who will be there when you struggle and want to give in.

7. **Get busy serving the Lord** in your life - quit having so much time to spend drinking, and get out dealing with people about Christ!

III. Brief Summary of Conclusions

A. There are two kinds of wine - new (fresh squeezed) and old (alcoholic).

B. God forbids and warns against the distribution of old wine, unless it is only for medicinal purposes.

C. Jesus never drank old wine - He always drank it new, fresh from the grape.

D. Drinking wine and strong drink "in moderation" is impossible for a Christian, just like committing adultery in moderation is impossible!

E. Drinking beer is the same as drinking wine in God's eyes.

F. The Christian who seeks to be filled with God's *Holy Spirit* MUST **abstain** (stay totally away) from *intoxicating "spirits"*.

G. There is a CURE for addiction to alcohol - becoming a slave to nothing and nobody outside of Jesus Christ through His perfect word!

H. Therefore, the only way out of addiction to alcohol is found in repentance, and surrender to Christ on a daily basis, seeking to be filled with the Spirit as you study, and live by the perfect words of the living God - the Bible!

Date Lesson Completed _____ *Discipler* _____

THE CHRISTIAN AT WORK
A Study of the Christian and His Work Related Responsibilities
Lesson Eighteen
Memory Verse: *Romans 12:11*   **Lesson Verse:** *1 Corinthians 10:31*

> *"Whether therefore ye eat, or drink, or whatsoever ye do, do all to the glory of God."* 1 Corinthians 10:31

I. Introduction

A. The Bible has a great deal to say about how you are to conduct yourself on your job, either as an employee, or an employer. About one-fourth of a person's adult life is spent on a job. It is essential for the Christian to learn how the Lord would have you work, and fulfill your responsibilities there. Be careful not to restrict your Christian testimony to just church and home.

B. This lesson is intended to help you be the type of employee, or employer that God would have you to be.

II. Basic Principles

A. **All Christians are Supposed to Work - not be Lazy!**

1. We were made *to work* (Gen 2:15; 3:17-19). We were not made to have the "easy life." The easy life comes in heaven, and after hard work!
2. Primarily on a full-time job for a man (2 Thes 3:10-12).
   a. If a man who is able to work, is not working, he ought not to eat! Nobody should pity that man, and that man ought to FAST and seek a job until he gets it – it is that important to his character!
   b. If a man is not working, his health will only collapse! As will his family!
3. Primarily at home for a woman (Titus 2:3-5; 1 Tim 5:13,14). And, don't tell me THAT is not work enough!
4. God hates laziness, idleness, and slothfulness (Pr 6:6-11; Rom 12:11).
5. If you are not working, and yet not dying in a hospital, then you are sinning against God, against your family, and against yourself! Get a job!

B. **All Christians are Servants of the Lord.** In other words: "Serve your Lord throughout your entire day at home, and at work"

1. Romans 1:1 says that the Christian's primary job is to serve _____. So, when we labour at anything, we are to do it for HIM!
2. Serve the Lord mowing grass, building houses, making clocks, digging ditches, designing computers, standing guard – whatever you do, do it as unto the Lord!
3. Serving *God* is a *full-time job* - not just when you go to church (1 Pet 3:15; 2 Tim 4:2). We need to SERVE the Lord Jesus by always doing things for others!
4. Serve the Lord especially at church! The Bible is very clear that every Christian is an integral part of a local church, and that each member's contribution is vital to that local fellowship of believers. God expects every Christian to be involved in doing the Lord's work by witnessing, and caring about the needs of others (1 Cor 12:12,13; Eph 4:11-16).

C. A Job is What God Gives You so that you *Can* Serve

1. The world says your first responsibility is first to your self! But God says, your first ministry is to your _____ (1Tim 3:1,4,5; 5:8).
2. Your second ministry is to your church family (Gal 6:10; Heb 10:25).
3. Your third ministry is to reach the lost (2Cor 5:18,20).
4. By meeting those responsibilities, your own needs will be met!

Your job in life is meant by God to financially support all of the above ministries. But, without your job, you will be very limited in serving God in the above ministries. Don't let Satan trick you into laziness, and defeat.

D. Your Attitude at Home or at Work is *Critical* to Your Testimony

1. Attitudes toward your job. You should view your job as a *ministry* opportunity, not just a job.

    a. For most Christians, your fellow workers (or your neighbours) are the greatest exposure you have to unsaved people. Your life may be the only true witness of the Lord Jesus that they may ever see.

        1) You are a _____ representing Jesus Christ in a dark world (Matt 5:14-16)
        2) Your life should reflect and demonstrate the Bible in living colour (2Cor 3:2)! An "epistle" is just another word for a letter. We are a living letter, written by God for all to read about HIM!

    b. A mother has the greatest opportunity to present Christ to their children! Don't let anybody demean or mock motherhood!
    c. You will have a much greater influence on those you spend the most time with. Although total strangers are an opportunity for a witness, those who can see a consistent testimony of a Christian's life are much easier to win.

2. Attitudes toward the company and management you work for:

    a. Serve in your job as if _____ was your employer (Eph 6:5-8; Col 3:22-24).
    b. Have a grateful attitude at work! Don't get caught up in the complaining that normally goes on! The same is true among women - don't get caught up complaining to other women about your family, and the work load! That brings a bitter spirit into both your life, into your home, and into the homes of the people you talk to!
    c. Respect the authority of your employer's position.

        1) Obviously no employer will be correct on every point, and you certainly can disagree with them, but you are to submit to their leadership, using it as an opportunity to show them a testimony of the Lord (Titus 2:9,10). *Purloining* means to rob from your employer, as in "pinch", "pilfer", or "pocket" the change.
        2) This only goes until they cross clear Biblical lines of right and wrong (Example of being asked to sell liquor, etc.).

    d. Respect your company's **property**. Care for it as if it was yours. It does not belong to you, so do not "partake" (Lev 19:11)!
    e. Respect your company's time.

        1) Do eight hours of work for eight hours of pay (2Cor 8:21; Col 3:22).

2) Be efficient! That means work hard, and at your best! The Biblical word is "diligence."

3) Also, you are getting paid to work, not witness. Use appropriate times to talk about the Lord (like on breaks, etc.).

  f. You are to do the very best that you can to help the company *succeed* and make your employer look good (Rom 12:11; 1Cor 10:24; Prov 10:4). Joseph is the greatest example of this principle in the Bible. See Genesis 39:1,2,21,22 all the way through to chapter 50 as they record his labours for others, including:

1) For his father, Jacob
2) For his master, Potiphar
3) For the prison keeper
4) For Pharaoh!

  g. Mind your own _____ - to a limit (1Thes 4:11)

  h. If you suffer wrongfully on the job, suffer it _____ (1Pet 2:20). This will usually be a testing of your resolve to live like Christ on the job – don't fail here!

  i. Finally, don't let someone else's laziness affect your work; (2Thes 3:10-13).

E. What About Those Under Your Leadership?

1. Are you treating your people justly and equally? Do you set standards for them which you refuse to keep yourself? (See Col 4:1; Eph 6:8,9)
2. Are you consumed by your own self-interests without considering the needs of those employees around you (Philp 2:3,4)?
3. Are you *defrauding* your employees (taking unfair advantage of them) so that they suffer, and you don't? See James 5:1-5.
4. Even in a position of leadership, you should always maintain the attitude of a _____ (Mark 10:42-45). Remember that Jesus, the Lord of Lords, came to minister, and was a servant!

III. Some Issues to Settle

A. "What if my job conflicts with spiritual things?"

1. There will always be some conflict of priorities between church activities and your work schedule. You cannot quit your job and take time off work because of a few minor conflicts. Remember, your job is a ministry opportunity. However, you must not use your job as an excuse to neglect your responsibilities to your church. Maintain a right balance in this area.
2. When your job responsibilities are contrary to Bible principles, then you must draw the line (Acts 5:27-29):

  a. Refuse to lie or steal for your employer, or violate other clear commandments of God.

  b. Guard against temptations on the job (flirting, loafing, complaining, losing your testimony, etc.).

  c. Don't be influenced by sinful activities around you.

  d. Refuse to do things that you know are contrary to the Bible

1) Selling _____, or strong drink (Hab 2:15)
2) Manufacturing and selling _____ (Acts 19:24)
3) Selling Pornography, or even things doubtful (Rom 14:23)

4) Working on Sunday just so you can get more money.

3. IDEA – if you just can't find a decent job, that allows you to be a Christian, then you ought to consider STARTING your OWN BUSINESS!

B. **"How do I find the right job that God wants me to have?"**

1. Have you taken the matter to God in prayer (James 1:5; Philp 4:6,7)?
2. Will the new job destroy what God is trying to develop in your life? You may have an area in your life that God may be focusing on through a co-worker or employer, and if you change jobs, you may be escaping God's refining process.
3. If you are having to move, or being asked to move to another city, is there a church there which can provide for your spiritual needs?
4. If you have a job, but are looking for a job, ask yourself, "Am I running away from something I should be facing and trying to correct?"

C. **"Can a woman work outside the home?"** (Titus 2:3-5) Yes and No.

1. The godly home takes an immense amount of work! According to Proverbs 31:10-31, a godly woman works more than most people realize!
2. The following conditions need to be met for a woman to work a job:

   a. If she is not married. Obviously she needs to work if she has no other responsibilities. And, she needs to excel!
   b. If married and not expecting children. However, this usually hinders the husband and wife from wanting children, which is wrong.
   c. If absolutely necessary. There are times when the wife does need to work a job, but she needs to allow her husband to be the breadwinner, and be willing to step back home when bills are under control.

D. **"How do I handle persecution on the job?"**

1. Most "persecution" in our culture is a result of the Christian's own ignorance or lack of personal commitment to the Lord. If you are being "persecuted," it is probably for one of two reasons: your behavior is improper, or your testimony is offensive to someone (1Pet 3:16,17). If it is the latter, don't worry, that is how the Light of the gospel is perceived by the world - as an offense.
2. Expect a certain amount of adversity from the world if you are truly serving Jesus Christ (2Tim 3:12).
3. Learn how to commit that adversity to the Lord, and leave it in His hands to resolve (1Pet 2:18-23).

E. **"Don't I always deserve a promotion, or a better job?"**

1. Are you trying to be a leader over too many things? Consider the following, whenever a promotion or transfer opportunity presents itself:

   a. A great Bible principle is, "*He that is faithful in that which is _____ is faithful also in _____ ...*" (Luke 16:10). Be sure that you can handle what you have now well. And then go further.
   b. The more responsibility that you have, the more potential there is for problems to arise (James 3:1; Eccl 8:9).
   c. The more responsibilities you have, the more time and energy is demanded. Be sure your new responsibilities will not hinder your service for God (not having adequate time for family, church, and your primary ministries; 2Tim 2:4). Keep a balance in your life.

2. Ambition is: "A strong desire to achieve (accomplish) something." Like *aspiration*. Ambition is the drive behind human effort. Without ambition, human effort has no goal, or purpose. Effort becomes only tasks, and requires task-masters to complete. The book of Proverbs gives God's best advice on ambition and life goals.

   a. Wrong Ambitions

      1) To only provide for self, and your own happiness (Gen 3:5,6)

      2) To **dominate** (3 John 1:9,10; Mark 9:33,34; Luke 20:46)

      3) To love _____, instead of labour (1Tim 6:10; Eccl 5:12)

   b. Right Ambitions (1Tim 6:5-7). People should have right ambition

      1) To provide for your _____, and the future (1Tim 5:8; 2Thes 3:10; Prov 13:22). There is nothing wrong with planning, and preparing financially for the future. There is no faith in relying on others when you could have prepared for bad times yourself!

      2) To do one's best (1 Kings 3:7-14), with God's help.

      3) To please _____ (2Tim 2:3-5)

      4) To store up _____ in heaven (Matt 6:19,20)

Date Lesson Completed _____ *Discipler* _____

CREATION AND EVOLUTION
A Study of Where We Came From - Our Origins
Lesson Nineteen
Memory Verse: *Romans 12:11*   **Lesson Verse:** *Genesis 1:1*

*"In the beginning God **created** the heaven and the earth."* **Genesis 1:1**

I. Introduction

A. At this point in your discipleship training you should realize foremost, that the basis for what you believe is found in God's word, **the Bible**. Before you got saved, your basis for truth and fact were basically vague. You may have had a belief concerning a subject, but with no real support. With God's word in hand though, truth and fact become quite clear! Especially in relation to science! Bible believers do not run and hide behind "*religious views*." We go to the Book of books and see what God says! Because when it comes to facts, the evidence overwhelmingly proves the creation account of the Bible, and not evolution's theory!

B. This lesson will provide the new Christian with the FACTS to both reinforce his or her faith in the Bible, and also to deal with any scientist who may believe in the theory of evolution.

II. Where Do We Begin?

A. **Some Presuppositions** (World Views). Either you believe...

1. In the beginning GOD... (an *Almighty Creator*)
2. In the beginning, DIRT... (an *Almighty Accident*)

B. **Some Misconceptions**

1. "Evolution is a proven fact." Wrong. Neither evolution, nor Creation is proven, because we cannot now see either theory in operation today. Both ideas are theories that must be accepted by faith. The person's conclusions for their faith must be based upon truth though - the evolutionist *has no proof*, only more theories. The Creationist has the words of the Bible which can be proven in a court to be true. It has been consistently proven there are no false statements in the Bible!

2. "The Bible, and Religion are just the same." Nothing could be further from the truth. The Bible is God's final word. Religion is man's attempt to replace the need for the Bible.

3. "The Bible is religious, and therefore not scientific." How that could be true is beyond reason! Yes the Bible is religious, but only because it speaks from outside human perceptions, and it speaks about more than just the future. It accurately describes all major scientific laws of physics without contradiction.

4. "Only ignorant people believe the Bible." Ignorance is when a person is unaware of something beyond their current understanding. All people therefore are ignorant. But there are those who desire to be willfully ignorant of anything besides what they currently believe to be true - these are usually "scientists."

C. Some Definitions

1. What Science is

a. Science is a body of knowledge that can be demonstrated and observed as fact. If something cannot be proven with observable evidence, then it is only **a theory**, and not *science*. Scientific facts are called **laws**. For anything to become scientific law, it must stand up to two processes: **observability** (it can be seen) and **repeatability** (it can be repeated). Anything that cannot be repeated, or observed now, is only a THEORY - it can never be fact.

b. A **Scientific Law** is a verifiable fact that has been observed and repeated, and **proven** to be true. Science is supposed to be based on Laws, not theories. Up until 1880, science was ONLY interested in developing LAWS based on FACTS. But now science has to be popular, and has been swayed towards focusing on generating theories, while ignoring established facts.

2. What Evolution is. Evolution is a *theory* of the origin of all things based upon **a process of continuous "innovative" change**. It states the universe is continually *improving* itself. It may take *billions of years*, but it is supposedly gradually improving! This usually means without allowing for an outside Creator's help. It represents the acceptance of *anything* that can explain the existence of this universe, as long as it does not allow for the existence of God.

3. What Creationism is: Creationism begins with the theory that an intelligent Designer ("God") created a perfect creation, and that that creation is currently falling apart (not improving). Creationism states that creation was a one time event, and is not now occurring. Biblical creationism takes the Bible literally when it says God created everything in six 24 hour days.

> Neither EVOLUTION, or CREATION is an established FACT - neither can be observed, nor repeated - they are BOTH theories. The question is, which theory makes more sense?

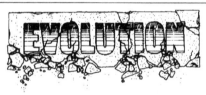

III. Where Did The Universe Come From?

Let's face it; the universe is here. The basic problem is *how did it get here?* In order to be scientific, we will have to go by what we can observe and by what we can demonstrate. Let's look at the only four possible explanations of how this earth got here.

A. **The universe has always been here.** This theory states that matter is *eternal*, and therefore has just always been here.

B. **The universe has not always been here.** There was a time, when "naturally," *nothing* produced *something*! This explanation describes matter coming into existence from nothing (by chance), and then *life* coming into existence from *dead* matter (all by *accident*).

C. **The universe is not really here, but just an illusion.** You just *think* that it is here! This theory pleases Buddhists (who believe life is only an illusion that needs to be "resolved") and produces more drug addicts.

D. **The universe started suddenly, when a Creator made it.** This is what Jesus Christ believed (Mark 13:19), King David (Ps 8:3; 19:1), the apostle John (John 1:1-3), and Paul (Col 1:15-17), to name a few!

E. There can only be **four** possible explanations for the existence of this universe. Can you come up with any other explanation that is not covered by one of the above four? The first two explanations are the basis for ALL evolution theories. Of the four, which is most scientific (observable) and logical? To settle this, let's look at the proven laws of science, and allow them to determine the answer.

Against the
LAWS
of Physics!

IV. Evolution - A Science Contrary To Evidence (1Tim 6:20)

A. **Some Scientific Laws *Against* ANY Form of Evolution.**

1. *The Laws of Thermodynamics (Heat Energy).*

   a. *The first law* says energy and matter can be transformed (changed) and altered, but cannot now be <u>created</u> or <u>destroyed</u>. This Law does away with **Theory B**. A universe that accidentally "big banged" *out of nothing* is <u>unscientific</u> since matter can't naturally be created (see Nehemiah 9:6). Evolution requires you to believe everything "accidentally" came from nothing!

   b. *The second law* states that energy in a closed system[1] will run out. This is called **ENTROPY**. All forms of energy run down like a watch. For example: things do not grow toward order and cleanliness by accident (ask any housewife with kids). Nothing is in the process of "evolving" (getting better, and more advanced, and more powerful), but rather EVERYTHING which can be seen demonstrates *dissipation, disintegration, decay* and *degeneration.* Nothing is "improved" unless it is worked on by an outside force! This Law is stated in Isaiah 51:6, and does away with **Theory A** since if the universe had always been here, it would have "burned-out" long ago! Even though matter and energy cannot disappear, energy is always slowing down - *never increasing (and never being replaced)!* An example is the burning of a fire log. The log burns, and produces heat energy. That energy is then gone from the log, and cannot be produced from the same log anymore.

2. *The Law of Cause and Effect.* To every action, there is an opposite and equal reaction. For every effect that we see in the universe, there had to be an original *cause.* Evolution requires that all of ORDER came from CHAOS being "helped along" - again "accidentally."

3. *The Law of Biogenetics* demonstrates that life ONLY comes from life! Every living organism comes only from living organisms (John 1:1-4)! Never has life "spontaneously" come from a dead thing.

4. *Mendel's Laws.* Gregor Mendel (1822-1914) proved *scientifically*:

   a. Only *genetic* characteristics are inherited (things that are already coded in the DNA molecules of a gene) - only things that the parent already had "in" themselves, are passed on to the next generation. Nothing *new* can be passed on except for mutations which are 99.9% disastrous to the next generation.

   b. Variations are built-into the DNA code of an organism - this allows for variations in a specific kind of animal - i.e., a dog's genes have many variations already built-in (Doberman, Terrier, Greyhound), just as a cat's genes have many variations, etc.

---

[1] By "closed system," it is meant that if no energy is available to improve the state of a object from an outside force, then it is a closed system. All evolutionists believe in a "closed system" of science, or else they would have to accept the fact that God exists and has affected this universe!

c. Variations outside of the limits of the genetic code **do not occur**. The variations do not include the ability for offspring to turn into anything BUT what the parent was - i.e., a cat ALWAYS produces a cat! Never a *cat-dog*, or a butterfly, or a frog, etc.

d. No "new" characteristics appear in ANY species (it would be like trying to play keys on a piano that aren't there) except by *mutation* - which ALWAYS means a degradation of the offspring's quality of life - which is opposite of the evolutionary theory.

e. All mutations are proven to be destructive to the off-spring, because they are "degenerative" and not evolutionary - the next generation ALWAYS becomes sterile.

B. **Some Scientific Laws *Proving* Evolution... NONE!**

1. Evolution requires that there would exist some natural force that is "guiding" everything toward higher and higher levels of complexity.
2. This "Law" would be called, a law of "increasing organization."
3. This "law" does NOT exist anywhere!!!

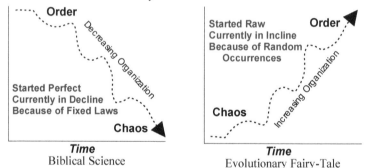

Time
Biblical Science

Time
Evolutionary Fairy-Tale

C. **Order Out of Chaos?** Could you believe that a delicate and beautiful Swiss watch could come from an explosion in a steel mill, or that a dictionary could come from an explosion in a print shop? Then how could a rational person believe that all the beauties and perfection of nature result from an explosion of hot gasses back at the "*big bang?*" Only if you are told again and again that it MUST have happened!

D. **Find the Fossil Evidence.** The theory of evolution contends that life appeared "spontaneously" on the earth, and that over millions of years, life forms changed and became more complex. Man is assumed to be the product of this process. Fossils, the remains of dead plants and animals, have supposedly left a record of the organisms that once populated the earth.

E. Modern research has shown that in recorded history, species are constantly moving toward *extinction*. Every day, more than 50 species become extinct. If evolution were true, one would expect to see the process providing examples of emerging species in their "transitional forms." The question arises, "where are the emerging species and their transitional forms?"[2] The fossil record shows no transitional forms - only fully developed creatures, in all strata!

INFINITE COMPLEXITY

There are NO "Simple" Building Blocks and there are NO "Simple" Solutions!

F. **Life is NOT Simple!** No matter where you look, there is infinite complexity to this universe. Evolutionists hope that the universe is very simple, and "just grows upon simple building blocks." Those *simple building blocks* just do not exist!

G. **Conclusion**

We then are left with **Theories C** and **D**. Either you believe Genesis 1:1, or lose your mind! Modern scientists simply ignore these facts, and pretend they don't exist. They reject **Theory D** pretending that since it is *religious* and not "scientific" that it is not true!

V. Noah's Flood - The Key to Geology

2Peter 3:3-8 tells us that people who scoff at the Bible are "willingly ignorant" of the Creation and the Flood. In order to understand science and the Bible, we must not be ignorant of those two great events in Earth's history.

A. Over 250 Flood legends from all parts of the world have been found. Most have striking similarities to the Genesis story of a man building a boat to save his family, and the animals.

B. Noah's ark was only built to float, and safely carry its cargo - not to sail.

C. The ark has been proven to be large enough to hold all the required pairs of animals, people, and food with room to spare (625ft long, 104 wide, 62 high). It wasn't until 1850 that someone built another ship that big!

D. God told Noah to bring two of each *kind*, not of each species or variety. Noah only had two of the dog kind which might have only included the wolves, coyotes, foxes, etc. The *kind* grouping is probably closer to our modern family division in taxonomy. This would greatly reduce the number of animals on the ark. Animals have obviously diversified into many varieties in the last 4,500 years since the Flood.

E. Noah did not have to go and get the animals. God brought them to him (Gen. 6:20, "*shall come unto thee*").

F. The mountains, as we have them today, did not exist until during the Flood when "the mountains arose and the valleys sank down" during the total upheaval of the earth's crust at the time (Ps. 104:5-9, Gen. 8:3-8).

G. The water in the oceans right now would cover the earth **8,000 feet deep** if the surface of the earth were smooth.

H. The continents were not fully separated until 100-300 years after the Flood. The people and animals that came off the Ark had ample time to migrate anywhere on earth by then.

[2]Concerning transitional life forms. These "transitional forms" of creatures in their evolutionary struggle upward would have had a rough time surviving. What about animals with "half wings," that were not quite ready to fly? They would have a tough time digging for grubs or running from anpredator in that state!

I. The top of Mt. Everest (from 26,000-29,000 feet) is made up of sedimentary rock containing fossils of **seashells** and other ocean-dwelling animals.

J. Sedimentary rock is found <u>all over the world</u>. Sedimentary rock is laid down only by running water.

K. Petrified clams in the closed position (found all over the world, including Mt. Everest) testify to their rapid mud-burial while they were still alive. Some petrified clams are as large as 6 feet wide!

L. Bent rock layers, fossil graveyards, and poly-strata fossils are best explained by a cataclysmic Flood.

M. People choose to not believe the Flood because it was <u>the judgment of God</u> on sin (2Pet. 3:3-8), which will also occur in the future, but then by fire.

VI. Evolutionary Hoaxes, Scams, and Abuses

A. Dating Methods - Billions? Millions? Or Just Thousands of Years Old?

1. ***Date the fossils by the "strata" they are found in.*** Most scientists believe that layers of the earth's crust (called *strata*) represent different time periods, and were laid down over millions and even billions of years. In the 1800's, each layer was labeled by its depth and rock type. Then, the fossils found within each layer were classified by that layer (i.e., Cambrian, Jurassic, Carboniferous, etc).

2. ***Date the strata by what fossils are found in it.*** As time went on, strata were not found to be uniform in layering, and so the fossil type that was found in each strata was used to label the strata. The problem is this: based upon a preliminary assumption in the 1800's that all the strata in the world were laid down uniformly, all fossils and strata are classified based upon each other's preliminary labeling - i.e., the strata is identified by the fossils it contains, and the fossils are classified by the strata they are found in - circular reasoning! Not science!

3. **The "Flood" ruined everything!** A creationist approaches the problem from the vantage of the world-wide flood of Genesis 7 & 8, which sorted the fossils and strata in a *cataclysmic*, not *uniform* fashion. In other words, the flood messed EVERYTHING up!

B. So-Called "Missing Links" of Human Ancestry

1. **Java Man** (*Pithecanthropus*). In 1890, a skull cap, femur, and two molar teeth were grouped together as belonging to the same person. The skull is that of an ape, but the teeth and the femur bone of an human. What was not published was that they were found 45 feet apart from each other, along with many other bones of apes, humans,  and other animals. It was a grocery store of "parts" to construct any animal you wanted! Java man has since been reclassified as human.

2. **Neanderthal Man** (*Homo sapiens neanderthalensis*) - 1856, in Neanderthal, Germany, a skull cap and limb bones were found. It was grouped with a set of skeletons found all over Europe that had the following characteristics: prominent eyebrow ridges, low forehead, long narrow brain case, protruding upper jaw, a strong lower jaw lacking a chin. The overall skeletons were short, and stooped-over. Anthropologists believed it to be a "missing link" between man and ape because it seemed to have shuffled along when walking. However, 150 years later, it is now admitted that these skeletons were of people that suffered

from rickets, and syphilis. Neanderthal Man was just a variation of the modern human kind with disease!

3. **The Piltdown Man** (*Eoanthropus*). In England, in 1912, a human skull cap and an orangutan's jaw were grouped together, along with a tooth as a hoax to prove another so-called "missing link." It was believed by the scientific world for over 40 years until tested for age, only to find that the tooth had been filed down to look human, and the jaw bone stained to look as old as the skull cap.

4. **The Peking Man** - all the "evidence" of this ape-man was lost in World War II, and is not available for examination.

5. **The Nebraska Man** (*Hesperopithecus*) - an entire skeleton of an ape-man was constructed based upon a single <u>tooth</u> of a supposed "missing link." The tooth was discovered to be of a **rare** pig found in Paraguay.

6. **Lucy** (*Ramapithecus*) - once widely accepted as the direct ancestor of humans, it has now been realised that this skeleton is merely an extinct type of orangutan - not an early human.

And they call all this "SCIENCE?"

VII. Biblical Explanations

A. **Creation.** Creation came about exactly as the Bible says it did in Genesis 1:1, where God simply created everything out of nothing. God was the ***First Cause*** - we are the ***Effect***! From that initial creation material, God personally moulded and fashioned the worlds and each creature therein (Gen 2:7,19; Heb 11:3). The initial creation was instantaneous, but the resulting "finish work" took six literal days to finish. Why six days? Not because God had a speed limitation, but rather to show a pattern for man's work-week (Ex 20:9-11). After the sixth day, God stopped working (Gen 2:2), and the universe has been carrying on the work of maintaining itself since then (Gen 1:21,22,27,28). There is nothing new now being created (Eccl 1:9), which is exactly what Albert Einstein discovered (about 3,500 years too late)!

B. ***Macro*** **verses** ***Micro*** **Evolution**

1. The evolutionist believes in something called MACRO (or BIG) evolution that allows for things to change "vertically" from one species to a higher level. This is also called "transformation." This change process is assumed, has never been observed, and is totally unscriptural.

2. The creationist believes in something called MICRO (or small) evolution that allows for organisms to change "horizontally" from black to red, and to white, but still be the same species. This is called "variation," and it is observed, is scientific, and is scriptural.

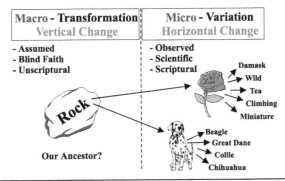

Macro - **Transformation**	Micro - **Variation**
Vertical Change	Horizontal Change
- **Assumed**	- **Observed**
- **Blind Faith**	- **Scientific**
- **Unscriptural**	- **Scriptural**

Damask
Wild
Tea
Climbing
Miniature

Our Ancestor?

Beagle
Great Dane
Collie
Chihuahua

C. The Dinosaurs.

1. *Their existence*. According to the Bible, Dinosaurs did exist on this earth.

   a. The first type of dinosaur is referred to as _____ (Job 40:15-24) and was a land-based animal that would match a *Diplodocus*.

   b. The other dinosaur is referred to as _____ (Job 41:1-34). It was a water-based animal. It is probably the basis for all the legends about **dragons**.

   c. All the bones that "scientists" have unearthed and attached together to represent animals, were alive mainly before Noah's flood (only 4,500 years ago). Remember, all of them became extinct at the same time pointing to a *cataclysmic* event.

2. *Their demise*. The cataclysmic event was the _____ of Genesis chapters 7 - 9 where water _____ the earth (Gen 7:19) killing every breathing thing that was not on the ark. At the end of the flood, all the water was drawn into now deeper oceans and the polar regions!

3. Most of the dinosaurs that got off the ark were extinct within the next 1,000 years due to the changes that occurred in the earth's atmosphere following the flood (a thinner atmosphere, with no water-canopy above the atmosphere that was present before the flood).

4. Another reason for their disappearance is that the dinosaurs were hunted by mankind - would *you want* one around your home?

D. Calculating The Age of the Universe

1. **Moon Dust**. Exploration of the moon has provided us with more evidence of the trustworthiness of the Bible, and the flaws in evolutionary thinking. Scientists know that many millions of tons of cosmic dust fall each year on both the earth and the moon. We don't notice it here because of erosion. But there is almost no erosion on the moon. So, the dust piles up continually on the moon's surface. If, as evolutionists believe, the universe is billions of years old, the accumulation of dust there should be great, amounting to many feet in depth. Prior to the first moon landing, most scientists predicted that the loose lunar dust could be between 50 and 100 feet in depth, presenting serious difficulties for the moon craft. When man finally reached the moon, it was discovered that the dust was between 1/4 inch and 3 inches deep. Since there is no method by which the dust could be carried away, the shallowness of it means it has not been accumulating for long. That, in turn, means the age of the moon and earth must be measured in *thousands* of years, not millions or billions supposedly required for evolution to have taken place.

2. **Half-lives**. This is the study of the present rate of decay of an element. You track how fast something is decaying, and calculate back how long it has been since it was 100 percent. Uranium is constantly breaking down into helium, yet the atmosphere has such a small amount of helium that the earth couldn't be older than a couple of hundred million years old - not 4.5 billion!

3. The **earth's magnetic field** is decaying at a rate that only 30,000 years ago, it would have been so strong it would have pulled in the moon!

4. The **continents** erode too quickly for them to be billions of years old.

5. The **oceans** should be super saturated with salt if billions of years old.

6. **Comets** only last 10,000 years – they could not be billions of years old!

7. **Human Artifacts throughout the Geologic Column.** Man-made artifacts - such as a hammer in Cretaceous rock, a human sandal print with a trilobite in Cambrian rock, human footprints and a handprint in Cretaceous rock – point to the fact that all the supposed geologic periods actually occurred at the same time in the recent past.

8. The **pressure of oil and natural gas** is so high that it could not have been underground for millions of years - only for several thousand years, or else the pressure would have "leaked out" long before now!

9. **Population Statistics.** World population growth rate in recent times is about 2% per year. Normal growth rate throughout human history would be about half that number with wars, disease, famine, etc. wiping out approximately one third of the population on average every 82 years. So, starting with just eight people, and applying these growth rates since the Flood of Noah's day (about 4,500 years ago) would give a total human population at just under six billion people. Yet, an evolutionary view will run into major difficulties, because, if you started with one "couple" just 41,000 years ago, it would give us a total population of 2×10^{89} people! The universe does not have space to hold so many bodies.

10. **Design in Living Systems.** A living cell is so awesomely complex that its interdependent components stagger the imagination and defy evolutionary explanations. A minimal cell contains over 60,000 proteins of 100 different configurations. The chance of this assemblage occurring by chance is 1 in $10^{4,478,296}$ (this number is an absolute impossibility).

11. **Design in the Human Brain.** The human brain is the most complicated structure in the known universe. It contains over 100 billion cells, each with over 50,000 neuron connections to other brain cells. This structure receives over 100 million separate signals from the total human body every second. If we learned something new every second of our lives, it would take three million years to exhaust the capacity of the human brain. In addition to conscious thought, people can actually reason, anticipate consequences, and devise plans - all without knowing they are doing so.

E. **Inherent Age**

1. When God created man, Did He create him as an adult or baby? When He created the chicken, He did not create an egg, for it would have required a Hen to protect and hatch it. When God created the earth, He created a fully mature world that *looked* "billions of years old," and yet was only a few seconds old! This universe may look old, but it is only because God created everything *mature* and ready to reproduce themselves, from the simple atomic and genetic levels all the way up to the most complex of galaxies (Gen 1:11,12,21,22)!

2. This explains why the universe is so immense, since your starting point is no longer a "*big-bang*" but rather **God**. If the big-bang started everything, then you would have to have hundreds of billions of years to have spread everything out as far as it now is. With creation, God just simply set everything in its place, demonstrating the immensity of the power of God (Ps 8:1-9)!

F. **The Biblical Record**. The Bible gives all those names and ages of people from Genesis chapter 5 on for a reason. If you take the time, you can count back from King Solomon (lived around 1,000 years before Christ's birth, **B.C.**), and see that creation took place around 4,000 years BC! We are living around 2,000 years AD (after His birth), making for a total age of **just 6,000 years**, not 4.5 billion years!

VIII. Some Final Conclusions

A. The Fight Against God

1. When you teach Creation, you are attacking the very foundation of the unbeliever. His basis for why he lives the way he does is rooted in their rejection of God. Creation points all men back to accountability to this all powerful Being called God, and convinces them of their sinfulness!

2. Romans 1:18-23 states that God's existence is proved by this earth being here, and a person has to corrupt his thinking and ignore a Creator in order to go his own way. Verse 25 says they "_____" the truth of God into a lie. For example: notice that Jesus' birthday is changed into a celebration of Santa Claus (a lie), and the resurrection is changed into Easter bunnies (a lie), and so on!

B. The Fruits of Evolution

1. No human theory launched upon mankind has made such an impact as Darwin's theory of evolution. It simply *eliminated* all absolute moral values, and man's accountability to God. Evolution accepts man only as an animal, responsible only to himself. It provides the framework for a spiritual *quagmire* - suicide, animalistic murders, perverted sexual behaviour, drugs, divorce, abortion, lying, stealing, rape, child abuse, homosexuality, and a host of other ills that violently affects our world.

2. What difference does it make? Well, if God does not exist; if He did not create us, then man is truly no more than an animal. There will be no day of judgment. There is no life after death. There are no absolute moral values - no rights and wrongs. If Darwin's "*survival of the fittest*" is true, then we have no moral restraint to prevent the adoption of Adolph Hitler's philosophy of eliminating "sub-human" races and undesirable people. According to evolution, "undesirable" racial or ethnic groups, old people, crippled people, mentally retarded people, unwanted babies in mothers' wombs, the poorly educated, the weak and sick, and any other undesirable being should be eliminated because they can only be viewed as a burden to society. They use resources that could give the more "highly evolved" among us more pleasure.

3. There is however a sure solution for these problems - a return to the solid foundation of the Bible (and its morality), and faith in the Lord Jesus Christ. Apart from this solution, there is no hope for this world. *Certainly evolution offers none.*

C. The Fruit of Scientific Creationism

1. ***All people are of immense value to God.*** "*For God so loved the world, that he gave his only begotten Son, that whosoever believeth in him should not perish, but have everlasting life.*" John 3:16

2. ***Every human being is separated from God*** by an immense universe filled with deterioration caused by sin. God is NOT this universe, but is outside it, and if He created it, then He is GREATER than it!

3. ***This Creator has intervened in history*** several times (at the creation, with the flood, in the birth of Jesus Christ, etc). Especially when our Creator took on Himself a human body 2,000 years ago in Bethlehem to save lost sinners by paying for their sins with His blood!

4. **The Bible is scientifically accurate** and demonstrates a trustworthy authority in all of life (Psalm 119:160). You can therefore TRUST it in ALL matters of which it speaks!

D. The Real "Big-Bang" (2Peter 3:6-14) - *Yet to Come!*

1. Forget about the evolutionary "Big Bang" - it is a hoax!
2. What every person must prepare for is the FUTURE coming Big Bang, where EVERYTHING will burn with melting heat, so that even the "_____ *shall melt with fervent heat*" (2Peter 3:10).
3. Not only is everything going to melt, it will "*pass away with a great* _____" - a BIG BANG! God said this 2,000 years ago (2Pet 3:15)!
4. If EVERYTHING in the universe is going to be done away with (Matt 24:35), then what kind of persons ought we to be (2Pet 3:10-14)?

   a. Having a holy _____ - what we say, and how we say it (2Pet 3:11).
   b. A godly life (2Pet 3:11).
   c. Looking forward to the coming of God to rule (2Pet 3:12).
   d. Diligently living in peace (rest, not anxious), without _____ and _____ - the world ought to see a big difference in your life!

Date Lesson Completed _____ *Discipler* _____

THE FUTURE
A Study of Heaven, Hell, and Eternity
Lesson Twenty

Memory Verse: *Romans 12:11*   **Lesson Verse:** *Isaiah 46:9,10*

> "...I am God, and there is none else; I am God, and there is none like me, **declaring the end from the beginning, and from ancient times the things that are not yet done,** saying, My counsel shall stand, and I will do all my pleasure:"
> Isaiah 46:9,10

I. Introduction

As you read and study the word of God, you undoubtedly will come across many Scriptures that refer to *future* events. These passages are called *prophetic*, and are very precious to the Christian because they clearly demonstrate that our God has everything under control, and all things will work out just as He has planned! Nothing will surprise the Lord! He knows the end from the beginning (Rev 22:13). On top of that, He has revealed all of important history and future events in one unique, supernatural Book, the Bible (1Cor 2:9,10; 2Pet 1:20,21)! In this lesson we will briefly study the incredible subjects of **heaven, hell,** and **the future!**

II. A Look At Heaven

A. **There are actually *three* Heavens.** The word 'heaven' means, the open space above you. The word 'firmamant' means the sky.

Third Heaven - God's Dwelling!

The Second Heaven - Space

The First Heaven - Air

The Earth

1. **The First Heaven** - Genesis 1:6-9,20 "*And God called the firmament Heaven...*" This 'heaven' refers to the earth's atmosphere, and is just above us and around us. It consists of air, and the clouds. The birds fly around in this heaven. It does not extend very far up above the earth's surface.

2. **The Second Heaven** - Genesis 1:14-17. The second heaven is filled with the planets, stars, comets, galzies, supernovas and nebulas that are beyond our atmosphere, and yet do not reach to God. The second heaven is the Universe itself. What we call "outer space."

3. **The Third Heaven** - *This is where God dwells* (Matt 6:9; Ps 113:4,5). It is not anywhere near this planet (Acts 7:48-50). It is outside of this universe, and separate. It is where born again believers go when they die or are taken to at the time of the rapture (1 Thes 4:15-17; John 14:1-3).

B. **What is Heaven Like?**

1. Heaven is a *real* place (Rev 4:1-3; Col 3:1,2). It is not a "state of mind," or state of "non-existence" (ie, Buddhist "nirvana")

2. It is *a holy place* (Ps 20:6). "*Now I know that the LORD saveth his anointed; He will hear him from his _____ heaven...*" There is no sin nor sinner there.

3. Heaven is *a joyful place* (Luke 15:7,10). There is joy among the _____ over sinners that repent here on earth.

4. Heaven is *a place of no trouble*. It has no death, sorrow or pain, "*And there shall be no more death, neither sorrow, nor crying, neither shall there be any more _____, for the former things are passed away*" (Rev 21:4).

5. Its size is *immeasurable* (Jer 31:37). It is bigger than this universe, because it is actually outside of this universe – and this universe is immeasurable!

6. Our home in Heaven is in *an entire city* (Heb 11:16) called the _____ Jerusalem (Rev 21:2,15-27). A furlong is $^1/_8$ mile. So, it is 1,500 by 1,500 by 1,500 miles! Truly, there is a lot of room in God's heaven!

III. What About Hell?

A. **Definition:** The Bible says *hell* is a place where the devil, his angels, and unbelieving people will spend eternity without God. They will suffer eternal punishment and separation from God.

1. There are 162 references to hell in the New Testament alone, which speaks of the doom that awaits the unbeliever, and over 70 of these references were made by Jesus himself! References include: Mt 13:41,42; 5:29,30; 10:28; 11:23,24; 16:18; Jam 3:6; Rev 20:13,14.

2. Old Testament references include: Deut 32:22; Ps 9:17; Ps 55:15; 86:13; Prov 9:13-18; 15:24; Isa 5:13,14; 14:12-15.

B. **Why did God create Hell?**

1. God created hell because He is holy and cannot allow *sin* in His Heaven.

2. Those who do not accept Christ's gift and trust completely in Him are destined to go to hell because they are still in their sins (John 3:18,36; 1Cor 15:16,17).

3. Therefore, hell was created for Satan, his angels, and all unbelieving persons (Mt 25:41; Rev 20:10).

C. **Where is Hell?** This *lake of fire* is a fire that exists in another dimension, and is located below us, **IN** the earth (Isa 14:12,15; Mt 12:40). Ephesians 4:9 states that Jesus _____ into the centre of the earth before He arose.

D. **Characteristics of Hell** (Read Luke 16:19-31)

1. It is REAL. It has a location (centre of the earth), and an eternal effect on all who dwell in it.

2. It is not volcanic lava, but is much like it. Lava shows us that there is something burning just a few miles under our feet.

3. It is _____ (Rev 14:11) - it is for ever, like heaven

4. It is a place of _____ (Luke 16:24) - not annihilation (Mt 23:33).

5. It is a place of darkness, pain, suffering, and isolation (Jude 7).

6. It is bottomless (Rev 9:2)! It has no bottom, only sides (because it is at the centre of a sphere)!

7. Those who died in Sodom and Gomorra are STILL suffering God's "_____ *of eternal fire*" in hell (Jude 1:7).

8. Everyone in hell is a would-be soul-winner (Lk 16:27,28)!

9. Hell is an unnecessary place for people if only they will put their complete faith and trust in Christ's all sufficient death on the cross - it was only made for the devil and his angels, not for any human!

10. Therefore, hell is NOT the grave, but a horrible place that no man should go to, and from which Jesus died to save people from!

E. **Jesus died to save sinners from Hell!** Jesus did not come only to bring sinners to a wonderful place called Heaven, but more importantly, to save them from the real place called Hell (John 3:16)! A person needs to get saved TODAY because *tomorrow* may be too late (2Cor 6:1,2)!

F. How Long Will The Lost Be In Hell?

1. The Bible says that all in hell will be there "*for* _____" (Rev 20:10).
2. Will God give persons in hell an opportunity to escape; a second chance? _____
3. When is the opportunity for people to be saved from hell (2Cor 6:1,2)? _____.
4. Let us be busy reaching the lost by preaching the gospel of salvation *now*, while people have the chance!
5. This is God's reason for Christianity's existence - *to warn people of hell!*

IV.A Brief Outline of Coming Future Events - *What's Ahead For the Universe? God* created this universe (Gen 1:1) and for sure *God* will end it (2Pet 3:10,11)! The study of the future comes mainly from Revelation, Daniel and Isaiah. Here is a brief outline…

A. The Soon *Rapture* (catching away) of true Christians to heaven
B. The Seven Years of Tribulation (Tribulation means, terrible trouble)
C. The Second Coming of Jesus Christ - at the battle of *Armageddon*
D. The Millennial Kingdom of Christ on Earth (His 1,000 year rule here)
E. The Final End of this World - at the battle of Gog and Magog
F. The Great White Throne Judgment of all the unsaved of history
G. The New Heaven and New Earth that will never pass away!

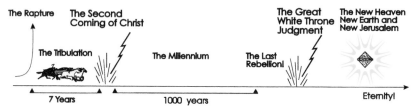

V. A Brief Study of Future Events

A. Some Background Facts

1. The Bible is full of prophecies related to the coming of the Messiah, Jesus Christ, to this world. Jesus has already come once – as a baby, born in a manger, and destined to die on a cross 2,000 years ago.
2. However, that FIRST coming did **not** fulfil one-fourth of the prophecies about the Messiah. The remaining prophecies relate to a *second* coming where He, as King of Kings will yet reign on earth.
3. The Jewish people are God's people – whether they believe or not. They, as descendants of Abraham, are special to God. That does not mean they are saved, but that they are special to God and are always part of His plans in this world.
4. Christians are neither Jews, nor Gentiles (Gal 3:11). No matter what we were before conversion, we are now totally new creatures in God's kingdom.
5. We do not replace Israel, but have a special relationship with Jesus as His BRIDE.
6. Ever since the time of Abraham, the Jewish people have been the main focus of God's work in this world.
7. When Jesus was born, He preached to and ministered to the Jews first (Matt 15:22-24; Rom 1:16). Since the Jews rejected Jesus as their Messiah, the Gospel has extended into all the world, and to all people.

8. But someday soon, Christians will disappear in an event called the Rapture, and God will focus once again on the Jewish people, and save them during the Tribulation.

B. **The Rapture of Christians**

1. When Jesus comes the second time, He comes in two parts.

   a. The first part is referred to as *the Rapture*, or the "*catching away*" of Christians to heaven!

   b. The second part (of the second coming) is His actual physical return to earth to rule and reign as King of kings and Lord of lords

   c. This may sound complicated, but that is because it is! But be patient! It is part of an awesome future that is just ahead of us!

2. Let's examine the following Scriptures that describe a catching away of God's people BEFORE God's judgment:

   a. 1Thes 4:13-18 refers to Christ's people someday soon being "*caught up*" into the air and taken to heaven with Jesus.

   b. Philp 3:20,21 describes is a "*changing*" of our bodies for heaven as we go up.

   c. John 14:1-3 Jesus says He will come back to "*receive*" His church to heaven like a Groom comes for His Bride at a wedding.

   d. 1Cor 15:51,52 describes it as all happening "*in the _____ of an eye*".

3. There are several example of "*Raptures*" in the Bible. Including:

   a. Gen 5:21-24; Heb 11:5 Who was "taken up"? _____

   b. 2 Kings 2:11 Who went UP? _____

   c. Gen 19:15,16,22 Who was pulled out of Sodom before judgment fell? _____

   d. Gen 7-9 Who was protected from the judgment of the flood? _____

   e. Each time, God "took" someone out of the way, so He could judge

4. Only a few signs will give any kind of signal that the Rapture is about to happen:

   a. Israel has to be in her land again – and they have been since May 14, 1948!

   b. Europe (Rome) will take control of the land of Israel "for their safety and peace", just like Rome was in control at Christ's first coming.

   c. The world will *start* experiencing all the troubles of the coming tribulation, in an ever increasing manner (Mark 13:3-10).

5. We are NOT in the Tribulation yet. It is only the preparation for it

   a. Jesus said in Mat 24:6 "*... see that ye be not troubled: for all these things must come to pass, but the end is not _____.*" And in Mat 24:8 "*All these are the _____ of sorrows.*"

   1) When Jesus uses the word SORROW, He is talking about the sorrow and pain of a woman who is about to give birth to a child!

   2) In the same way, the world is having the beginning pains before the coming Tribulation

   3) Obviously the world has always had wars

   4) And always battled diseases, and earthquakes and famines

   5) And that is why so many people constantly mock at Jesus' words

6) But Jesus is saying MUCH more than just a list of normal troubles and disasters…

7) Jesus is saying that these events and about 100 more will grow in number EXPONENTIALLY – like the pains leading up to a birth!

8) Jesus said these signs would appear like birth pains (Matthew 24:3-8).

9) Birth pains, or labour contractions, are sharp pains which INCREASE in intensity and frequency in the moments leading up to birth.

10) They become MORE frequent and have greater strength leading up to the big moment.

11) So it is with world events leading up the coming judgment of God!

b. What is so different about today?

c. We, right now, are experiencing an increase in:

1) **Wars and rumours of wars** – there have been more wars in the past century than in all of history combined

2) **Famines** – they will continue to increase, no matter how hard people try and protect crops

3) **Diseases/Pestilences** – more and more epidemics and pandemics (HIV, H1N1, SARS, Covid19, etc).

4) **Earthquakes** – ALL OVER THE WORLD, not just in normal hot spots

5) **Persecution of Christians** - the most persecuted people group today are Christians – and it is going to get worse

6) **The Rise of a United Europe** - a revived Roman Empire will come to power in the end times (Daniel 2:36-45, Daniel 7, Revelation 17).

7) **The Rise of a Global Government** (Rev 13:1-7) that will rule over *"ALL kindreds, tongues* [languages], *and nations"* on the face of the earth.

8) **The imposition of ONE Religion** on the entire world (Rev 13:8)

9) And **the control of everyone economically** (Rev 13:16-17) through a numbering system called the "Mark of the Beast" (Rev 13:16-18).

10) All of this is in place right NOW!

d. So, things will not get better and better like politicians keep promising – they will only "_____ worse and _____" (2Tim 3:13)

e. Christianity itself will start to fall apart, and become almost powerless in the world (2Thes 2:3; Luke 18:8)

f. Do YOU see any of the above happening? **Yes / No**?

6. Does anyone know when the Rapture will happen? (Matthew 25:13). **Yes / No**

7. So, What happens AT the moment of the Rapture?

a. Without any real warning, Jesus will break through the clouds from heaven and be visible only to Christians (1Thes 4:16; Titus 2:11-13)

b. Born again Christians will hear the sound of a trumpet, a **shout** from heaven saying *"come ____ hither"* (Rev 4:1) (only Christians will hear this).

c. All the bodies of Christians who have died since Jesus' resurrection, will break out of their graves (no matter how long they have been dead and decayed) , and they will come back to life, and fly straight to Jesus as a resurrection of the New Testament believers (1Thes 4:16).

d. All the Christians who are alive at that moment, no matter where they are, will ascend straight to Jesus, being changed in an instant on their way up, leaving everything behind them (1Thes 4:17).

e. And so shall we "_____ *be with the Lord*."

      f.   The whole world will just continue as it always has.

      g.   They probably won't even wonder what happened to us!

8. *Who* and *what* shall be left behind after Christians are taken home to heaven?

    a.   All your possessions (house, clothes, money, gold, silver, investments, car, your job). So, "*Lay up for yourselves* _____ *in* _____." (Mt 6:20)

    b.   Your and my *unsaved* family and friends will be left behind.

    c.   All the unsaved will be left behind under a ***one world*** government, lead by the anti-christ with a one-world religion, and a one-world currency forming a cash-less society as seen in Rev 13:11-18. (The anti-christ will be leading the world against God and Israel).

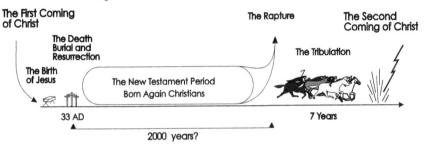

The First Coming of Christ   **The Rapture**   **The Second Coming of Christ**

The Death Burial and Resurrection   The Tribulation

The Birth of Jesus   The New Testament Period   Born Again Christians

33 AD   7 Years

2000 years?

C. The Tribulation

1. This is a **seven year** period of troublesome time that will begin right after the Rapture of Christians to heaven.

    a.   During this time, the antichrist (also called *the Beast*) will actually take over the entire world (Rev 13:1-9).

    b.   There will be at least 2 more world wars that will be fought during this time.

    c.   The Jewish people will be severely persecuted again and have to run for their lives to escape the anti-christ's wrath.

    d.   And there will be plagues and sufferings like never before (Mt 24:21)!

    e.   The time of the Tribulation is referred to as "_____ *trouble*" (Jer 30:7).

        1) The Tribulation is directed at the Jews, to get them to repent. Not at Christians.

        2) The Tribulation is directed at the world, to judge it with God's wrath.

        3) There are no Christians living now who will go through the Tribulation (1Thes 5:9)!

2. The Great Deception (2Thess 2:1-12)

    a.   At the time of the Rapture, God will send "*strong* _____" into the world to make people believe only lies.

    b.   No one left here on earth will believe the Bible, or Jesus at all.

    c.   They will ALL start to follow the antichrist, believing HE is the promised Messiah, and that Jesus was a fraud.

3. How Long will the Tribulation last? Seven years

    a.   Daniel's last week of Man's History, each day a year

    b.   Seven years of ever increasing Hell on Earth

    c.   Until the day of Christ's Second Coming! Called Armageddon!

4. There are Actually Two Tribulations (Mat 24:29, 21)

    a. The seven years are divided into two halves of 42 months each (3 ½ years)

    b. The first half is the build-up to the crowning of the antichrist in a rebuilt Jewish temple, in Jerusalem. It is simply called the Tribulation when an antichrist shall rise to political power

    c. Right until the Middle of the week of years comes the *Abomination of Desolation* (Mt 24:15-22) when the antichrist will set himself up *as "____"* on the throne of the Mercy Seat in the Holy of Holies in the rebuilt Temple in Jerusalem (2Thes 2:3,4).

    d. The second half is the wrath of God, mixed with the wrath of Satan, against the entire world. This is the beginning of the GREAT Tribulation!

5. Right in the middle of the seven years, *144,000 Jewish Gospel witnesses* will boldly testify of the Gospel during the last half of the Tribulation, and will turn many people to repentance (Rev 7:1-8; 14:1-5). Note that these are ***male, virgin Jews***, and not people from the Jehovah's Witnesses!

6. While all that is happening on the earth, here is what's occurring in heaven:

    a. Christians are receiving their **rewards** for serving Him (2Cor 5:10; 1Cor 3:10-15). This is called ***the Judgment Seat of Christ***.

    b. Then follows a grand feast called the ***Marriage Supper*** when Christians will be united with Jesus Christ in heaven (Rev 19:1-9).

D. **The Second Coming of Jesus Christ** (Rev 19:11-15) – Armageddon

1. As far as sinners are concerned, the most important subject in the Bible is that of Salvation, and Jesus Christ's *first* coming as Saviour to die on the cross. Yet, as far as God is concerned, the most important subject is Jesus Christ's *second* coming as Sovereign King to literally rule and reign on earth for 1000 years with Satan defeated, and paradise RESTORED.

2. This "*day*" is THE MOST discussed topic in the Bible. It is the day when good finally wins over evil; when everything that is wrong is made right; when God personally takes care of the Devil! This "day" is always referred to in the Bible as a BATTLE with great devastation and calamity. It is called, *the day of the Lord* (Joel 1:15; 2:1,2)!

    a. This battle takes no more that 24 hours to complete!

    b. The battle involves *burning up the* _____ (Mal 4:1-3)

    c. The battle will be fought in *Armageddon*, the Valley of Jehosephat (Rev 16:16; Joel 3:9-16; see also Micah 4:3).

    d. The battle is in reaction to Jerusalem being taken over by the antichrist (Zech 14:1-9).

    e. The "deceiver" of the world (the antichrist) will be captured and "cast **alive** into a _____ " (Rev 19:20), Satan himself will follow later.

> PRINCIPLE: THERE WILL BE NO PEACE ON EARTH UNTIL THE PRINCE OF PEACE COMES BACK, AND BY A FINAL DECISIVE BATTLE, BRINGS REAL PEACE!!!

3. Thank God none of us will have to endure such an event – all because of grace!

E. **The Millennial (1,000 year) Kingdom of Heaven on Earth** (Rev 20:1-4).

1. This is a time that Christ will rule and reign on the earth for _____ years.

2. During this time, there will be real peace on this earth.

3. The entire earth will be like, Paradise restored (Isaiah 11:4-9)!

4. Satan will be bound in Hell for the duration of Christ's kingdom (Rev 20:1,2).
5. And all the saints will rule and reign *with* Christ on the earth at this time (Luke 19:12-27; 1Cor 6:1-3).
6. What will YOU probably be doing during Christ's kingdom?
7. Your reward will be based upon your efforts NOW!

F. **The End of this World**

1. There is one final battle, bigger than Armageddon even. It is called the Battle of "_____ *and Magog*" (Rev 20:7-11).
2. During the Millennium, man has been allowed to return to paradise, and yet, he will still desire to go back to his "old sinful ways", just as the children of Israel wanted to "go back to Egypt!"
3. It is at the end of the 1,000 year reign of Christ that Satan will do his finalé by leading a <u>final rebellion</u>.
4. He will fail, and will finally, and completely be cut off from ever "infecting" this universe again, by being thrown into the "*lake of* _____", where he will be tormented for how long? _____

G. **The <u>Great White Throne Judgment</u>** (Rev 20:11-15).

1. It is at this judgment that all of humanity, from wicked Cain to those born in the Millennium who rejected God's salvation, will stand before God (Gen 4:8; 1John 3:12) to be judged according to their works.
2. At this judgment, all unsaved people will give an account of their "works" to see how well they match up with Christ's work on the cross. God will allow everyone to try to justify their sins. But of their name is not written in the Lamb's Book of "_____", they will face God's righteous judgment for ever!
3. They will realize that there is <u>no comparison</u>, and will then be cast into the Lake of Fire to join *their god, Satan*, while Christians will spend all eternity with *their* God! A person's eternal end is determined by *who* their God is (Eph 2:1-7).

H. **The New Heaven, New Earth, and the New Jerusalem** (Rev 21:1-3, 22:1-5)!

1. No longer will God be separated from man because of sin! The barriers between heaven and earth are done away, and God and man will forever be together in a new universe not infected with sin!
2. The new earth will be perfect and eternal – it will never pass away.
3. And the New Jerusalem will be the Christian's home for ever, full of mansions with room for everyone (John 14:2,3)!

VI. What Should We Do While We Are Waiting For Jesus to Come Back?

A. Realize that Jesus could return right now! So we should live for him 100%.
B. We should live holy and godly
C. We should be expecting Him to come for us any minute
D. We should be listening for His shout, and the sound of a loud trumpet from the sky
E. Ask God to use you to save your relatives, and to make you a soul winner!
F. Paul said in 2Tim 4:8 "*Henceforth there is laid up for me a _____ of righteousness which the Lord, the righteous judge shall give me at that day and not to me only, but unto all them also that love his _____.*"
G. Jesus says in Rev 22:20, "*...Surely I come _____. Amen. Even so, _____ Lord _____.*" Make that your prayer as well!

| Date Lesson Completed _____ Discipler _____ |

DISCIPLESHIP
A Study of The Ministry of Discipleship - Feeding Hungry Hearts
Lesson Twenty One
Memory Verse: *Romans 12:11*   **Lesson Verse:** *2Timothy 2:2*

> *"And the things that thou hast heard of me among many witnesses, the same commit thou to faithful men, who shall be able to teach others also."* **2Timothy 2:2**

I. Introduction

A. There is no shortage of Biblical materials in our Western world: Bibles, books, tapes, Gospel tracts, study helps, and the like are found in plentiful supply. If there is a missing ingredient, it is the process of *Biblical discipleship*, i.e., a loving, caring, selfless Christian, who is committed to teach another person *"all things whatsoever Jesus commanded"* (Matt 28:20).

B. The purpose of this lesson is to acquaint the Christian with the principles and importance of Biblical discipleship. Revival, evangelism, discipleship and missions are the life-blood of the church, and are all energized only by effectual, fervent prayer, in a spirit of charity.

C. Up to this point, you have been *discipled*. With the completion of this study lesson, you will see the importance for you to go and yourself become a *discipler*!

II. Discipleship's Purpose

A. As you now know, all Christians are not disciples! Discipleship, like salvation involves a conscious decision to follow the Saviour, no matter what the cost (Lk 14:26-33). You became a Christian when the word of God was extended to you through someone who cared to tell you about the gospel. Becoming a disciple of Jesus was the next step for you after you got saved. But now the Lord extends His word through you to reach others, and to disciple them.

B. There are five primary goals that serve to fulfill the Biblical command of what we call the "Great Commission" of Matthew 28:19,20. They are the very purpose of us being on earth, and are as follows:

1. Evangelize the **lost** (Acts 1:8; 26:18; Mark 16:15) - bring them to repentance, and total dependence upon Christ.

2. Establish growing **churches** by gathering together regularly to worship God, and minister to one another (Acts 11:19-26). This means more than Christians just getting together for fellowship, but as a unified body of believers, set on growing, and living the Christian life!

3. Build-up (strengthen) the disciples of Christ (Mt 28:18-20; Eph 4:11-16; 2Tim 2:2). This is discipleship's role!

4. Bring churches and disciples to **Christ-likeness** (Rom 8:29; Gal 4:19) - become mature! This takes a lot of time, and personal experience.

5. Bring **glory** to God (Rom 11:36; 1Cor 10:31; Isa 43:7). All that we as Christians do is to bring glory to God!

III. Where Discipleship Fits in a Christian's Life

A. Although Christ certainly evangelized and established His church, He never built what we would call a "big" church during His ministry, for it was not His immediate intention to do so. His goal was to leave behind **twelve men** that could do what He had done, and reproduce it on a world-wide scale until He returned (Jn 14:12).

B. In the establishment of New Testament churches, Paul the apostle understood and taught this principle when he said, "*And the things that thou hast heard of me among many witnesses, the same _____ thou to faithful men, who shall be able to teach others also*" (2Tim 2:2). The command being, what you have learned and lived, now must be taught to someone else!

C. Jesus said in Matthew 28:20, "_____ them to observe all things..." This is not only to be from the pulpit, but rather by way of a personal, people-oriented process, *one-on-one*! It cannot only be done by the Pastor!

D. Let's compare what Discipleship IS, and what it is NOT:

Discipleship is NOT...	Discipleship IS...
an activity	an attitude
a programme	a philosophy – a way of thinking
a series of book-lessons	a way of life
education only	edification and exhortation
instructions only	your life, a living example
a handbook	a heart to heart ministry
a rapid formula	a long lasting relationship

E. Discipleship is intended to establish all new Christians in the following Four *Foundations* of the Christian life:

1. In the _____ of God (Matthew 4:4)
2. In fellowship with other _____ (Hebrews 10:25)
3. In the structure of the New Testament _____ (1Cor 12:27)
4. In the ministry for Christ (Romans 12:11)

You may remember, the above four areas were covered in the previous pages of this Discipleship Study Guide.

IV. What Discipleship Accomplishes

A. Discipleship establishes the new Christian in the foundational truths of Biblical Christianity (the principles you have learned over the previous lessons).

B. Discipleship provides the new Christian with a caring, comforting friend to help him through the difficulties of spiritual transformation from baby to mature. You have been helped along by your discipler, but are now becoming ready to fill the role of a caring and comforting discipler yourself.

C. Discipleship affords the new Christian additional spiritual protection through the counsel and prayer support of a mature Christian.

D. Discipleship provides mutual accountability between you and your new disciple, which will help keep you motivated, and will motivate your disciple to grow in Christ, and walk in faith.

E. Discipleship provides personal Christian fellowship, which you know to be so important for a new Christian to have.

F. Discipleship provides encouragement while the world goes out of its way to attack and discourage all young disciples of the Lord.

G. Discipleship also brings the new Christian to "perfection" or maturity in Christ, so that he or she also becomes a discipler of the Lord Jesus.

V. How Discipleship Works

A. Christ started with 12 students. Those twelve men took Christ's words to the world and turned it "_____ *down*" (Acts 17:6).

B. If every Christian, who has repented of their sins, and asked Christ to save them (Rom 10:13), would become a disciple in order to become a Discipler, then the world could be turned to Christ in just 65 years. Watch:

Year 1 You get saved and get into a Bible preaching church, and get under a Discipler, or Mentor. You start with just **2** (you and your Discipler) - that is all you need!

Year 3 You finish being discipled, and then win someone else to Christ, and get them into church, and begin to train them. Your previous discipler also goes and turns someone to Christ, and starts discipling them. Now there are **4** Christians.

Year 5 You encourage your disciple to reproduce himself, and you go and get another person saved, and in discipleship. There would then be **8** Christians. Not a lot to show for 5 years, but watch.

Year 7 There would now be **16**, strong, dedicated, Christians who would be the basis for a very strong and vibrant church, reaching out and affecting the world for Christ!

C. This goes on with everyone, every two years winning someone else to Christ, training them in the Bible, and then encouraging them to win someone and train them, and so on, until year 65, when **8,589,934,592** will have been reached!

D. The above number is based upon *every* Christian doing his or her part, and on every Christian living more than 65 years! Obviously, that won't happen, but truly, we can do what Christ said must be done, even with 6 billion people on this planet - but only if we would set out to do it with all our heart (Dt 5:29; Luke 1:37)!

VI. What Discipleship Involves

Luke 9:23 can be correctly called **the Disciple's Motto**, and expresses what Discipleship involves for both the discipler and the disciple.

A. "*If* _____ *man...*" - Your Desire - especially if you are a Christian!

B. "*will come after me...*" - Your Decision - It is up to you if you will or not

C. "*let him* _____ *himself...*" - Your Denial - *Make the necessary time*

D. "*take up his cross daily...*" - Your Dedication to the cross instead of a crown.

E. "*and* _____ *me...*" - Your Determination to keep your eyes on Jesus, no matter how hard the path becomes.

VII. So, How Can *You* Be a Discipler?

A. **Teach a Sunday School Class in church**. No matter what age group you teach, you will be making investments into lives that will last an eternity.

B. **Be a committed friend to a new Christian**. Listen to them and work with them through their struggles in prayer, and discussion, always encouraging them that they are not alone, and that with a full confidence in Christ, they cannot fail!

C. **Provide helpful materials**. Use select videos and maybe cassette tapes that have helpful information for new Christians. Get these from your church, or maybe purchase them yourself, so that you have them on hand.

D. **Use this or another Discipleship Course**. You have worked all the way through these lessons, so you at least are familiar with the material. You would need to go back through the material before each time you meet with a spiritually hungry Christian. If you are not confident in understanding certain things, then, pray and search out the answers, or call on the Pastor.

E. **Have your own Bible Study**. Ask the pastor to help you start up a simple Bible study in your home, or at work during breaks. There may be an opportunity for you to regularly get together with another young Christian in God's word, feeding them, and training them in living the Christian life. Hey, if you have the time, use it wisely *for the Lord!* Don't leave it only to the pastor, or his wife!

VIII. The Final Challenge is *to You*!

Just as you have been discipled...

Go, and do thou likewise!

Lead someone to Christ, and then disciple THEM!

Date Lesson Completed _____ *Discipler* _____
What was your START date? _____

Section FOUR Test
The Ministry For Christ

NAME: _____   DATE: _____
                                        SCORE: _____

The following questions will help you identify how much you have learned in your Bible Study time. Answer as many as possible, and take your time so that you can think and remember the answers. Most answers are obvious. Some questions however will be hard. All questions come from the material in the previous Section of the **First Principles** Study Course. God bless you as you examine what you have learned, and become confident in knowing and growing in God's wondrous word!

1. Write out *word-perfect* Romans 12:11 _____
   _____

2. There are three parts to Christ's Great Commission in Matthew 28:18,19. List them:
   1) _____ 2) _____ 3) _____

3. There are many reasons why Christians are commanded to take the Gospel to this world. List one: _____

4. When you are witnessing to a person, what is the Holy Spirit trying to do in their heart? _____

5. When you go soul-winning, list some things that you should have on hand:
   _____

6. What must the sinner realise about themselves before they can be saved? _____
   _____

7. What are the two things that a sinner must do in their heart to be saved?
   1)_____ 2) _____

8. Concerning employment, the Christian is really, always serving who?
   _____

9. Is it important how a Christians acts and reacts on the job? _____. Explain why:
   _____
   _____

10. Are there limits to what a Christian can be asked to do on a job (i.e., selling liquors, manufacturing idols, lying for the boss, etc.)? _____. Explain how you know where to draw the line? _____
   _____
   _____

11. Should you expect to draw persecution on the job when you hide your Christianity?
   _____

12. List the two kinds of wines in the Bible: 1) _____, 2) _____

13. According to Proverbs 20:1, what mocks the drinker? Drunkenness, or the wine itself? _____

14. God compares leaven (yeast) to what? _____

15. God says that a Christian is to use alcoholic wine for what general purpose (that is, if they have no other resource available)?
   _____

16. A Christian can drink as long as it is in moderation: **True**, or **False** (circle one)

17. Can an alcoholic get complete victory over alcoholism? **Yes**, or **No** (circle one)

18. According to Romans 6:14, *"sin shall not have* _____ *over you."*

19. Define *ambition*: _____

20. Can Christians have right ambitions? Yes / No

21. Define the word evolution: _____
_____
_____

22. What event do evolutionists believe started this universe? _____
_____

23. There are many scientific laws that totally disprove evolution. Give one of those laws: _____

24. How many days did it take to fashion this entire universe? _____

25. List something new that can be *created* right now? _____
_____

26. How old is this earth, if we go according to the biblical record? _____

27. Dinosaurs are described best in what book of the Bible? _____

28. List the three heavens: 1) _____ 2) _____
3) _____

29. A Christian's place in heaven is in a city called the _____ Jerusalem.

30. Explain why did God create hell? _____
_____

31. Give a brief description of hell: _____
_____

32. What Scripture can best be used to describe hell? _____

33. How long will the lost be in hell? _____

34. What is the next event that the Christian is to be looking forward to? _____
_____

35. How long will the Tribulation last? _____

36. Who are the 144,000 witnesses in the Tribulation? _____

37. Explain the Judgment Seat of Christ: _____
_____

38. The Second Coming of Christ is referred to as the Battle of _____

39. The Second Coming is also referred throughout the Old Testament as *"the day of the* _____*."*

40. What period of time follows the Tribulation, and the Second Coming of Christ?
_____

41. How long will the Millennium last? _____

42. Who will rule the world during the Millennium? _____

43. At the end of the world, there is a final judgment called *"the Great* _____ *Throne"* judgment. Who will be there? _____

44. There will be three new things after the end of the world. What are they?
1)_____ 2) _____ 3) _____

45. Once a person has been discipled, it is now their privilege and purpose to become a what? _____

46. When Christ sent out his disciples, they basically turned the world _____ down. How many people had been discipled by Christ? _____

47. If every born again Christian did their part in soul-winning, and discipling, is it possible to reach the world in our lifetime? _____

Well Done!

FINAL REVIEW

Let's check to see whether you have grown spiritually since we began this Study Course...

1. Have you been born again, the Bible way? **Yes, No.** When? _____
2. Have you been baptized? **Yes, No.** When? _____
3. Have you read your Bible all the way through yet? **Yes, No.**
4. What Book in the Bible are you reading currently? _____
5. Are you committed to reading your Bible through every year? **Yes, No.**
6. Do you believe the King James Bible is the *preserved* word of God in the English language? **Yes, No.**
7. Have you memorized the four main memory verses listed so far? **Yes, No.**
8. Please give the four main memory verse locations: 1) _____
   2) _____ 3) _____ 4) _____
9. How many Scriptures would you guess have you memorized so far? _____
10. Are you faithful in attending church (every Sunday possible)? **Yes, No.**
11. Are you setting aside time for, and actually praying almost every day? **Yes, No.**
12. Is God answering your prayers? **Yes, No.**
13. List a recently answered prayer: _____
    _____
14. Is there anyone in your life you are currently having problems with? **Yes, No.**
15. Are you letting that person hold you back from serving the Lord with your whole heart and life? **Yes, No.**
16. Is your home-life developing, and becoming more Christian? **Yes, No.**
17. Are you tithing? **Yes, No.**
18. Have you led anyone to Christ since starting this discipleship course? **Yes, No.**
19. Name one person you have led to Christ recently _____
20. Name a person that you are burdened about their salvation _____
21. Have you started to disciple anyone since you completed this discipleship course? **Yes, No.**
22. Have you determined what God's will is for your life? **Yes, No.**
23. If yes, what is it? _____
24. Have you found something to do as a ministry in church? **Yes, no.** If so, what is it?
    _____

You have now completed the entire First Principles Bible Study Course!
Praise God!

You have come a long way for Christ!

Never Stop Growing!
Read your Bible
Faithfully attend Church meetings
Evangelize
Pray about everything
and do everything you do
will all your might!

MEMORY AND LESSON VERSE LIST
A List of All Memory Verses Given in This Study Guide

The following list is provided to help you remember both the Scripture verses and their theme that was the basis for each of the lessons in this Discipleship series. Please take the moment and make sure that you have all of the following verses memorized, and that they are copied onto your Scripture memorization cards for later review. These verses will come in handy so many times in the future, and when used as the weapons that God intended them to be against temptations and doubts, they will establish you as a true light in this dark world.

Lesson Number	Subject	Memory Verse	Lesson Verse
1	Biblical Salvation	Matthew 4:4	1 John 5:12
2	Eternal Security		1 John 5:13
3	Believer's Baptism	*The Word of God*	Acts 2:41
4	The Word of God		Hebrews 4:12
5	Bible Study Techniques		2Timothy 2:15
6	The New Testament Church	Hebrews 10:25	Hebrews 10:25
7	Bible Memorization		Psalm 119:11
8	Knowing God	*Fellowship With Other Believers*	1Peter 1:8
9	Praise and Worship		Psalm 9:1,2
10	The Lord's Supper		1Cor 11:26
11	Prayer	1 Corinthians 12:27	Psalm 5:2
12	The Will of God		Romans 12:1,2
13	Spiritual Warfare	*The Structure of the Church*	1Cor 10:13
14	The Christian Family		Genesis 1:27
15	Finances		Philp 4:19
16	Personal Evangelism	Romans 12:11	Mark 16:15
17	Wine and Strong Drink		Proverbs 20:1
18	My Job and Employer	*The Ministry of Christ*	1Cor 10:31
19	Creation and Evolution		Genesis 1:1
20	The Future		Isaiah 46:9
21	Discipleship		2Timothy 2:2

This completes the **First Principles** Discipleship Lesson Course. The next stage of your growth involves either the study of individual Books of the Bible, or the next series of Lessons called **Practical Doctrine**. Contact your pastor or Discipleship Director for more information and his recommendation.